HANDBOOK OF PROPERTIES OF TECHNICAL & ENGINEERING CERAMICS

Part 1: An introduction for the engineer and designer

HANDBOOK OF PROPERTIES OF TECHNICAL & ENGINEERING CERAMICS

PART 1
AN INTRODUCTION
FOR THE ENGINEER
AND DESIGNER

R. MORRELL

NATIONAL PHYSICAL LABORATORY

LONDON: HER MAJESTY'S STATIONERY OFFICE

CONTENTS

Section 4: Applications of technical ceramics

Section 5: Manufacturers and suppliers

Section 6: Materials and design expertise in ceramics and brittle materials

Section 7: Standards related to ceramics, glasses, graphite, cemented carbides and components made from them

PART 2: DATA SHEETS (separate volumes)

Group A – High-alumina ceramics

Group B – Aluminosilicate ceramics and porcelains

Group C – Oxide and mixed oxide ceramics

Group D – Silicon carbide ceramics

Group E – Silicon nitride ceramics

Group F – Non-oxide ceramics

Group G – Technical glasses

Group H – Glass-ceramics

Group I – Machinable ceramics

Group J – Halides

ACKNOWLEDGEMENTS

This two-part Handbook has been compiled from a combination of literature review, discussions with manufacturers, and an in-house test-programme at NPL. The inception of the project was encouraged by Professor J P Roberts (formerly of Sheffield University) and by Mr W E C Creyke (formerly of Pilkington Brothers PLC, and former President of the Institute of Ceramics). It has been supported by the Materials and Chemicals Requirements Board (formerly the Engineering Materials Requirements Board) of the Department of Trade and Industry.

The author would like to thank the following members of NPL for the parts they have played in bringing this Handbook to fruition: D J Clinton, for microstructural analysis and hardness testing; L A Lay, for work on the chemical corrosion including compilation of Section 2.9; J M Cox, for X-ray analysis of materials examined; A Grandjean, for preparation of test-pieces and of photographs and micrographs; W P Byrne, for mechanical testing; J A Champion and G O Lloyd, for vigilant reading and commenting upon the text.

In addition, thanks are due to D B Binns, formerly of the British Ceramic Research Association Ltd, for a literature review; R Taylor and S P Howlett* of the Department of Metallurgy, UMIST (*now at Doulton Industrial Products Ltd), for the successful execution of a programme to measure the thermal diffusivity of a range of ceramic materials; R C Major, formerly of Smiths Industries Ceramics and Ignition Company Ltd, for reading and commenting valuably on much of the text of Part 1.

Information on commercial products has come from many manufacturers, but especial thanks are due to the research staff of: Allied Insulators Ltd, Anderman and Ryder Ltd, Doulton Industrial Products Ltd, Feldmühle A G, A G Hackney Ltd, Hewitt and Sons Ltd, Morganite Electroheat Ltd (now Kanthal Electroheat Ltd), Pilkington Brothers PLC, Royal Worcester Industrial Ceramics Ltd, Smiths Industries Ceramics and Ignition Co Ltd, Steatite and Porcelain Products Ltd, Geo. Wade Co Ltd. Without the valuable discussions held it would not have been possible to gain the appreciation of manufacturing processes and commercial considerations needed to format and write this Handbook in a meaningful manner.

Finally, the author would like to thank the typing and word-processing sections of NPL for their services in preparing the text, and the graphics sections for preparing the line diagrams.

SECTION 1

Introduction

1.1

The effective use of ceramics in engineering

From the engineering point of view, brittleness is the reason why designers and engineers act very cautiously when the possibility of using a ceramic arises. In some respects this is justified. Experience with glassware in the laboratory, or with teacups at home, engenders some resistance to using brittle materials, and thus such materials tend to be used only as a last resort. Increasingly, however, ceramics are being used for critical components outside their traditional area of electrical insulation. They are used for enhanced properties which are quite unlike those of any other group of materials. These include:

hardness and wear resistance
resistance to chemical attack
resistance to oxidation and high temperatures
dimensional stability
optical properties
specific electrical properties.

Of course, not all ceramics possess all of these characteristics. Each type of material, each proprietary product, has both advantageous and disadvantageous properties when it comes to engineering performance. An alumina ceramic may be hard and strong, but may not withstand severe thermal shock. A silicon carbide may be acid-resistant, but not alkali-resistant. Each commercial product, sometimes even each component shape of each commercial product, has to be considered separately.

The customer for ceramic components has had nowhere he can turn for unbiased advice and guidance on the use of ceramics in engineering. The people with most experience are generally the manufacturers, who are usually intent on selling their own products, however suitable or unsuitable for optimum performance. Alternatively there are specialists who may know much about principles and the science, but little about the ins and outs of commercial products. The scientific literature is rather unstructured and unbalanced, weighted primarily in favour of the exotic or the unobtainable. Most inexperienced customers have needed to learn the hard way, by trial and error, by buying and testing.

This Handbook has been written to try to improve upon this situation. Its aims are to try to clear a straightforward path through the jungle of scientific and commercial literature, to provide property data for design purposes, and to enable the inexperienced user to enter a new field with less trepidation and less waste of effort than previously. Even if this Handbook does not answer all the questions that come to mind, the author hopes that at least the reader will learn how to approach the use of ceramics in an appropriate way, and will be in a better position to negotiate with suppliers from a basis of some understanding and background knowledge.

All Handbooks have some limitations, and this one is no exception. It has been written with the fact in mind that all commercial products are proprietary, and are thus subject to variation, not only in compositional terms, but also in performance resulting from different methods of making the finished product. In these respects it is undesirable (and almost impossible) to draw comparisons between outwardly similar commercial products. Some attempt is made where appropriate to discuss some of these factors and the influence they may have on properties, but there is no reference to the advantages or disadvantages of any particular product. In this way the author avoids the risk of unfair comparison on the basis of incomplete information, and allows market factors such as a manufacturer's willingness to help, or his ability to make the product to particular tolerances for a particular cost, to enter into the equation of choice. Although the user therefore does not have an outright recommended product he has the chance of obtaining deeper insight and can then compare competing products using his own terms of reference suited to his particular needs.

This Handbook is divided into two parts:

Part 1 – contains general information on properties, how they are measured, what they mean with respect to ceramics, and in broad terms a comparison of properties of basically different types of ceramic. Also included are notes on manufacture of ceramics and design of components, on principal applications for ceramics, on sources of advice, on manufacturers' names and addresses, and on standard test procedures and specifications related to ceramics.

Part 2 – contains detailed data on engineering ceramics divided into narrow groups based on composition, performance and applicability to end use. Each Data Sheet describes all aspects of products that fall within its specification.

In this way, detailed data are separated from generalities, but by studying the generalities, the reader should be able to conclude which types of material are candidates for his application, and can then turn to the detailed data to learn more about their suitability.

1.2

What are engineering ceramics?

The usual definition of a ceramic is a material based on inorganic non-metallic compounds and produced by the action of heat. This is an all-embracing description which can be applied to materials not normally called ceramics, but which have ceramic-type properties, notably brittleness. So in addition to materials comprising:

    oxides (including silicates)

    carbides

    nitrides

    silicides

    borides,

one could include:

    glasses

    carbon and graphite

    inorganic cements

    silicon, gallium phosphide and semimetallic compounds

    many salts, such as rock salt.

For the purposes of this Handbook the range described above must be restricted to those materials used in an engineering sense for stress-bearing applications, i.e. those which are fine-grained and strong, and find uses as mechanical components. Unfortunately there is no single term which adequately covers all such materials, but the nearest is probably 'engineering ceramics'. 'Technical ceramics' is too wide a term, and 'special ceramics' is too narrow a term, both of these also being in current usage. The Japanese term 'fine ceramics' is also appearing in the literature, not to be confused with domestic claywares.

The coverage of the Handbook is summarized in Table 1.1. In addition to fine-grained polycrystalline ceramics, also included are some technical glasses, such as fused quartz, soda-lime glass and borosilicate chemical glass. These are often employed in the engineering sense covered by the definition above. Glass-ceramics – finely crystallized glasses – are used for technical components, as are single crystal quartz and sapphire. Use is often made of 'machinable' ceramics, synthetic or natural products which can be turned or drilled, particularly for 'one-offs' or for prototypes. All these are included. For comparison purposes, rather less detailed sections on carbon and graphite, on cemented carbides and other cermets, and on kiln furniture products are included.

The following are excluded:

Heavy refractories (bricks and blocks)

Structural claywares (bricks, pipes, etc.)

Table 1.1 Principal types of engineering ceramics

Detailed data in this Handbook are given for:

Clay-based products:	Traditional quartz porcelains, special porcelains, aluminous porcelains, refractory porcelains. Cordierite ceramics, mullite ceramics, some stonewares, electrical refractories.
Talc-based products:	Steatite ceramics, forsterite ceramics.
Oxide ceramics:	Alumina (Al_2O_3), zirconia (ZrO_2), titania (TiO_2), beryllia (BeO), magnesia (MgO), and mixed oxides.
Nitride ceramics:	Silicon nitride (Si_3N_4), boron nitride (BN).
Carbide ceramics:	Silicon carbide (SiC), boron carbide (B_4C), vitreous carbon.
Boride ceramics:	Titanium diboride (TiB_2).
Silicide ceramics:	Molybdenum disilicide ($MoSi_2$).
Technical glasses:	Soda-lime, borosilicate, various forms of vitreous silica (SiO_2).
Glass ceramics:	Various types.
Single crystals:	α-quartz, sapphire.
Machinable ceramics:	Sintered fused silica, pyrophillite, glass-ceramics, machinable alumina, massive talc.

General comments only on the following types of material:

Kiln furniture:	Aluminosilicates.
Cermets:	Hardmetals (usually carbides, often based on WC), oxide/metal systems.
Carbon and graphite:	Comparative data only, except for vitreous carbon.

Note: This list gives generic names only. Each name may cover a wide range of different types of product – see index to Part 2.

Domestic claywares (fine pottery, porcelain, etc.)

Special electrical ceramics (high permittivity or magnetic ceramics used primarily for their electrical properties)

Special technical glasses (special compositions for particular properties)

Cement and cement-based materials (structural and engineering concretes, special cements, refractory concretes)

Natural minerals (rocks, etc. with the exception of machinable materials)

Coatings and flame-sprayed ceramics (because properties depend on preparation conditions and substrate).

Engineering ceramics have descended from porcelain over a period of a hundred years or more. Porcelains were first used in a technical sense with the advent of electrical power, and since that era technical ceramics have progressed to an enormous diversity of oxide and non-oxide products, especially in the last 30 years. Traditionally, ceramics are made from natural minerals; clays, quartz, feldspar, and other common rocks. Nowadays, most of the more advanced materials are synthetic in origin, with researchers striving to improve the quality of the product with improvements in the processability of the synthetic starting batch.

With the principal exceptions of clay- and talc-based materials, most engineering ceramics are called by a chemical compound name or a contraction of it (e.g. alumina for aluminium oxide). This name usually reflects the principal but by no means the only chemical component of the material in question. Other components are present for various reasons, often to improve processability by lowering the temperature required to consolidate the material. Very often these components control the overall performance of the product, and in this way differences arise in the behaviour of outwardly similar commercial products from different sources. From the user's point of view, care must be taken in using such chemical names without qualification. Generally speaking, one has to be rather more specific in order to define products more closely. The subdivision of the material spectrum used in Part 2 is a demonstration of this need.

In addition to requiring a different approach to component design to that for metals or polymeric materials, note should be made that engineering ceramics also need a different approach to actual procurement of components. With the exceptions of glasses, glass-ceramics and single-crystal materials (which are melt-formed), and pyrolytic products (which are formed from the gas phase), all ceramics are manufactured by powder technology methods. The appropriate powder batch is shaped by one of a variety of methods into what is known as a 'green body', usually in the shape or close to the shape of the final product. A high-temperature firing process then converts it into the final hard ceramic, the 'fired body'. In this state it is much more difficult to shape. As a general rule, therefore, ceramic components are made to final dimensions (usually to as-fired tolerances of $\pm 2\%$) by the primary manufacturer as part of the total process. For smaller levels of tolerance machining is normally required using diamond tools. The customer should therefore consider purchasing the final component when possible, rather than buying in blanks to machine. A ceramic manufacturer's expertise is usually centred around the manufacture of components to customers' requirements, and this may well be the cheapest way of getting what is required.

1.3

How to use this Handbook

Let us begin by assuming that the user finds that the performance required of particular components, or perhaps particular parts of a component, exceeds that achievable by the use of cost-effective metallic or plastic materials. For example, the component may get hot, or see a high level of wear, or see a severe chemical environment. In this situation the user may find that a ceramic component or insert is an attractive proposition. What material should he use? How can he find out about the properties? How should he set about designing his ceramic component? Where can he get it? These are the basic questions. A typical sequence of events he can follow is shown in Table 1.2, together with parts of this Handbook that should be referred to. Part 1, Section 2 describes in general terms the comparative properties of various types of ceramics, and what the property data mean (they may depend on how the test is done). This, coupled with reference to Section 4, a summary of uses of various types of ceramic, should guide the user to suitable generic types. If detailed property information on various versions of the materials within each generic type is then required, reference can be made to Part 2. The reader should not be put off by the depth of detail in places; it may be irrelevant to individual needs, but note should be made of the first few sections in each Data Sheet which describe composition, microstructure and manufacturing methods. These may influence decisions.

With ceramics, there is often an interrelation between manufacturing method and component design. This may be the cost-controlling factor, so consultation with Section 3 of Part 1 may help guide the user in general terms. However, there is no substitute for early discussions with appropriate manufacturers on particular products. They are in the best position to know what is feasible with their products within their plant capability. They may make useful suggestions which make the design easier to make and therefore cheaper. Section 3 is intended to supplement such discussions, acting as a broad introduction, rather than substitute for them. At the end of each data sheet in Part 2, manufacturers' names and product codes are given, and a complete list of names and addresses with fields of operation is given in Part 1, Section 5. However, it should be borne in mind that all products are proprietary and are liable to change at any time. If something different is offered, check back to the appropriate section to examine any stings in the tail.

Any new application for a ceramic material is an iterative learning process. Ceramics often do not work because they are too brittle for the imposed loads, but there are successful applications when the component is engineered in an appropriate way. This may be the most difficult part of the product

Table 1.2   Design steps

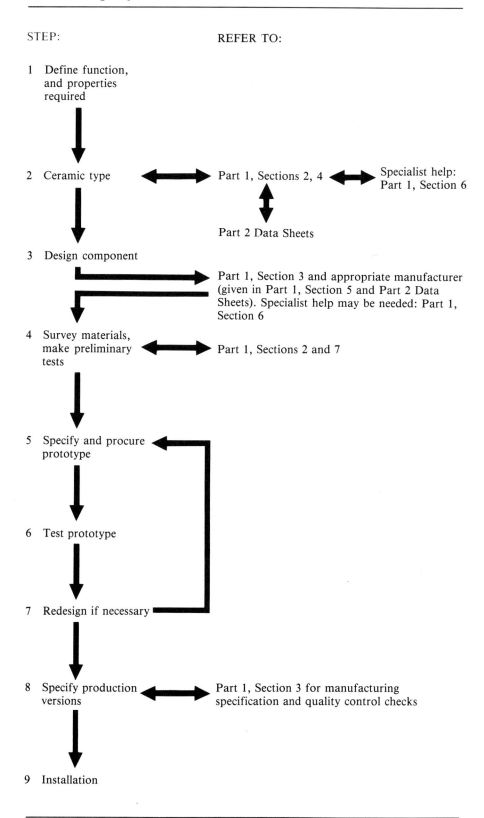

STEP: REFER TO:

1   Define function,
    and properties
    required

2   Ceramic type   ⟷   Part 1, Sections 2, 4   ⟷   Specialist help:
                                                            Part 1, Section 6

                                 Part 2 Data Sheets

3   Design component

                               Part 1, Section 3 and appropriate manufacturer
                               (given in Part 1, Section 5 and Part 2 Data
                               Sheets). Specialist help may be needed: Part 1,
                               Section 6

4   Survey materials,
    make preliminary   ⟷   Part 1, Sections 2 and 7
    tests

5   Specify and procure
    prototype

6   Test prototype

7   Redesign if necessary

8   Specify production   ⟷   Part 1, Section 3 for manufacturing
    versions   specification and quality control checks

9   Installation

development process. The manufacturer may be able to provide some help, based on his experience with other customers, but often the user is on his own. He may wish to seek specialist advice, and reference to Section 6 may help in the right direction.

Once the prototype is fully developed, it will be necessary to negotiate for a supply of the component in the final form. Tolerances, inspection, and proof-testing will all need to be specified, backed up with agreed procedures. Reference to Section 3 may help here, and if agreed test procedures are required, Section 7 lists a wide range of standard test methods, both British and International, which may be of use.

In conclusion, this Handbook is intended to help the inexperienced to gain information and understanding without rummaging through text-books or journals so that he can negotiate with manufacturers from a standpoint of some knowledge and can ask the right questions. We do not pretend this Handbook is complete; it has been compiled in finite time from a relatively limited review of available data. We hope that from time to time it can be updated, especially with respect to product codes and the development of new materials.

SECTION 2

The properties of engineering ceramics

A summary of types of ceramic together with comparative property data

2.1

Introduction

In this Section, we aim to do two things:
1. to give a general impression of the relative properties of the more common types of engineering ceramic
2. to give descriptions of how such properties are normally measured on ceramics, and what the data produced mean in relation to material performance.

The information on materials comparison is necessarily somewhat broad and superficial in approach because it is impossible to condense adequately the detail given in Part 2 data sheets without considerable loss of specificity. Our intention is to assist the reader in coming to the right conclusions with regard to broad material type that might satisfy his requirements. For any particular combination of properties it should be possible to identify likely types of material, the detailed properties of which can then be found in Part 2. We do not intend this Section to act as a guide on its own, but to be used in conjunction with Part 2. The reason for this is that any generic name for a type of material, for example, 'high-alumina ceramics' covers a very wide range of fundamentally different materials with different properties. Successful performance of any one product does not in any way imply that all products under the generic name will also be suitable. It will be up to the user to refer to data sheets for particular types of product in Part 2, and then to discuss individual products with their respective manufacturers.

An important aspect of understanding technical information on materials is understanding what property data mean. On most data sheets or brochures for engineering ceramics are disclaimers to the effect that the data are 'typical', or 'obtained on laboratory specimens', or 'from test pieces'. In other words, no manufacturer is in a position to guarantee that the data shown apply to all real components, even if the same test can be done on the component as is usual for test pieces. There is a dependence of material performance upon the component shape and treatment during manufacture. 'Test pieces' tend to be specially made to suit the test requirements, which may be laid down in Standard specifications or procedures. The manufacturing treatment may be different from that for many real components. Manufacturers would probably not deny that some data in brochures have been obtained from test pieces prepared by the route giving the most advantageous answer. In this Section an attempt is made to relate the applicability of test data to the performance of real components in real situations.

2.2

Composition and microstructure

The composition of a ceramic and the microstructure produced by the fabrication method are crucially important in determining the properties and performance, just as with metallic materials. However, unlike the case with metals, this microstructure cannot usefully be changed by plastic working either at room temperature or at high temperatures. The vast majority of materials we are considering in this guide are fired to a high temperature at which the microstructures they finally possess are developed. Thus one must normally accept the product as it is supplied.

Virtually all ceramics start life as powders or mixtures of powders which are shaped and then subjected to heat to consolidate them. (Exceptions are of course bulk glasses and glass-ceramics, and single-crystal materials.) The powder types and properties determine how consolidation takes place. Ceramists generally divide this process into four types:

1. 'Vitrification'

A term used mainly for clay-based ceramics, describing the tendency of some components to melt to a viscous liquid during high-temperature firing, this liquid cooling to a glassy phase. A 'well-vitrified body' is one in which the process of melting has enabled a dense impervious material to be obtained.

2. 'Sintering'

A term used, in its pure sense, to imply the densification of a body at high temperatures in the absence of a liquid phase, i.e. by solid-state diffusion processes. However, the term is often used in situations where some liquid is also present to help redistribution of solid material by solution and reprecipitation.

3. 'Reaction-bonding' or 'reaction-sintering'

A term used to signify the process in which components within a material react together to form an effective bond between pre-existing particles, or to produce the required phase in situ. In many cases, one of the reacting components may be introduced in the liquid or in the gaseous state during firing. 'Self-bonding' is sometimes used for products in which the bond is chemically the same as the pre-existing particles.

4. 'Hot-pressing'

A term used to imply that pressure is required to assist a high-temperature densification process which would not proceed adequately without pressure, or which produces materials with more advantageous properties than those made by pressureless densification.

In addition, a fifth manufacturing process may be used for certain types of ceramic:

5. 'Chemical Vapour Deposition'

This is a process whereby components in final or near final shape are produced by reaction between gases. Clearly its use is restricted to ceramics the chemical components of which can be obtained in the gaseous state. Silicon carbide can be produced by reaction of a silicon-containing gas such as a silane, and a carbon-containing one such as carbon monoxide. The reaction is made to take place over a heated former or substrate of suitable shape, upon which the ceramic is deposited in a form that depends on the prevailing conditions. The technique can be used for making thin coatings on existing components, or the deposition can be made over an extended period of time to build up thicker sections and a free-standing shape can be made after removal of the substrate. The term 'pyrolytic' is also applied to products made in this way.

Of these routes, simple firing of a powder shape in air in a high-temperature kiln, i.e. vitrifying or sintering the product, is preferred from the point of view of reliability and cost. Other processes require rather more careful control and are used for special types of material, more especially non-oxide ceramics which are exceedingly difficult to sinter. Further detail on these routes is given in Section 3, but it should be appreciated that these terms are often used to refer to types of product; hence the reason for defining them at this stage. It is not our intention to discuss precise details of manufacture, powders, etc., except in broad terms as they affect the fired product.

Some further definitions are given here for the terms used in this and subsequent sections:

COMPOSITION:
Expressed as percentages by weight of individual components, usually in mineral form (e.g. as a feldspar, or as alumina (Al_2O_3)).

PHASE:
An identifiable crystalline species or a distinct amorphous or glassy species within a microstructure.

PHASE CONTENT:
The relative proportions of different types of crystalline or glassy phases within a material expressed as a percentage (or a volume fraction).

PHASE TRANSFORMATION:
Occurs when a phase is no longer thermodynamically stable in its environment, and changes to another structure, often with a change in volume and properties.

GRAIN SIZE:
Difficult to define in three dimensions because only a cross-section is seen. Where a grain size is discussed here, the term 'mean linear intercept size' is implied (see ASTM E112–1974), being the average distance between the intercepts of grain boundaries with a straight line drawn across a photomicrograph of a polished section. In many materials there is a range of actual grain size and shape, and where a range is quoted the figures are intended only as an indication of the largest and the smallest grain cross-sections observed. In most cases the mean grain size is implied. The grain size

observed on the surface of a fired sample may be different from that in the bulk.

POROSITY:

Open porosity is the ratio of void space in a sample accessible from its exterior surface to its total bulk volume, expressed as a percentage (or a volume fraction).

Closed porosity is the ratio of void space in a sample not accessible from its exterior surface to its total bulk volume, expressed as a percentage (or a volume fraction).

Total porosity is the sum of the open and closed porosities.

DENSITY:

Bulk density is the ratio of the mass of a sample to its geometrical volume including all porosity.

True density is the ratio of the mass of a sample to its volume including closed pores but not open pores.

Theoretical density is the average density of the solid phases within a body, i.e. excluding all porosity.

TEXTURE:

A directionality of the microstructure produced by the method of shaping which tends to orientate non-equiaxed particles into a preferred direction. Extrusion is a manufacturing route in which this commonly occurs.

2.2.1 Clay-based and other silicate ceramics

This group of materials is extremely wide-ranging in compositions, microstructures, and hence properties, and thus only the generalities of microstructure can be discussed. The group includes porcelains of various types, steatite and forsterite, aluminosilicate-based materials, and cordierites, all of which are made in fine-grained forms. The group also includes materials of coarser grain size such as chemical stonewares and aluminosilicate materials used for kiln furniture. Although large grains generally lead to mechanical weakness (see Section 2.5), coarse particles are included in the starting batch as a means of restricting shrinkage during drying after shaping and during firing. In this way, improved dimensional control can be obtained. Large pieces are therefore made more readily. However, restriction on shrinkage means that porosity is not eliminated to the same extent during firing, and this may be undesirable. In this and the following Sections, the International Electrotechnical Commission (IEC) classification scheme for electrotechnical ceramics is followed so that the various types of material are grouped in a manner that eventually may be agreed internationally. This scheme (designated IEC 672 and to be adopted as BS 6045) does not cover all types of technical ceramics, but primarily those of use for electrical insulation, so other classes not described in the scheme are inserted at appropriate points.

2.2.1.1 Siliceous and aluminous porcelains

Porcelains are well-vitrified ceramics based on a mixture of clays, feldspars and a filler. The composition depends on the end use and the appearance required. Historically, porcelain compositions have been designed to use indigenous raw materials, and thus there are substantial differences between manufacturing procedures in the UK and in other countries which continue today even in the field of technical ceramics. In this Handbook we are primarily concerned with technical applications, and the majority of technical porcelains have been designed to have high strength for use as insulators. There are others which have been designed for specific improved properties, e.g. for resistance to chemical attack or to thermal shock, or to have improved thermal conductivity, etc.

Porcelains with <30% alumina, IEC class C-110

Most conventional electrical porcelains fall into this category. They are composed of a mixture of clays, a feldspar, and some siliceous filler material, usually ground sand or flint. The raw material batch varies widely, but UK materials are typically made with 45–55% of a mixture of plastic and non-plastic clays, 25–35% of a feldspar (an alkali aluminosilicate mineral), and about 20% of quartz. The feldspar is a flux in the sense that it produces a low-melting reactive glass on firing which vitrifies the material. The actual composition is chosen so that the material does not shrink excessively on drying, does not distort excessively as it shrinks on firing, and does not require an unacceptably high firing temperature to achieve the vitrified state. In other words, the raw batch must above all have good processability for reproducible and trouble-free production. The properties achieved are not greatly dependent on the composition provided the manufacturing standard is maintained.

The microstructure consists typically of quartz grains surrounded by a matrix phase composed of a glassy phase produced by the feldspar, interpenetrated by a mass of mullite ($3Al_2O_3.2SiO_2$) crystals (Figure 2.2.1). The quartz particles may be slightly rounded by dissolution in the matrix phase during firing. There is always some closed porosity, but the classification requires zero open porosity, and this is usually achieved by processing the material in the wet state and producing shapes by extrusion, plastic moulding, and turning. An important feature to note is the quartz phase. At 573°C on cooling after firing, the high or beta-quartz transforms to low or alpha-quartz with a considerable volume decrease. The strain involved tends to cause the particles to crack away from the matrix, leaving boundary cracks

Figure 2.2.1
Microstructure of a typical quartz porcelain showing cracks around the quartz filler particles.

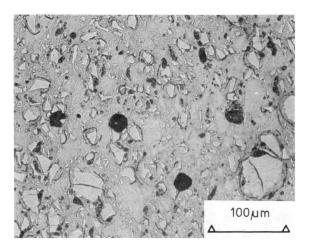

100μm

visible in the microstructure. This effect is most noticeable in materials with quartz particles greater than about 20 μm across.

There is some tendency for the firing shrinkage and the final properties to be slightly anisotropic as a result of preferred orientation of the clay particles during plastic working. This is often not obvious in the appearance of the microstructure.

In materials with low initial quartz contents that are subject to high firing temperatures, the quartz phase may disappear. The result is a rather lower expansion coefficient and improved thermal shock resistance, and such materials are used for laboratory ware.

The use of more refractory clays, particularly in continental European compositions, leads to the need for higher firing temperatures, often with a period of reducing atmosphere in order to prevent swelling caused by oxidation of divalent iron and to retain a dead white colour. The resulting microstructure is very similar to that shown by UK-type materials.

Pressed porcelains with <30% alumina, IEC class C-111

For complex shapes in porcelain, a direct shaping method is die-pressing using granules of batch which have a water content rather lower than that normally used for extrusion or plastic working, typically 10–12%. Since air can be trapped between the granules during pressing, a more porous body is produced on firing. The classification C-111 allows for up to 3% open porosity, but the microstructure is otherwise similar to that produced by wet shaping methods, C-110 above. There is a little less tendency to obtain anisotropic shrinkage on firing, and the properties are also less anisotropic. However, pressed porcelains need to be glazed to avoid moisture penetration, and have a limited dielectric breakdown voltage gradient, so they cannot be used for high-voltage applications.

Cristobalite porcelains, IEC class C-112

In some porcelain materials, the choice of indigenous raw materials results in the appearance of the silica phase cristobalite rather than quartz. Cristobalite can also be produced by over-firing quartz-containing materials. Cristobalite has a transition like quartz but at around 180–250°C depending on the chemical purity and environment. Properties and performance appear similar to those of class C-110 materials.

Aluminous porcelains with 30–50% alumina, IEC class C-120

This class covers porcelains of similar type to C-110, but in which alumina is a main constituent, partially or completely replacing quartz. Since alumina has no phase transformations, there is no tendency for internal cracking on cooling and the strength of the material is generally rather greater than that of quartz-containing materials in the unglazed state. Some materials, notably from Japan, contain cristobalite as well as alumina.

Aluminous porcelains with >50% alumina, IEC class C-130

C-130 materials are those feldspar porcelains in which there is a high filler content of alumina replacing quartz as in the class C-120. Microstructurally the appearance is intermediate between that of class C-120 for lower alumina contents, and that of debased alumina ceramics at higher alumina contents (i.e. classes C-780, C-786). As the alumina content is increased, so the strength and Young's modulus also increase.

For materials with a similar alumina content, but which contain little or no feldspar, a rather higher firing temperature is required to produce vitrification and densification. These materials are in the C-600 category of refractory porcelains in which the principal crystalline phase is mullite, not alumina. The term 'aluminous porcelain' is sometimes misleadingly applied to such products as well.

2.2.1.2 Steatite and forsterite ceramics

This class of ceramics is designed primarily for electrical applications, but steatites are also used for mechanical purposes where high strength is not required. The common factor in this group is that the principal crystalline phases are magnesium silicates, enstatite ($MgO.SiO_2$) and forsterite ($2MgO.SiO_2$). The major source of magnesia for this category of material is talc. Talc is a mineral of plate-like habit which in massive form can by itself be fired to a ceramic body. Earlier this century it was commonly used for radio components in this form, called steatite. However, owing to the desirability to shape by powder pressing or extrusion methods, and to obtain zero open porosity materials, raw material batches now include other ingredients to improve handleability from the ceramic manufacturing point of view. The term steatite now applies to all talc-based ceramic materials. The plate-like nature of talc, while making it easy to press shapes, can lead to problems in manufacture due to alignment of the particles in extrusion and to a lesser extent in die pressing. This can lead to differential shrinkage on drying and firing, some lamination effects, and some anisotropy of properties, such as strength. Ceramic formulations and powder processing procedures are designed to reduce the risk of this occurring, and problems are met with less frequently nowadays.

Low-voltage steatites, IEC class C-210

This class of materials has a typical raw material composition containing 80–90% talc, 5–10% plastic clay, and 5–10% feldspar. In the fired state, the material comprises predominantly enstatite, together with some silica phase (quartz or cristoballite) in a glassy matrix produced by vitrification of the felspar and clay. The clay content aids plastic workability, but more than about 10% causes firing problems due to the narrowing of the acceptable firing range and the formation of the phase cordierite ($2MgO.2Al_2O_3.5SiO_2$). Steatites in this category are allowed a small level of open porosity, 0.5%, and a lower level of strength compared to the following class C-220, hence their limitation to low-voltage use.

Normal steatites, IEC class C-220

This class covers steatites normally made for medium- and high-voltage use, and having no open porosity. The specification requires higher resistivity, higher dielectric breakdown voltage, higher strength, and lower dielectric dissipation than for class C-210. The last of these properties is controlled by the glassy phase, the composition of which becomes very important (even more so in the following category of low-loss steatites). To reduce dielectric loss, and at the same time improve the firing range, feldspar may be replaced by barium or calcium carbonate in the raw material batch. A relatively high-loss alkali-containing glass is thereby replaced by crystalline alkaline earth aluminosilicate phases of lower dielectric loss. A typical raw material batch might be 70–80% talc, 10–18% plastic clay, 6–10% barium carbonate, and 0–4% calcium carbonate. In addition there may be added magnesium carbonate to raise the MgO content, and some zirconia-containing material. The microstructure consists essentially of a fine-grained mixture of enstatite and a barium-containing phase such as celsian ($BaO.Al_2O_3.2SiO_2$), with a minimum of residual glassy material between the grains.

Low-loss steatites, IEC class C-221

Compositions in this class are designed to reduce as far as possible the dielectric loss by reducing the amount of residual glassy phase. For this category, compositions are similar to those of class C-220 above, but greater emphasis is placed on ensuring that alkali levels are low to minimize the amount of glass formed. Microstructures tend to be very similar to those of class C-220.

Porous steatites, IEC class C-230

The specification for this class implies that the materials should be open-porous versions of a low-loss steatite with typically 30% open porosity. Such a material will have a similar solid microstructure to that of class C-221 material but with the addition of a high level of controlled porosity. Uses are limited to low-voltage applications where machinability or improved thermal shock resistance is required at the expense of open porosity. It is not in regular manufacture in the UK.

Forsterites, IEC classes C-240 (porous), C-250 (dense)

Forsterites are versions of steatites in which the magnesia level is raised by the addition of MgO or $MgCO_3$ so that the crystal phase forsterite, rather than one of the forms of enstatite, is produced. The specific advantage of forsterite ceramics is that their expansion coefficients are higher than those of steatites, are a good match to titanium and other metals such as some nickel-iron alloys, and are nearly linear over the temperature range up to 1000°C. The materials are therefore used for ceramic-to-metal assemblies in applications requiring low dielectric loss, such as high-frequency power devices and microwave tubes. The high thermal expansion coefficient brings a disadvantage in that resistance to thermal shock is poor. Raw material batches are typically 40–60% talc, 30–40% MgO or dolomite, with small amounts of barium and calcium carbonates to act as fluxing agents to produce a low-loss body. Microstructures are similar to those of steatites except that forsterite is the major crystalline phase. The porous category is similar to C-230 for steatites, and allows 30% open porosity.

Massive talc bodies

As indicated above, blocks of mineral talc can be used directly as a machinable ceramic material, although uses are nowadays rather limited. Other names are 'soapstone', 'steatite', and 'lava block'. 'Lava' is a synthetic version. The material can be machined very readily, even carved by hand, and can then be fired to a hard ceramic state. In the firing process there is considerable shrinkage, which in the natural versions is not isotropic. The talc dehydrates and recrystallizes to one of the forms of enstatite depending on the maximum temperature achieved. This can cause problems in the long term because of a slow phase change that occurs at room temperature, from the high-temperature form, protoenstatite, to a low-temperature form, clinoenstatite, with associated volume changes. This does not occur readily in steatite products, because the grain size is kept small, e.g. 5 μm and below, and the change is essentially suppressed.

The microstructure of fired talc contains one of the forms of enstatite in a siliceous glassy matrix. Fired talc is nearly always open porous.

2.2.1.3 Cordierite, celsian and zircon porcelains

IEC class C-400 is for a group that is termed 'materials based on alkaline earth aluminosilicates'. As such it incorporates materials based on cordierite ($2MgO.2Al_2O_3.5SiO_2$), and celsian ($BaO.Al_2O_3.2SiO_2$). These are vitrified materials, essentially of low porosity, the specification allowing 0.5% open porosity. Their major application is where greater thermal shock resistance than that offered by siliceous or aluminous porcelains is required, such as in fuse tubes. Celsian porcelains are not in common production nowadays.

A material not covered by the IEC classification is zircon porcelain, which is included in this section for convenience.

Dense cordierite, IEC class C-410

Cordierite ceramics have a notoriously narrow firing range, and careful control of firing is required. Cordierite is not common as a mineral, and in any case is not easy to process into a ceramic, so cordierite ceramics are made by firing an appropriate mixture of clay and talc with some added alumina. A typical composition might be 40% clays, 25% talc, 30% sillimanite (as a source of extra alumina), and 5% feldspar as a fluxing agent. The amount of flux is limited to this level otherwise the advantage of a low coefficient of expansion is lost. The microstructure is generally very fine, and consists of cordierite crystals in a glassy matrix, with some residual sillimanite not dissolved by the vitrification process. The material may be self-glazing, which is an advantage in that low-expansion glazes suitable for cordierite materials are not easy to produce. The composition may vary considerably from the chemical formula. In particular, the amount of iron in the raw materials determines the ease of firing, increasing iron content decreasing the firing temperature and imparting a darker colour to the fired product. Also, reducing the amount of talc in favour of increased sillimanite content tends to increase the amount of mullite produced, with a small increase in expansion coefficient. This is a more refractory material. A wide range of possible variations in composition achieves the primary objectives of a low expansion coefficient, dense, and readily fired material. Some of these materials, by virtue of not possessing the low specified level of open porosity, fall into class C-500.

Dense celsian, IEC class C-420

Celsian porcelains are the aluminosilicate equivalent of barium-fluxed steatites in that there is a minimum of glassy phase to produce a material of very low dielectric loss and better thermal shock resistance than steatite. The major crystalline phase is celsian ($BaO.Al_2O_3.2SiO_2$), produced from a mixture of clay and barium carbonate, and a filler may be incorporated to help minimize distortion in firing. These materials are not made in the UK at present but are available from overseas suppliers.

Zircon porcelain

Formerly widely used for applications such as spark plugs and other insulators requiring higher mechanical strength than offered by conventional porcelains, this material has now been largely superseded by high-alumina ceramics of class C-700, and by aluminous porcelains. Body compositions contain 60–75% zircon ($ZrO_2.SiO_2$), 5–25% fluxes and 10–20% plastic clay, and are fired typically to 1300–1400°C. The major crystalline phases are zircon and mullite, together with a glassy phase, which may be present only in small amounts in materials of low dielectric loss formulated with a non-alkali flux. These materials are not in current production in the UK, but are made by a number of firms overseas.

2.2.1.4 Porous materials based on aluminosilicates

In the IEC classification scheme, this category, C-500, is set aside for porous materials which might be used for refractory purposes where low voltage electrical insulation is required. Compositions range from less than 30% to more than 99% Al_2O_3. Typical applications include insulators for heating elements of all types, and for thermocouples. However there is also a very wide range of non-electrical ceramics that can be considered to fall into this overall class, such as materials with coarse aggregate particles used for crucibles and tubing for high-temperature processing. Materials with coarse aggregates are clearly not appropriate for some electrical applications where components with intricate shaping are required, such as heating-element formers with fine threads and holes. However, when discussing composition and microstructure, it is impossible to separate electrical and non-electrical materials. So, in addition to those materials which fall into the IEC classification subclasses, other materials designed for non-electrical use are included below where appropriate.

Aluminosilicates, IEC class C-510

This category includes a range of fired clay products that contain primarily refractory clay, with added quartz, sillimanite or alumina as appropriate to obtain the required refractoriness. No fluxes are added as a rule, apart from those present in the major constituents as impurities. As a consequence, dense bodies are not achieved on firing, and the specification for this class allows up to 30% open porosity. This type of material, but without a coarse filler, may be used for domestic gas fire radiants and related applications, where even higher levels of porosity are advantageous in improving resistance to thermal shock damage. The microstructures tend to be very fine, and consist of mullite crystals in a highly siliceous glassy phase, interspersed with extensive and fairly fine interconnected porosity. This structure acts as a bond for the coarse aggregate particles when these are included.

Another category of materials that fits into this class are porous so-called refractory porcelains, of the types which if dense would fall into class C-600. The porosity level may be low, typically 2–10% open porosity, but microstructures are similar to those in class C-600.

Magnesium aluminosilicates, IEC classes C-511, C-512, C-520

As with class C-510, these categories are for a wide variety of material compositions which are primarily designed for refractoriness and thermal shock resistance, but with the difference that they contain deliberate additions of magnesia (as the carbonate) or talc. Distinctions between these classes rest on performance. Class C-520 should have a high level of cordierite, and hence the lowest thermal expansion coefficient and the greatest thermal shock resistance. Apart from these features there is little that can be discussed about microstructure and composition in general terms, apart from the comment that crystallite sizes tend to be very small for most cordierite-based materials, and that porosity is usually fairly fine and uniformly distributed.

Cordierite has the lowest thermal expansion coefficient of all the crystalline phases in the three-oxide system $MgO-Al_2O_3-SiO_2$. To minimize thermal expansion, and thus maximize thermal shock resistance (but see also Section 2.6.2.2 on thermal shock), compositions as close as possible to that of cordierite are required. These are usually based on a mixture of clay, talc, and alumina, rather than the single oxide components, in order to achieve a greater level of reactivity, cordierite being formed more readily on firing. Materials of this type, which might be considered as falling into the class C-520, are used for automobile exhaust catalyst supports, experimental heat exchangers of various types, and other applications where severe thermal cycling up to 1000°C is involved. Of note is the microstructural anisotropy that has been advantageously developed in certain types of thin-walled honeycomb extruded cordierite products. By suitable choice of raw materials, the cordierite grains produced on firing are aligned so as to minimize the (crystallographically anisotropic) thermal expansion in the plane of the honeycomb walls (see US Patent 3,885,977).

Porous aluminous materials, IEC class C-530

This category (with an unspecified range of alumina contents) includes materials more refractory than those containing magnesia or those of substantial silica content included in class C-510. The allowable range of thermal expansion coefficient indicates that compositions over the range 50–85% Al_2O_3 can be included. The resulting crystalline phases are most likely to be mullite and alumina (for compositions above about 75% Al_2O_3), unless non-clay aluminosilicate minerals such as sillimanite and kyanite are included, which are not decomposed in the firing schedule. Microstructures are individual to particular products, but in general tend to comprise coarse filler particles of calcined clay, sillimanite or kyanite, bonded by a matrix originating from a fine particle size mixture of clay and alumina (or other source of Al_2O_3).

Porous high-alumina products

For products of more than about 80% alumina, see Section 2.2.2.1.

2.2.1.5 Aluminosilicate and mullite ceramics

This class, IEC class C-600, covers impermeable fine-grained materials which are used mainly for thermal shock resistant gas-tight tubing and for high-temperature electrical insulation where high strength and high dielectric strength, resulting from low porosity, are required. There are two subclasses according to Al_2O_3 content. Some of these materials have a small level of a fluxing agent included, and are sometimes known as refractory porcelains, and also (confusingly) as aluminous porcelains.

50–60% alumina content materials, IEC class C-610

Materials of this composition range are made from mixtures of clay and alumina, or clay and sillimanite or kyanite, or any other combination which contains the required amount of Al_2O_3. A small amount of a flux, which may be a feldspar or a non-alkali type such as MgO or CaO, is usually added to aid vitrification and densification to a closed porous state. In the fired state, the microstructure consists of a mass of small mullite crystals in a matrix of glassy phase which is highly siliceous in composition but contains the fluxing materials and most of the impurities from the clay. Typically, there is about 60% by volume of interconnected mullite crystals. There is some residual porosity, but this tends to be distributed as relatively large pores throughout the mass.

60–80% alumina content materials, IEC class C-620

This composition range encompasses that of mullite itself. In thermodynamic equilibrium in the typical firing temperature range up to 1650°C, the binary oxide system Al_2O_3–SiO_2 will comprise mullite and silica (usually cristobalite) below 71.8% Al_2O_3, and mullite and alumina above 71.8% Al_2O_3. In an actual material which may contain a few percent of additional components, the approach to thermodynamic equilibrium will depend on the firing conditions and the starting raw materials. The amount of mullite produced will depend on the percentage of silica compared to other non-aluminous components. For example, if a material has a nominal 75% Al_2O_3 content, uses alumina as a starting material, and contains say 15% SiO_2, and 10% CaO, this is a non-refractory material with a high flux level. It would not be fired to a high temperature, and the microstructure would comprise Al_2O_3 grains in an essentially glassy matrix which might partly devitrify on cooling to give some anorthite ($CaO.Al_2O_3.2SiO_2$). Such a material is strictly a highly debased alumina ceramic which is outside the range of alumina content allowed by class C-700, and in the IEC scheme and in this Handbook is classed as an aluminous porcelain (C-130). On the other hand if the material contains little CaO and more SiO_2, but the same alumina content, incorporated perhaps partly as sillimanite, the mixture is more refractory and a higher firing temperature is used. There is a closer approach to equilibrium, and extensive mullite formation, at the expense of alumina, can be expected. Such a material will have a lower coefficient of expansion and lower thermal conductivity than an aluminous porcelain of the same Al_2O_3 content. The refractoriness is determined by the amount and type of the glass. Although the intention of the IEC specification is to cover thermal shock resistant impervious materials (by comparing it with the DIN scheme on which it is based), materials that have properties meeting the specification for the subclass are not restricted in chemical or phase composition, and can have a wide range of crystalline compositions. Generally they are all very fine-grained, and have no open porosity, and most have some glassy bonding phase.

2.2.1.6 Chemical stoneware

By definition, stonewares should not be open porous. They can be used without a glaze, and chemically inert liquids should not penetrate them. This distinguishes them from materials to which the term stoneware is sometimes applied, but which are in fact earthenwares, and are porous and require a perfect glaze layer to prevent ingress of liquid. In this way a distinction can be drawn between materials designed for use in chemical plant, which should be impermeable, and materials of similar composition which are used for sanitary ware and for pipes such as sewers and gullies.

Chemical stonewares are a group of materials which are intended for use in corrosive environments, such as acid plant, etc. The materials are used in towers, pipes, supports, etc., in large pieces, and as such must be made with accurate control on shrinkage and dimensions. This is achieved economically by incorporating an 'grog' or coarse aggregate into a mixture of clays, a feldspar as a flux, and flint or fine sand. Apart from the grog, they are similar to electrical porcelain, but generally do not have the same low porosity level, tend to have less flux, and are primarily designed for cheapness rather than for quality. Corrosion resistance is similar to that of a conventional electrical porcelain as a result of the choice of flux level. However, it is generally recognised that chemical stoneware relies for its impervious nature on a skin which, if damaged, may admit liquid to the possibly open porous interior structure. Corrosion resistance tests must take this factor into account. The inclusion of talc or magnesia in the batch gives improved thermal shock resistance when this is required, due to the formation of cordierite which lowers the thermal expansion coefficient.

2.2.1.7 Aluminosilicate kiln furniture

The purpose of kiln furniture is to support a heavy load of shaped ceramic pieces during firing, and consequently it needs to be able to withstand thermal shock, both upward and downward, and to be strong and refractory so that it does not fail or distort unacceptably in use. Specialist manufacturers of kiln furniture have to operate between the constraints of dimensional control to the customers' requirements, cost, and desirable material properties. Most manufacturers have a wide range of compositions in frequent production, and most are based on aluminosilicates of various types. However, the current trend in the ceramic and allied trades is to fire products faster and to a higher temperature in order to save energy. It is therefore desirable to minimize the mass of kiln furniture that has to be heated, and at the same time, to use a more refractory system. The combination of good thermal shock resistance and refractoriness in cordierite-containing materials is becoming marginal for many applications and there is a trend towards using more expensive materials based on silicon carbide (see Section 2.2.3).

Aluminosilicate bodies used for kiln furniture are composed mainly of clays and a fairly coarse aggregate which may be a calcined and graded fireclay, or an aluminosilicate mineral such as sillimanite or kyanite. Talc is commonly added to produce cordierite in the fired product. The fired microstructures are composed essentially of the virtually unchanged aggregate particles bonded together with a matrix phase composed of fine crystals of mullite and cordierite (if talc is added) with a small amount of glassy phase, usually highly siliceous and containing impurities from the clays. There is always open porosity and this may improve resistance to thermal shock damage.

2.2.1.8 Machinable aluminosilicates

All ceramics can be machined with diamond tools, but from the engineering point of view it is sometimes useful to be able to fabricate a trial shape in a ceramic material that can be machined readily by ordinary machine tools. There are a number of such materials available; one has already been mentioned in section 2.2.1.2. Others are discussed elsewhere in this text, but in this section some comments are made about another popular type, pyrophyllite.

Pyrophyllite is a natural mineral found in a number of regions around the world in thick deposits. It is a massive, non-plastic version of a clay, an aluminosilicate of plate-like habit with some iron and alkali present as impurities. It is quarried in blocks and is supplied usually as plates, blocks, or rods. It can be machined readily by normal tools to accurate dimensions, and can be used in the as-machined state. Firing it to a ceramic form makes it stronger, but this has to be done cautiously, otherwise differential shrinkage can cause cracking. It is a hydrated mineral, and during firing, a ceramic bond is not developed until a temperature of around 1000°C is reached. Above this temperature vitrification commences, but the temperature should not be raised above about 1250°C, otherwise the form of silica known as cristobalite appears, which with its phase change at 180–250°C makes the material very susceptible to thermal shock; in fact the material may crack on cooling after firing. Material fired to a temperature in the range 1100–1250°C is generally acceptable, and has a low coefficient of expansion and good resistance to thermal shock. Maintenance of dimensions during firing can, however, pose a problem. As quarried, pyrophyllite is anisotropic, having been subjected to pressure across the geological bedding plane of its formation. This is reflected in dimensional changes during firing which are different in and across the bedding plane. In our experience, the orientation of the bedding plane is not well controlled in quarrying, and therefore shrinkage may be uneven, a circular shape tending to go oval. If experiments to find shrinkage as a function of firing temperature are made (for example, to obtain zero net shrinkage), the orientation of the bedding plane needs to be taken into account. Of course, the shape can be trued up afterwards by diamond grinding, but it is simpler to avoid this where possible. The microstructure of fired pyrophyllite is usually very fine, and in the correctly fired state consists of mullite crystals in a glassy matrix. As indicated above, over-firing devitrifies the glassy phase and cristoballite is produced.

2.2.2 Oxide-based materials

This Section deals with materials containing mainly synthetic oxides rather than major amounts of processed minerals. Many of the materials are not pure single oxides in the sense that they may contain other components which act as a bond for the major oxide, and at the same time make the material easier to manufacture, and perhaps more reproducible. These secondary components often form a glassy phase, and the composition of this glass is crucially important in determining the engineering properties.

Many sintered oxides are covered by the IEC classification scheme: e.g. class C-700 covers high-alumina ceramics with upward of 80% Al_2O_3 and no open porosity, and class C-800 covers BeO, MgO, and ZrO_2. The scheme is followed where appropriate, but there are other materials which are not covered.

2.2.2.1 High-alumina ceramics

Alumina-based materials are probably the best known group of engineering ceramics, and are manufactured by a number of firms in the UK, each of which tends to specialize in particular established markets. Materials are made in a very wide variety of types suitable for particular applications, and consequently there is a wide range of compositions and microstructures, particularly among the 'debased' materials which contain moderate amounts of other components, principally SiO_2, CaO, and MgO. The easiest way of discussing this variety is to commence with pure Al_2O_3, and then examine the influence of additional components.

First, some general comments are made:
1. Materials for high-temperature applications, such as tubing, thermocouple sheaths, boats, etc., need to have a minimum of glassy phase which is not refractory, and a large grain size up to 200 μm is advantageous. The alumina content is typically more than 99%, but for temperatures below about 1200°C, glass-containing materials may be used if their electrical characteristics are adequate.
2. Materials for high strength need to have a fine grain size, typically less than a mean value of about 8 μm. This is most readily obtained in debased materials which can densify in firing without excessive grain growth from the original alumina particle size.
3. Materials for wear resistance need also to have fine grain size, generally finer than materials for 2. above, 3 to 5 μm being typical mean values.
4. Materials for resistance to chemical corrosion need to be chosen with great caution, because many 'standard' varieties are designed for purposes other than corrosion resistance. Furthermore, materials stated to be acid-resistant may not also be alkali-resistant. Tests at NPL have shown that even in materials of 99.5% purity, the glassy phase determines corrosion resistance, and in fact some 95% aluminas show better performance than 'high-purity' products.
5. Electrical and dielectric properties depend on composition. Electrical resistance is greatest and dielectric loss factor is lowest in materials of highest alumina content and lowest alkali content.
6. Some alumina ceramics designed for electrical insulation have relatively coarse grain sizes, and are weaker than materials for general mechanical and electrical uses. The reason for this is that they may be more readily metallized in the high-temperature molybdenum-manganese process, and distort less under load at high temperatures than fine-grained materials.
7. Some materials are deliberately coloured, usually for commercial reasons, but sometimes because the choice of composition suits a particular manufacturing method or final product. In the former case, colouring agents

do not significantly affect engineering properties. Further comments on colour are given at the end of this Section.

8. Materials are usually classified by their oxide content, i.e. the percentage of Al_2O_3. Care needs to be exercised in using this figure to compare performance because depending on the nature of the other components and the firing schedule, it does not necessarily indicate the percentage of Al_2O_3 crystals in the microstructure. Some Al_2O_3 may be included as a clay in the starting batch, and may end up in the glassy phase.

9. The IEC classification divides 'high-alumina ceramics' into four classes based on nominal alumina content. In this Handbook, which deals with applications other than the electrical and electronic ones for which the IEC scheme was devised, it is necessary to use alternative groupings, partly by application, in order to cover all materials manufactured. In addition, there are a large number of materials which by virtue of their nominal alumina content could be placed in either of two IEC categories. The ranges chosen here avoid this problem by being placed at alumina content levels between those commonly being manufactured. At the same time it should be appreciated that in view of the diversity of material compositions, grain sizes, and shaping techniques, classification in this way does not guarantee properties. For some applications it may well be that a material with lower alumina content may have more appropriate properties for a given application than one with higher alumina content, even though the general trend of properties with alumina content may suggest that a higher alumina content could be used to advantage.

High-purity aluminas ($>99.9\%$ Al_2O_3) (IEC class C-799)

Very high purity alumina powders are used to produce essentially single-phase ceramics of fairly uniform grain size. Since densification on firing is by solid-state sintering, firing without externally applied pressure tends to result in grain growth, and a small amount of MgO, typically 0.05%, may be added to suppress this. Otherwise, mean grain sizes may reach 20–50 μm. Products fired in air usually contain some residual closed porosity, although recent developments in the production of the starting powder mean that it is now possible to achieve very low levels of residual porosity, $<0.2\%$. Complete elimination of porosity can be achieved by firing in a reducing atmosphere, often hydrogen, and coarse-grained materials produced in this way, such as those used for sodium vapour lamp envelopes (Figure 2.2.2), may be translucent or transparent. If pressure is applied to enhance sintering (i.e. hot-pressing), then fine-grained materials may be made without the use of an MgO addition, e.g. with equiaxed grains 1–2 μm across, and almost pore-free.

Aluminas with $>99.7\%$ Al_2O_3 (IEC class C-799)

Very high purity levels are not normally used for refractory products on grounds of cost. The starting raw material may be 99.8% pure, and is either used at this purity level or has some MgO added. This addition, typically at the 0.1% level, controls grain growth at high temperatures during sintering. Refractory products without added MgO are ideally suited for very high temperature use, but have large mean grain sizes, up to 100 μm, and are relatively weak (Figure 2.2.3). When MgO is added the grain size is considerably reduced and the product (Figure 2.2.4) is stronger, an advantage for rods or tubing of small diameter or wall thickness. Both types of material have some porosity, and in the coarse-grained materials some may be open. Pores tend to occur at grain boundaries in finer-grained materials, but may also be within grains in the coarser-grained materials.

Figure 2.2.2
Microstructure of a sintered translucent 99.9% alumina, showing no residual porosity.

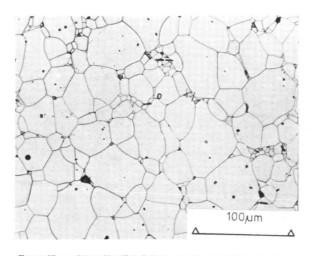

Figure 2.2.3
Microstructure of a so-called 'recrystallized' 99.8% alumina with very large grain size and some porosity.

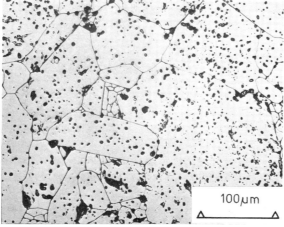

Figure 2.2.4
Microstructure of a 99.7% alumina with some MgO added for grain size control (c.f. Figure 2.2.3).

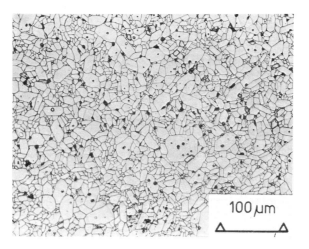

Aluminas with 99.0–99.7% Al_2O_3 (IEC class C-799)

Many alumina ceramics for electrical and engineering applications fall into this group. Other components may be added as well as MgO, primarily for control of electrical properties. The production of a stable glassy phase in small amounts also assists process control. Microstructurally, the glassy phase is very difficult to observe, and the materials appear essentially single-phase under the microscope. The average grain size is in the range 2–25 μm, depending on the product, fine-grained ones being particularly strong, while the coarser-grained ones are primarily designed for electrical insulation and resistance to high-temperature deformation in metallizing. In the latter category, there may be a wide spread of grain size within an examined cross-section (Figure 2.2.5 and Figure 2.2.6).

Aluminas with 96.5–99.0% Al_2O_3 (IEC classes C-799 and C-795)

Materials in this category have a deliberately-formulated glassy phase produced by the addition of small amounts of SiO_2, MgO, and CaO, often for the express purpose of controlling behaviour in the molybdenum-manganese metallizing process.

Their microstructures all show evidence of a glassy phase at the grain boundaries and in isolated pockets. However, a high proportion of the grain boundary area may be glass-free, revealed only by thermal etching. Some for general engineering applications have fine grain sizes, whilst others for metallizing have average grain sizes typically of 12–20 μm. Porosity is usually low, about 1–5%, and should be closed to qualify for the IEC class.

Aluminas with 94.5–96.5% Al_2O_3 (IEC classes C-795 and C-786)

These materials tend to have a rather lower firing temperature than those of higher alumina content because reliance is placed on densification by vitrifying the secondary components. Some materials have microstructures showing a uniform distribution of alumina crystals completely isolated from each other by a glassy phase. Others fired to rather higher temperatures than those required solely to effect densification show some recrystallization of alumina to give an interconnected network (Figure 2.2.7 and Figure 2.2.8). Porosity occurs almost exclusively in the glassy material. Some secondary crystalline phases are usually evident, if not in the microscope then almost certainly by X-ray powder diffraction. The identity of these phases depends not only on the added components, but also on the firing temperature and cooling rate, which determine the chemical state of the glassy material. Phases such as anorthite ($CaO.Al_2O_3.2SiO_2$), mullite ($3Al_2O_3.2SiO_2$), cordierite ($2MgO.2Al_2O_3.5SiO_2$), and calcium hexaluminate ($CaO.6Al_2O_3$) may be present, or may be induced to crystallize during prolonged heating at temperatures above about 900°C. The effect of these phases on properties is not known in detail. As with the previous group, materials for high-temperature metallizing have relatively coarse grain sizes. Some have ZrO_2 added to improve resistance to distortion during metallizing.

Some products in this group contain manganese and titanium oxides, and are dark brown in colour. The aim is to achieve densification at lower temperatures than for the conventional types by forming a manganese-containing liquid phase. Microstructures are substantially glass-free, fine-grained and reminiscent of a 99% Al_2O_3 product. Electrical properties and refractoriness are not so good as for the conventional types (Figure 2.2.9).

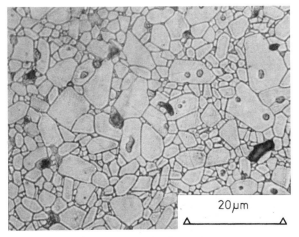

Figure 2.2.5 Microstructure of a fine-grained 99.5% alumina ceramic.

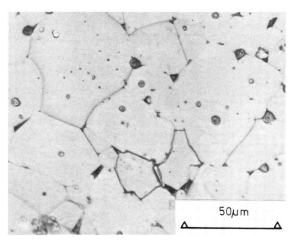

Figure 2.2.6 Microstructure of a coarse-grained 99.5% alumina ceramic suitable for high-temperature metallizing.

Figure 2.2.7 Microstructure of a 95% alumina ceramic showing the glassy phase between the grains.

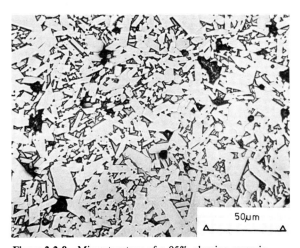

Figure 2.2.8 Microstructure of a 95% alumina ceramic showing some grain growth and development of alumina/alumina grain boundaries.

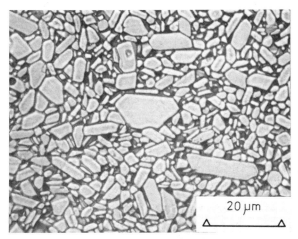

Figure 2.2.9 Microstructure of a 96% alumina containing MnO and TiO_2, with very little glassy phase evident.

35

Aluminas with 86–94.5% Al_2O_3 (IEC class C-786)

The vast majority of products in this range of alumina content are non-refractory and are intended for use as electrical insulators or mechanical components. The inclusion of substantial amounts of secondary components, typically SiO_2, CaO, and MgO, means that firing temperatures seldom exceed 1500°C, and there is a greater risk of distortion due to viscous sag. As with the previous group, products containing manganese and titanium oxides are available. Microstructural examination reveals that all materials are essentially glass-bonded, and some which employ non-equiaxed alumina particles as the starting raw material may show marked evidence of microstructural anisotropy, as well as anisotropy of properties (Figure 2.2.10).

Aluminas with 80–86% Al_2O_3 (IEC class C-780)

Two types of material fall into this category. One, as in the previous group, is non-refractory and applications tend to be limited to low temperatures and to non-critical uses, because strength is lower than with materials of higher alumina content. The other type is refractory, and contains much lower levels of fluxing components, i.e. the balance of the composition is primarily SiO_2. Such materials are composed mainly of mullite and alumina, and are refractory, similar to materials of class C-620. Materials in the IEC class C-780 should have no open porosity, should have a high strength and are usually fine-grained. The two types are not distinguished.

As noted earlier in Section 2.2.1.5, alumina ceramics with less than 80% Al_2O_3 fall into IEC categories C-620 and C-130.

Porous alumina ceramics

Porous materials of composition covering the range 80–99.9% Al_2O_3 are made for use as refractories, usually with a coarse grain size, and as filtration media, usually with a fine grain size and carefully controlled porosity levels. Refractory products with grain sizes up to 10 mm or more are intended for applications requiring high levels of resistance to corrosion or slag attack. The term 'fused alumina' may be used for such products. Some so-called 'recrystallized' aluminas, ones in which the fine initial particle size is allowed to grow as large as 1 mm during very high temperature firing, may also be open porous, and thus not fall within the scope of IEC class C-799.

Machinable alumina is essentially a porous, underfired, moderately fine-grained material containing usually at least 95%, commonly 98% Al_2O_3. It may be supplied in the form of blanks which have been fired sufficiently to bond the particles weakly together so as to make the mass rigid, but friable. Alternatively it may be supplied in a castable form, in which case it contains a calcium aluminate cement. Such materials can be machined, or rather chipped, to shape by tungsten carbide tipped tools. As they are dimensionally stable to temperatures typically in excess of 1200°C, they do not usually require refiring. The microstructure is of alumina grains weakly bonded to each other, with a high porosity level, typically 40%.

Alumina-titania ceramics

The permittivity of rutile (the stable form of TiO_2) is high, about 80, whereas that of alumina is lower, about 10. For some electronic applications it is desirable to increase the dielectric constant of alumina ceramics, and this may be done by additions of TiO_2. At high temperatures, alumina and titania

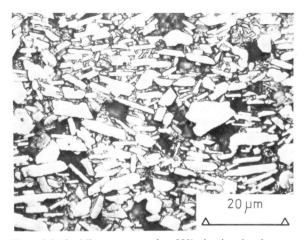

Figure 2.2.10 Microstructure of an 88% alumina showing alignment of the alumina grains in an extruded product with the extrusion axis horizontal.

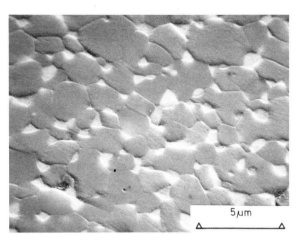

Figure 2.2.11 Microstructure of a zirconia-toughened alumina with fine grain size and very little porosity.

react to form a compound, aluminium titanate, but below about 1150°C, the compound dissociates slowly to alumina and titania. Strong ceramics of this type need a heat treatment below this temperature after firing to effect the dissociation. For applications requiring a rather higher level of permittivity than that offered by rutile itself, various forms of titanate, e.g. barium titanate and its derivatives, are commonly used. Other carefully controlled additions may be made in order to modify the temperature coefficient of capacitance. Products of this type are usually specials.

Alumina-zirconia ceramics

Recent developments in the field of toughening of ceramics involve additions of 10–20% by weight zirconia to alumina.

By careful control of particle size and zirconia stabilizer levels (see below), an enhancement of strength and apparent toughness over that shown by the best high-alumina products may be obtained. Such materials are being sold as machine tool tips, and other markets may follow. The microstructure of such material shows a uniform distribution of zirconia particles, usually in the size range 0.2–0.4 μm, in a 1–3 μm mean grain size alumina matrix (Figure 2.2.11).

Alumina-titanium carbide ceramics

Materials of this type have been developed for use as throw-away tool inserts for machining of metals. High-purity alumina in a fine-grained, hot-pressed form can be used for machining, but the addition of titanium carbide increases strength and stiffness by an extra margin. Typical compositions contain 20–40% TiC, and microstructures are fine-grained, two-phase, with very low porosity and essentially no glassy phase. The materials are hot-pressed under reducing conditions, and are black in colour.

Single-crystal alumina (sapphire and ruby)

Synthetic crystals of alumina, with or without dopants, can be grown by high-temperature processes. The term ruby refers to chromium doping and such materials are used for bearings and for laser elements. The name sapphire tends to be used for transparent, undoped alumina, which also has the mineral name corundum. Sapphire is used for windows and for other applications involving high temperatures, and for bearings and wear-resistant applications requiring high hardness.

Microstructurally, single-crystal alumina is featureless, but may contain crystallographic twins which can affect optical and thermal expansion properties. Examination between crossed polarizers will identify the presence of such defects.

Colour in alumina ceramics

Pure alumina ceramics are white when optically opaque. Materials with a small amount of MgO added for grain size control tend to be slightly yellow (the term 'peach' is sometimes used) when fired under oxidizing conditions, but white when fired in reducing conditions. This is associated with weak colour centres produced by impurities. Sometimes such products are cored, white in the centre and yellowish on the exterior. This reflects changes in gas-fired furnace atmosphere as the temperature is changed, initially reducing but becoming oxidizing at the maximum temperature when there is no longer open porosity which allows the interior to change colour at the same rate as the surface. This is usually of no consequence.

The colouring of materials pink, green or blue is done for commercial or identification reasons only. A small amount of a transition metal oxide such as Cr_2O_3, Fe_2O_3, FeO, NiO, CoO, or TiO_2 (and combinations) colours alumina crystals by producing optical colour centres. Manufacturers have in fact followed nature in its production of ruby (red), sapphire (blue), and other coloured varieties of corundum. This colouring changes properties other than optical ones very little, as the additions are bound in the alumina crystals in solid solution. The thermal expansion coefficient may change by a small amount if large amounts of colouring addition are made. Usually the addition is only a fraction of 1% by weight.

Materials deliberately coloured dark brown were originally designed for electronic substrates and other small components which were to be used in association with photodiodes, requiring low ambient light reflection. However, the same, or similar materials are sold for general engineering use. The brown coloration is usually due to MnO, a moderate addition of which to the raw material can lower the firing temperature by producing a reactive glass-forming bond. The colour can vary between the outer surface of a fired component and its interior, due again to variations in furnace atmosphere during firing.

Specks of metallic impurity in the unfired material, picked up during batch handling, pressing, machining, or setting for the kiln, can cause spots of colour in the fired product as these produce colour centres in the same way as deliberate additions. Deliberate coloration of the product tends to mask these spots. In some cases where there is a large speck of metal, reaction with any silicate phase can leave an undesirable fusion spot which may affect properties and performance. Inspection procedures in manufacture usually eliminate components with such defects at the surface.

2.2.2.2 Zirconia ceramics

There are relatively few commercial forms of dense zirconia ceramic available at the time of writing, and therefore generalizations like those described for alumina ceramics cannot be made. For electrical purposes, all zirconia ceramics fall into IEC class C-830.

Zirconia has three attributes that alumina does not possess; firstly, it is more refractory, having a melting point about 500°C higher; secondly, it can be machined readily to give a good surface finish which has a low coefficient of friction against metals; and thirdly it is a useful oxygen ion conductor at temperatures above about 500°C. However, because it is more expensive than alumina, it is not used for applications where alumina suffices.

Zirconia has the complication of phase instability. In its pure form, it is crystallographically monoclinic at room temperature, changes to a tetragonal form with considerable volume shrinkage at about 1200°C, and changes again to a cubic form at about 2370°C. These transitions mean that a pure zirconia ceramic, fired in the cubic state, would virtually disintegrate on cooling due to the various volume changes. However, it is possible to suppress these transitions and retain the cubic phase to room temperature by the addition of a stabilizing oxide, such as CaO, MgO, Y_2O_3, and combinations of these. In this way so-called 'fully-stabilized' materials can be made by conventional powder pressing and sintering routes. The long-term stability of the 'stabilized' state at high temperature is not guaranteed, because of the possibility of a very slow degradation of the solid solution produced by the stabilizing oxide, particularly when held at temperatures between about 800–1100°C. Materials stabilized only with MgO appear to destabilize most readily (according to the literature). Fully-stabilized materials are used for the manufacture of oxygen probes (devices for recording oxygen partial pressure in a gas stream), small crucibles, dishes etc., and heating elements for operation to high temperatures in air.

Materials which do not contain sufficient stabilizer to effect complete stabilization are known as 'partially-stabilized' (p.s.z.). While a proportion of the grains are in the stable cubic form, the remainder are unstable and at room temperature are in the monoclinic state. The unstabilized grains cause a degree of internal cracking at grain boundaries on cooling, which renders the material weaker than the fully-stabilized form, but rather better in resistance to thermal shock damage (see Section 2.5.2.3). ZrO_2 has a high thermal expansion coefficient and a low thermal conductivity, which give the fully-stabilized material poor thermal shock performance.

Development of tough partially-stabilized materials has been reported in the literature. These have now reached the market as reproducible commercial materials. The toughening is based on the extended controlled heat treatment at 1300–1400°C to precipitate the tetragonal phase on a very fine scale within crystals of the cubic, stabilized form. On subsequent cooling, the fine scale of the precipitate prevents it from transforming to the monoclinic form. However, in the neighbourhood of a free surface (including that of a propagating crack), transformation can occur with its associated volume increase, and this places the surface in compression. As a result, it is more difficult to cause a crack to propagate, and the material appears relatively tough and strong compared with both partially- and fully-stabilized forms in the as-sintered state. Ceramics with this type of strengthening could show advantages where resistance to impact is required.

Even more recent is the development of an all-tetragonal material, known as 'tetragonal zirconia polycrystal' (t.z.p.). This material is produced by hot-pressing or sintering a very fine starting powder of zirconia, retaining a fine sub-micron grain size which does not undergo the phase transformation to the monoclinic form on cooling. Toughness and strength are therefore enhanced in much the same way as in optimally-aged p.s.z., and strength figures in excess of $1 GNm^{-2}$ have been claimed. However, such a material is highly metastable, and there are reports of a tendency for uncontrolled destabilization at the surface, especially at elevated temperatures and in the presence of moisture. Current research is aimed at preventing the transformation by altering the surface composition in such a manner as to increase its stability. Clearly, reliable behaviour will need to be demonstrated before the material finds extensive application.

Table 2.2.1 summarizes typical stabilizer contents in various types of zirconia ceramics. This information is rarely given by manufacturers, so without direct interaction over the performance of a given product, it is usually not possible to establish precise stabilizer levels except by analysis.

Table 2.2.1 Typical stabilizer content of various forms of zirconia ceramic

Material type	Stabilizer type, mol%			
	CaO	MgO	Y_2O_2**	mixed**
Fully-stabilized*	10–15	12–16	6–9	any appropriate combination
Partially-stabilized	4–8	5–8	2–5	e.g. 2–5 MgO plus 2–5 CaO
Toughened, partially-stabilized	5–9	7–9	2–4	any appropriate combination
Tetragonal zirconia polycrystals (t.z.p.)	0–2	0–2	0–1	any appropriate combination

* Lower levels of stabilizer require higher initial firing temperatures to achieve the cubic state, and tend to be less stable in the temperature range 700–1000°C.
** Y_2O_3 is expensive, and is only used in high value products when essential. The tendency is therefore to use MgO and CaO where possible. Y_2O_3-containing materials are said to destabilize less readily at high temperatures than CaO- or MgO-containing materials.

Dense zirconia ceramics generally have a relatively large grain size, typically 15–40 μm, and may show evidence of some grain boundary phase, sometimes of glassy nature (Figure 2.2.12). This results from the impurities in the starting raw material, such as silica, iron, alkalis etc., combined with some of the stabilizer. As a rule, zirconia ceramics are not deliberately debased to produce a glassy phase in the same way as many alumina products.

In the case of optimally-toughened, partially-stabilized zirconia, electron microscopy reveals a second-phase precipitate in the form of small lenses with a crystallographic relationship to the relatively coarse-grained cubic matrix. The precipitate size is generally in the range 0.1–0.5 μm (Figure 2.2.13).

Coarse-grained, open-porous zirconia materials are made as refractories to withstand very high temperatures. They comprise stabilized zirconia grit bonded with a fine-grained stabilized zirconia matrix. They tend to be less pure than the fine-grained types used for technical applications, and may contain deliberate additions of materials such as clay to aid the formation of a bond.

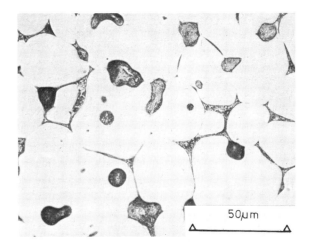

Figure 2.2.12
Microstructure of a CaO-stabilized zirconia showing coarse grains.

50μm

Figure 2.2.13
Microstructure within a single grain of an optimally-aged partially-stabilized zirconia, showing the tetragonal phase precipitate.

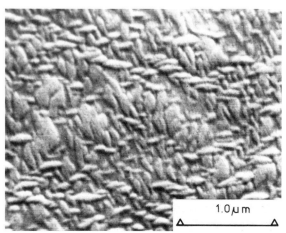

1.0μm

2.2.2.3 Titania ceramics, IEC class C-300

In many respects, titania ceramics have fewer uses nowadays than in the past when they were made in large quantities for applications requiring high permittivity. The formulation of titania-based materials can be very varied, depending on the dielectric properties required. For example, oxide additions of a variety of types are used to modify the temperature coefficient of permittivity. For such applications, materials based primarily on titania itself have, in the main, been replaced by materials based on titanates, compounds of titania and other oxides, but silicate-bonded materials (covered by class C-310) are still made in quantity for mechanical applications including thread guides. For such uses, a mixture of titania, with a small amount of a plastic clay and a flux, such as CaO, is shaped and fired to around 1300–1400°C. If fired in an oxidizing atmosphere, the material is generally pale buff coloured, but if fired in strongly reducing conditions, is black due to partial reduction of TiO_2 to a sub-stoichiometric form. This black form is semiconducting, and is used for thread guides for synthetic yarns so that static electricity generated by the running thread is discharged to earth.

Figure 2.2.14
Microstructure of a
silicate-bonded titania ceramic.

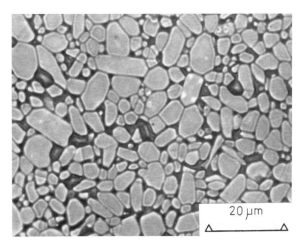

20 μm

The microstructure of titania-based materials comprising titania and a silicate bond is usually fine-grained with rutile as the major phase, and with some glassy phase acting as a matrix (Figure 2.2.14).

Various titanates are covered by other subclasses of the C-300 group, but are outside the scope of this Handbook.

2.2.2.4 Beryllia ceramics

Beryllia ceramics tend to be for specialized electrical or nuclear applications only, because the toxicity of beryllium and the cost of the raw material make manufacture expensive. However, the advantages outweigh the cost in some circumstances, such as in electronic devices, where a high thermal conductivity electrical insulator is required. Beryllia has the highest thermal conductivity of all insulating ceramic materials, approaching that of copper at room temperature.

The microstructure of beryllia ceramics is reported to be highly dependent on the starting beryllia powder. In particular, some manufacturing routes for beryllia powder produce a proportion of needle-shaped grains which become aligned during, for example, extrusion to form a rod. In the fired product, these grow preferentially, and give some anisotropy of properties. A material with mean grain size 5 μm may have needles in it 200 μm long. However, if the firing conditions are such that matrix grain growth is allowed to occur on firing, the needles may recrystallize, so a 25 μm mean grain size material may show no evidence of anisotropy. Grain growth inhibition is said to be more difficult in beryllia than in alumina, although commonly a small amount of MgO is added for this purpose. Most beryllia ceramics with more than 99% BeO have quite coarse grain sizes, e.g. in the range 8–100 μm with a mean of 20–30 μm. However, a fine grain size material can be made by close control of raw materials and firing conditions. Porosity is primarily at grain boundaries, and once it is reduced to a low level during firing, rapid grain growth occurs. Closed porosity levels are typically 1–5% by volume.

For general electrical purposes, materials containing about 96% BeO are available. These have a glassy bonding phase, much as in the debased aluminas, which helps densification at a lower firing temperature with less risk of grain growth. Because the glassy phase has a much lower thermal conductivity than the beryllia itself, the thermal conductivity of debased beryllias is significantly lower than that of 99% BeO materials.

Beryllia single crystals have substantial anisotropy of thermal expansion, so that in polycrystalline materials, thermal stresses are set up on cooling from the firing temperature. These are more troublesome than the slight anisotropy in alumina, and thus medium to coarse-grained materials tend to be rather weaker than their alumina equivalents.

Beryllia ceramics for electrical and electronic applications fall into IEC class C-810.

2.2.2.5 Magnesia ceramics

There are few commercially available dense magnesia ceramics of engineering type, primarily because magnesia possesses few property advantages over alumina. On the other hand, magnesia refractories are used extensively for their relatively high thermal conductivity, their refractoriness, and their resistance to basic slags. Magnesia ceramics tend therefore to be used in applications requiring resistance to corrosion at high temperatures.

Pure MgO will sinter to a coarse-grained, open-porous ceramic, but removal of all porosity and retention of a fine-grained form is difficult without hot-pressing. Some impervious products for crucibles, tiles, etc., are made from a magnesia with 2–5% of clay added. This helps the product to sinter by producing a liquid phase, observable as a second phase in the microstructure (Figure 2.2.15). Magnesia ceramics for electrical purposes are covered by IEC class C-820, which allows up to 30% porosity. The primary intention is that this class should cover the use of MgO in a form suitable for use as a crushable insulator in mineral-insulated cabling.

Magnesia single crystals may be used for infra-red windows and are optically transparent. Magnesia powder may be hot-pressed (usually with a small amount of lithium fluoride) to a transparent form.

Figure 2.2.15
Microstructure of a
silicate-bonded impervious
magnesia ceramic.

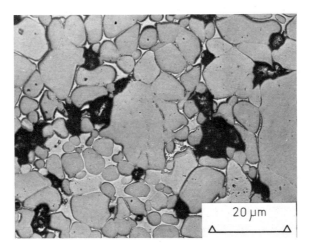

2.2.2.6 Spinel ceramics

The mixed oxide, magnesium spinel $MgO.Al_2O_3$, is made in fine-grained form for applications where the corrosion resistance of alumina is insufficient. Otherwise, the material shows no specific advantages over high-alumina ceramics. Hot-pressed transparent spinels have been made for some specialist applications. No useful comment can be made about microstructure because there are few commercial sources.

2.2.2.7 Zircon ceramics

Zirconium silicate is a natural mineral found mainly as a sand. It is used extensively in the steel industry as a casting sand, and in the glass industry in refractories to resist corrosion by silicate melts. It is a compound of silica and zirconia ($ZrSiO_4$), and is stable to about 1700°C. Above this temperature it dissociates to its component oxides, giving a zirconia precipitate in a silica glass.

Zircon porcelains, mentioned earlier, contain a substantial proportion of zircon, but rely on vitrification of other components to form a dense impervious ceramic. Zircon itself can be made into a ceramic, but care has to be taken that the high-temperature sintering process does not cause dissociation, otherwise cristobalite forms and the refractoriness of the material is reduced. Zircon ceramics are not commonly available, and are usually made to special order.

2.2.2.8 Other oxide ceramics

There is a range of other types of oxide-based ceramics for engineering applications. These include CaO, ThO_2, UO_2, and mixed oxides such as materials based on $LaCrO_3$. Materials of these types are not commonly available, and usually have rather specific applications. For example, $LaCrO_3$ materials are used for electric heating elements for furnaces. Some details are included in Part 2. In addition there is a wide range of oxides used specifically for electronic or optical properties, such as ferrites, zirconates, titanates and zirconate-titanates. It is not the intention of this Handbook to cover such materials.

2.2.3 Non-oxide ceramics

The vast majority of silicate and oxide-based materials are given a simple firing in air, or in a slightly reducing atmosphere, to effect densification either by vitrification or by sintering. With non-oxide materials, high-temperature processing to produce a bond between particles of the starting raw material generally has to be undertaken in the absence of oxygen. The reason is that virtually all useful carbides, borides and nitrides do not possess sufficient resistance to oxidation to enable them to be processed in air. Furthermore, most non-oxides of interest cannot readily be sintered in the absence of pressure, and the use of vitrified bonding phases is usually not appropriate. Thus in the main, non-oxide ceramics are made by specialized routes, and the composition and microstructure reflect the manufacturing method.

In this Section, the major non-oxide materials are described, together with their manufacturing methods. These methods were introduced in general terms at the beginning of Section 2.2, but the following notes are made with specific reference to non-oxides:

1. *Sintering* can be used for some materials, but tends not to be a particularly satisfactory method for non-oxides because of their refractory nature. It is usually necessary to add a dopant to enhance the sintering process at grain boundaries. For some mixed oxide/nitride systems, sintering in the presence of a liquid phase, or by reaction between components, is now well developed – see 4. below.

2. *Hot-pressing* can be used to densify a non-oxide. It is usually necessary to add a small quantity of an oxide or other material to aid the process.

3. *Reaction-bonding* is a common method of bonding precursor particles together. The usual technique is to produce the ceramic species in situ between the precursor particles by reaction of its components. For example, silicon carbide particles may be bonded by silicon carbide produced in situ by reaction between carbon and silicon in liquid or vapour form, or as silicon monoxide vapour. The term is also used to describe the conversion of a silicon powder compact to silicon nitride by heating in nitrogen.

4. *Bonding with a second phase* is used for a number of types of material. In a sense this is equivalent to vitrification in silicate materials. Examples are the bonding of silicon carbide with a clay-derived aluminosilicate, the sintering of silicon nitride materials with oxide additions, and the manufacture of metal carbide based materials with metals, notably cobalt. The manufacture and properties of hardmetals (tungsten carbide based cermets) are subjects in their own right, and are included here only in general terms for comparison purposes.

5. *Chemical vapour deposition* is a method of manufacture of components by reaction between gases. The product may be either a thin-walled free-standing component or a coating on another material. The method is used for graphite, boron nitride, silicon carbide and silicon nitride in particular. The term 'pyrolytic' may also be used.

6. *Reaction-converted materials* are those in which the original form is changed by a chemical reaction which alters the surface layer to advantage. For example, carbon or graphite can be converted to silicon carbide by heating in a silicon-containing medium such as silicon monoxide vapour. The reaction converts the surface layer of the original piece to silicon carbide, increasing the hardness while retaining the shape.

2.2.3.1 Silicon carbide materials

Silicon carbide is a hard semiconducting material and has been used in ceramics for many years. The high-temperature stable phase, alpha-SiC, is crystallographically hexagonal, and is the form normally made by the reduction of silica sand by carbon in an arc furnace. It exists in a number of forms with various stacking arrangements of the atomic planes. Beta-SiC is crystallographically cubic, and is produced by low-temperature vapour phase reactions. This form converts to the alpha form at temperatures in excess of 2000°C. Silicon carbide is very refractory, tending to dissociate at temperatures above 2500°C, and as a consequence is difficult to sinter, although this can be done. More usually other methods are used to make ceramics.

Clay-bonded silicon carbide

Bonding silicon carbide in this way involves the use of from 10–50% of a clay-based material. This type of product is usually fairly coarse grained and open porous, and is used as a refractory product in conditions requiring thermal shock resistance. A typical microstructure is shown in Figure 2.2.16. The refractoriness is clearly limited by the performance of the clay bond. The chemical bond between clay and grit is formed by a silica layer produced on the silicon carbide during firing. This layer is a viscous glass to which the vitrified clay adheres and which seals the surface of the grit particles against further oxidation. This same mechanism enables silicon carbide materials to be used in air to high temperatures with only low oxidation rates, whereas other non-oxides not containing silicon are not capable of forming the protective layer and thus have rather more severe temperature limitations on use in air.

'Self-bonded' silicon carbide

This term, or alternatively 'reaction-bonded' or 'reaction-sintered', is used for materials in which a silicon carbide bond is developed at relatively low temperatures between the grains of silicon carbide. Such materials are made by pressing a powder compact of silicon carbide powder, carbon and a temporary binder. The binder in the pressed shape is then carbonized, and the porous body subjected to liquid silicon (either by incorporating silicon powder in the starting batch or by infiltration by capillary rise), silicon vapour, or silicon monoxide vapour. This reacts with the carbon, producing silicon carbide which is deposited on the pre-existing grains, eventually bonding them together.

With the liquid infiltration method, the most commonly used for fine-grained, fully-dense products, some residual silicon remains visible in micrographs as a light-coloured phase in islands between silicon carbide aggregates (e.g. Figure 2.2.17). Processing techniques vary considerably between different manufacturers and result in a wide variety of microstructures. Materials may have a free silicon content between about 8 and 40 vol.%. Most have very little porosity, just a fraction of a percent of isolated pores in areas not completely infiltrated. Average grain sizes vary between about 2 and 50 μm, sometimes even greater, up to 1 mm. Often the surface skin on the as-fired product has a different microstructure from the bulk due to the processing method. During carbonization of the binder, the surface may be deliberately oxidized to remove some carbon. This creates a more porous skin through which silicon can infiltrate more quickly. A large piece can then be infiltrated more uniformly than by capillary rise through the less porous interior alone. The result is a skin containing a high proportion of free silicon. This is often removed by machining to the final required shape as most of the applications of this high-strength version are in mechanical engineering.

Figure 2.2.16
Microstructure of a
clay-bonded silicon carbide
used for refractory tubing.

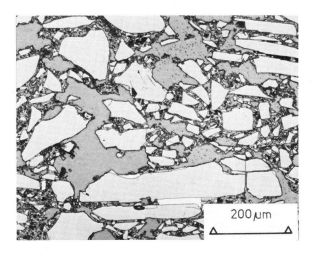

Figure 2.2.17
Microstructure of a
reaction-bonded silicon
carbide produced by the liquid
infiltration technique.

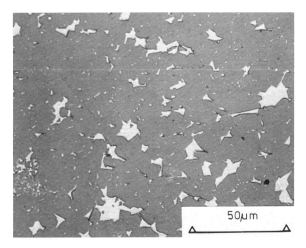

The porosity in the porous versions, such as those incorporating silicon powder or those subjected to vapour-phase reactions, can be closed by subsequent infiltration with liquid silicon. The same process may also be applied to the recrystallized type (see below), simply filled with silicon after the sintering stage. Such products tend to be indistinguishable from reaction-bonded types.

The interconnected matrix of silicon can be removed altogether by leaching in an HF/HNO_3 mixture, leaving an open-porous refractory material for use in situations where the presence of silicon vapour or liquid would be undesirable.

Hot-pressed silicon carbide

Hot-pressed products can be made provided a small amount of a secondary material, usually an oxide, is added to the starting material. A typical material might contain, say, 2% Al_2O_3, which is readily deformable at the hot-pressing temperature, and which is suitably refractory for subsequent use of the product. Hot-pressed silicon carbide is extremely fine-grained, has essentially zero porosity, and is hard and strong. However, it is also very

Figure 2.2.18
Microstructure of a sintered alpha-silicon carbide.

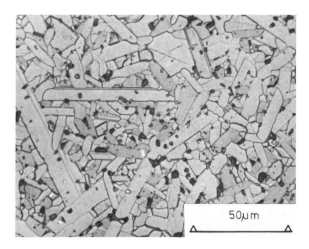

50μm

expensive to make because shapes have to be machined from pressed blanks. There is therefore increasing commercial interest in the production of an equivalent sintered material.

Sintered silicon carbide

Material of dense, engineering quality is made by high-temperature firing of silicon carbide powder with a suitable dopant added to enhance an otherwise sluggish sintering mechanism. Both alpha- and beta-SiC can be used, the latter tending to convert to the alpha form during the sintering although the extent of the transformation appears to depend on the dopant level and the firing temperature. Since the transformation is accompanied by grain growth of the alpha phase, the microstructure (typically as in Figure 2.2.18) can vary considerably. There is always some residual porosity between the grown alpha grains in the fine-grained matrix which may be primarily of the beta phase. See the relevant Data Sheet in Part 2 for further detail on this subject.

'Recrystallized' silicon carbide

This term is given to products which are of fairly coarse grain size, and which are sintered at high temperature to open-porous materials. The sintering process gives some additional grain growth and such materials have highly faceted surfaces. They are essentially single phase. Such materials are used for furnace elements, for refractory worktubes and holders, and for applications requiring very high refractoriness, particularly under vacuum or reducing conditions.

Silicon carbides for heating elements

Heating elements are made by a variety of methods, and these are usually proprietary. Some types are made by sintering a pressed or tamped alpha silicon carbide powder of a suitable range of grit sizes at a high temperature, usually 2200°C. Others are made by lower-temperature routes which produce beta-silicon carbide. Different manufacturers resort to different techniques in order to create a central zone of high resistance in a rod or tubular shape. One method is to infiltrate the element ends with molten silicon by capillary rise, e.g. by r.f. heating the end section. Another, applicable to tube geometries, is to cut a spiral of suitable pitch in the central zone. A further method is to make the end sections of lower resistivity separately from the central section, and then join them together in a separate operation using one of the self-bonding methods, such as carbon and silicon powders used as a cement.

The microstructures of heating element materials thus vary considerably depending on the manufacturing method. Generally speaking, those materials made from alpha silicon carbide grit as a starting material and which have experienced high-temperature sintering have the so-called 'recrystallized' appearance of faceted grains on the surface, and a coarse-grained appearance in cross-section. Those that have not experienced a temperature sufficient to cause sintering or recrystallization usually have much finer microstructures without the faceted appearance. Some examples are shown in Figures 2.2.19 and 2.2.20.

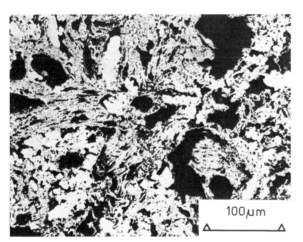

Figure 2.2.19 Microstructure of a beta-silicon carbide heating element made by reaction between silica and carbon.

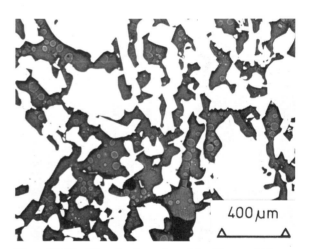

Figure 2.2.20 Microstructure of an alpha-silicon carbide heating element made by sintering silicon carbide at high temperatures.

Nitride-bonded silicon carbide

This is a reaction-bonded form, typically of relatively coarse grain size used for refractory materials. The material comprises alpha silicon carbide grit, to which is added silicon powder. The material is then moulded to the required shape, the temporary binder is removed, and the shape is then fired in a nitrogen atmosphere to a temperature of 1350–1450°C. In firing, the silicon reacts with nitrogen gas to form silicon nitride which bonds the silicon carbide particles together. Such a material contains typically 5–15% silicon nitride, and the remainder is silicon carbide, essentially unchanged by the firing. Alternative versions are available in which the bonding phase is an oxy-nitride, but details of the process are proprietary.

Nitride-bonded materials are open-porous, fairly coarse-grained, and are used for refractory bricks, tiles, tubes, and other shapes such as muffles and saggars. It is claimed that such materials have advantages over other forms of silicon carbide in terms of resistance to creep and to oxidation at high temperatures. Section thickness is limited to 80–100 mm by the need to obtain diffusion of nitrogen gas to the centre of the material.

Siliconized carbons and graphites

In these materials the surface layer of a carbon or graphite component has been impregnated with silicon. The reaction of silicon with carbon produces silicon carbide, which has rather different properties from the precursor carbon. In this way a component can be machined readily to size and required surface finish as a carbon or graphite, and the surface layer can then be hardened by the siliconizing treatment. The microstructure of such materials shows that there is a high content of silicon carbide in the immediate subsurface area, and this level drops with increasing depth into the material. The silicon carbide structure reflects the precursor carbon or graphite structure. The effectiveness of the siliconizing treatment depends on the conditions employed, and on the type of carbon or graphite, not all types being suitable. In particular, the depth of penetration of silicon will depend on the level of open porosity of the precursor carbon. The treatments tend to be proprietary in nature, but are based on heating the carbon or graphite shapes in silicon or silicon monoxide vapour. Depths of penetration of 0.25–2.5 mm are typical. The structures are usually open-porous after treatment. Figure 2.2.21 shows a typical microstructure.

Figure 2.2.21
Microstructure of a siliconized graphite showing the conversion of a surface layer to silicon carbide (the lighter phase). The outer surface is to the left.

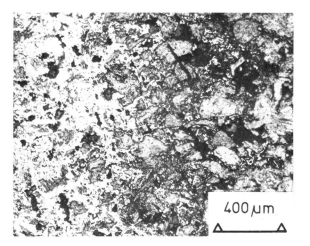

400 µm

C.v.d. or pyrolytic silicon carbide

Coatings or thin-walled components can be produced by reaction of a silicon-containing gas such as a silane or silicon tetrachloride with a carbon-containing gas. In such a reaction silicon carbide is deposited on a substrate heated to a suitable temperature. The morphology of the deposited material depends critically on the chosen conditions of deposition, particularly the temperature, gas mixture composition and flow rate, and the pressure. At low temperatures, small grains are deposited with low levels of porosity, but at higher temperatures there is an increasing tendency to produce larger, columnar grains and a rougher surface. Silicon carbide is usually deposited in the beta form, with a small amount of the alpha form.

2.2.3.2 Silicon nitride based materials

Silicon nitride materials have made their advance in the last 20 years primarily as a result of development efforts towards materials to replace metals as components in high-temperature engines. One of the primary advantages of silicon nitride is its low coefficient of thermal expansion, and hence its thermal shock resistance. Like silicon carbide, it can be used under oxidizing conditions to high temperatures because it too forms a protective layer of silica (SiO_2) on the surface, slowing down the rate of oxidation. Also like silicon carbide, it cannot be sintered readily, tending to dissociate at temperatures above 1850°C, and resort has to be made to manufacturing techniques which produce a bond by indirect methods.

Reaction-bonded silicon nitride (RBSN)

Reaction-bonding is the simplest and cheapest method by which silicon nitride ceramics are currently being made. The method is based on the conversion of a silicon powder compact to silicon nitride by heating in a nitrogen atmosphere. The reaction occurs by either a gas/solid or a gas/vapour reaction, depending on temperature, and produces very small crystals of silicon nitride which tend to fill the porosity in the original compact, with very little change in dimensions. However, since penetration of the gas to the centre of the shape being converted has to be maintained throughout the process, the materials are all open-porous, and claimed densities rarely exceed 85% of the theoretical $3.19 \ Mgm^{-3}$. Furthermore, particularly in the denser materials, conversion is seldom complete and a small amount of free silicon may remain. Weight gain during nitridation can be used as a monitor of the extent of reaction, and for complete conversion should theoretically be 66.49% (assuming no losses by vaporization of Si). In thick-walled items, the exothermic nature of the reaction can result in the melting of the silicon compact unless care is taken over heating rate. If this occurs, complete conversion of the solid mass of silicon is impossible. Although manufacturers are attempting to standardize their materials, it is probably true to say that RBSN on a commercial scale is somewhat variable as a result of two main factors: the starting raw material, and control over nitriding atmosphere. Extensive research in recent years has enabled the development of a fairly detailed picture of the factors affecting the nitriding process and the material properties achieved, so improvements in reliability should be expected in the future.

The variations of impurity levels in the starting raw silicon powder can be quite large, and somewhat erratic since semiconductor quality is not used. This can lead to variations in the nitridation process and in the microstructure produced, the latter affecting mechanical properties and oxidation resistance. Some of these factors are described in the relevant data sheet in Part 2.

The microstructure of RBSN is usually of submicron well-formed crystals of a mixture of two similar phases, alpha- and beta-Si_3N_4, with considerable interconnected porosity. The larger pores, $1–50 \ \mu m$ across, tend to result from voids in the original compact or from melting of silicon particles during nitridation. These are interconnected by channels which may be in the size range from $0.01–1.0 \ \mu m$ in diameter (Figure 2.2.22). In some circumstances, particularly at external surfaces, a whisker morphology of alpha-Si_3N_4 is developed (Figure 2.2.23), rendering the as-nitrided material a pale grey in colour, whereas the interior is generally dark grey. There is some scientific

Figure 2.2.22
Microstructure of a
reaction-bonded silicon nitride
showing the open pore
structure.

Figure 2.2.23
Whisker morphology of the
surface of as-fired
reaction-bonded silicon
nitride.

argument over the question of the respective origins of these phases which has yet to be conclusively resolved, but there is evidence that properties are affected by the relative proportions of the phases.

Hot-pressed silicon nitride (HPSN)

Unlike the reaction-bonded form, HPSN does not have the disadvantage of open porosity. However, because silicon nitride will not densify under pressure by itself at temperatures below its dissociation temperature of about 1850°C an oxide is added to facilitate densification by providing a liquid phase at the hot-pressing temperature, typically 1700–1800°C. This liquid phase solidifies and may crystallize after hot-pressing, and imposes a limitation on the temperature to which high strength is retained. However, at low temperatures the product, being essentially fully dense and very fine grained, is hard and strong and finds applications where these properties are required.

Typically an addition of 1–5% MgO is made depending on the requirement for refractoriness. During hot-pressing this reacts with silica impurity on the surface of the silicon nitride particles and produces a magnesium silicate glassy phase on cooling. Some solution of silicon nitride can also be expected, so the glass will show partial substitution of oxygen by nitrogen. Other impurities in the silicon nitride powder may be incorporated in the glass, and the resistance to high-temperature creep deformation will depend on the composition of the glassy phase, and hence on the impurity levels of the starting materials.

The microstructure of hot-pressed silicon nitride is usually very fine, with grains typically 0.7–1.5 μm separated by an intergranular amorphous phase (Figure 2.2.24). Other hot-pressing additions may produce other crystalline phases. Generally speaking such materials are at the research stage and most commercially available products contain MgO. The axiality of hot-pressing tends to produce an anisotropic microstructure with a smaller effective grain size parallel to the pressing direction than perpendicular to it. This has some effect on strength, but other properties are modified only slightly.

Figure 2.2.24
Microstructure of a hot-pressed silicon nitride showing the low porosity level and fine grain size.

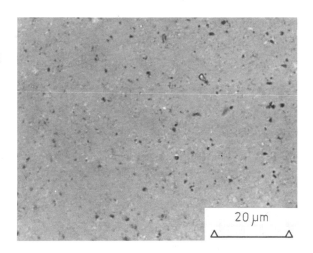

20 μm

'Sialons' and sintered silicon nitrides (SSN's)

These products are essentially varieties of silicon nitride which have been developed in order to employ sintering techniques instead of hot-pressing, which is expensive and limiting on shape, and reaction-bonding, which leaves the product with open porosity. 'Sialon' ceramics derive their name from an acronym of their principal components, Si, Al, O, and N. It has been found that the beta-silicon nitride crystal structure can accommodate aluminium in partial substitution for silicon, the charge deficiency being compensated by the equivalent substitution of oxygen for nitrogen to give a single-phase solid solution range, termed a 'beta-prime sialon'. Ceramic bodies of sialon composition can be made in two ways. Firstly they can be hot-pressed from mixtures of silicon nitride, alumina, silica and aluminium nitride in suitable proportions and secondly they can be sintered from similar mixtures but with additional components to enhance densification in the absence of pressure. In hot-pressing, the components react together in the presence of some liquid phase produced by the silica present, either deliberately added or as an impurity, and if the final composition lies in the solid solution range, the liquid eventually disappears to leave a single-phase material of nearly full density.

Over recent years, research effort has been aimed at sintering the materials to acceptable levels of density, and this has met with some success. The additive for sintering is usually an oxide or a combination of two oxides, and the composition of the starting powder mixture is such that not only is a high density achieved, but also the properties of the residual phase are controlled. This is particularly necessary in cases where the residual liquid phase is designed to crystallize to give good resistance to high-temperature creep and oxidation. The phases produced, typically mixed silicon-oxynitrides, need to be free from undesirable phase changes. As can be readily realized, such developments have made it necessary to study a completely new area of solid-state chemistry. Microstructure, properties and performance in terms of composition and manufacturing conditions are not well understood except in certain narrow areas. Microstructures are typically very fine grained, with substantial amounts of various second phases depending on the composition (Figure 2.2.25). Porosity may be as low in the sintered materials as in the hot-pressed materials. Manufacturing techniques are similar to those for oxide ceramics, and require the usual allowances for firing shrinkage and distortion. Firing is carried out in a nitrogen atmosphere. In view of the possibility of the dissociation of the starting silicon nitride at the sintering temperature (above 1800°C), pieces are typically packed in a buffering powder such as boron nitride.

Figure 2.2.25
Microstructure of a sintered sialon used as a machine tool tip.

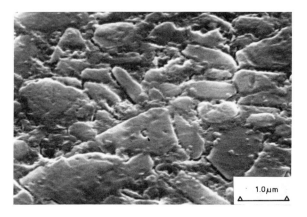

A similar method can be employed to sinter silicon nitride without the alumina in solid solution, but current developments are concentrating on a different route to sintering in order to reduce the shrinkage and thus obtain better control on dimensions. A compact of silicon with various oxides such as MgO, Al_2O_3 and Y_2O_3 is nitrided to a density higher than could be achieved by pressing the equivalent mix using silicon nitride powder. The nitrided body is then subjected to a high-temperature sintering process to effect full densification. Such materials are termed sintered silicon nitrides, and in some cases may be indistinguishable from sintered sialons in terms of microstructure.

C.v.d. or pyrolytic silicon nitride

This can be made by the reaction of a silicon-containing gas with a nitrogen-containing one, such as ammonia, over a heated substrate. As with pyrolytic silicon carbide, crystalline morphology depends on the deposition conditions. It can be made in transparent form. It is not generally commercially available at present.

2.2.3.3 Boron carbide ceramics

Boron carbide is one of the hardest of the commonly available ceramic materials. It is used for very abrasive conditions, such as in shot-blast nozzles, and for impact resistance, such as in air bearings and ballistic armour. However, it is expensive because of the difficulties of fabrication, and this tends to limit its application to critical areas where the improvement in performance compared to other candidate materials is economically worthwhile. Small shapes in boron carbide may be hot-pressed, and this remains the most common fabrication route. The microstructure produced depends on the carbon content of the starting material and the hot-pressing conditions. Porosity is generally very low, less than 1% in well-made material. Some free carbon may be present, but materials tend to be essentially single phase (Figure 2.2.26).

Boron carbide can be sintered, but requires a dopant, normally excess boron, and a very high sintering temperature, typically >2000°C. Porosity levels are higher than in hot-pressed materials, and the grain size tends to be greater.

Figure 2.2.26
Microstructure of a hot-pressed boron carbide.

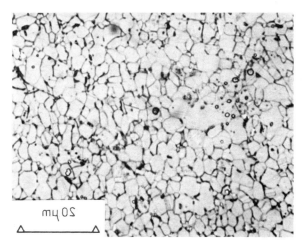

20 µm

2.2.3.4 Boron nitride ceramics

The three previous types of non-oxide materials are hard and difficult to make in dense form. Boron nitride is totally different in the sense that it has a crystal structure similar to that of graphite, i.e. it is platelike and in block form is soft and machinable like graphite. However, unlike graphite, it is an excellent electrical insulator, and is also not wetted by many metallic and non-metallic melts.

Boron nitride in solid form is usually made by hot-pressing boron nitride powder, and the material produced is anisotropic because of the tendency of the platelets to line up in planes perpendicular to the direction of pressing. The starting powder usually contains some oxygen, and this produces boric oxide, a glass former, which may affect properties, particularly the tendency to pick up moisture at ambient temperature. The microstructure of the hot-pressed material is very fine and is more or less impossible to observe in the bulk by polishing a section because the material is so soft.

Thin-walled shapes in boron nitride can be made by the c.v.d. or pyrolytic method, the material being deposited on a suitably shaped graphite or carbon substrate which is subsequently removed. The product has highly anisotropic properties because the platelet structure is orientated with the plane of the plate parallel to the plane of the substrate. Thermal and electrical conductivity parallel to and perpendicular to the substrate surface are quite different.

The boron nitride form discussed above is the one normally manufactured at low pressure. There is also a high-pressure cubic form which is totally different in the sense in which diamond is different from graphite. Cubic boron nitride (CBN) is now available as a grinding grit and is being developed in solid form (with a metal binder) for machining. It is exceptionally hard, but as yet is not available in ceramic form.

2.2.3.5 Boron nitride based composite ceramics

The ability to hot-press boron nitride with ease has led to its use as a matrix for other non-oxide ceramics. One important case is that of titanium diboride. A composite of titanium diboride and boron nitride is used for aluminium evaporators where resistance to aluminium at very high temperatures is required. The electrical resistivity of the material is controlled by the proportion of boron nitride.

Other materials have been produced but none have found regular application except for highly specialized uses, and they are not discussed here.

2.2.3.6 Carbon and graphite materials

Carbon and graphite materials are very widely used for a variety of engineering applications, and there is a very wide range of products available, worthy of a complete property review in their own right. Their inclusion in this Handbook is for comparison with ceramics in general terms. Carbon and graphite products comprise a mixture of precursor graphite or carbon particles pressed with a carbonaceous binder to a solid block. The block is then fired in reducing or inert conditions to carbonize the binder and bond the particles together. Precursor sources of carbon are usually coals which are coked to remove volatiles, and sources of graphite are usually natural deposits (e.g. from the Malagasy Republic). Binders are usually heavy oils or tars or other organic materials, the emphasis being on cheapness.

The microstructures, properties and performance of the fired materials reflect the source of the precursor material as this tends to be largely unchanged by the processing and firing. The microstructures tend to be complex, and to consist of islands of relatively high density originating from the precursor material, bonded by a lower density matrix, both parts usually being open porous except in products of the highest density. The graphite content of the material is determined by that of the starting mix, but can be enhanced by high-temperature firing as the amorphous carbon content starts to recrystallize. Many materials show some degree of anisotropy due to the orientation effects introduced by pressing or extrusion, and this is particularly noticeable in fine-grained graphite materials. This anisotropy is often visible in microstructures, and affects all properties.

Carbon fibre can be produced by the controlled carbonization of polymer fibre, and has particularly advantageous strength and stiffness for the production of fibre composite materials. One type of material worthy of mention in the context of this Handbook is the carbon/carbon fibre composite for refractory applications. If a polymer/carbon fibre material is made using a suitable polymer, and this composite is then carbonized at high temperature, the product is stable up to a temperature where additional graphitization occurs. It is usually open porous and has a low density but is stiff and strong.

Another material of note is so-called *vitreous carbon*. This is produced by the controlled carbonization of a cross-linked polymer which has a suitable structure to prevent, or at least delay, the formation of graphite during the carbonization treatment. The required shape is made in the polymer, and is retained during carbonization to give a product which appears glassy, is X-ray amorphous and has no open porosity, but a low density. It is therefore useful as a crucible material for containing reactive melts.

Pyrolytic graphite is produced on a removable substrate by a vapour-phase reduction process under controlled conditions. It is a highly anisotropic material in which the graphite platelets are aligned parallel to the substrate surface, and this anisotropy is reflected in all properties, particularly thermal and electrical ones.

2.2.4 Melt-formed ceramics and glasses

2.2.4.1 Glasses

The strict definition of a glass is 'an inorganic product of fusion which has been cooled to a rigid state without the formation of crystalline phases'. A glass is therefore not representative of an equilibrium state in phase terms, and should be considered as a metastable material at temperatures below the liquidus temperature. As a melt is cooled, structural changes take place to produce liquid-like thermal contraction. However, the viscosity increases progressively in this process and there comes a point, which depends on cooling rate, at which the viscosity becomes too large to allow the structural changes to take place. The temperature at which this occurs is called the 'fictive temperature'. Below this temperature the melt becomes a glassy solid with smaller, solid-like, thermal contraction properties (Figure 2.2.27). To circumvent the problem of variable fictive temperature, glass technologists have defined other characteristic temperatures in terms of equilibrium glass viscosity:

$10^{13.5} Nsm^{-2}$ strain point, at which thermal strain anneals in about 15 min

$10^{12.4} Nsm^{-2}$ transformation temperature, equivalent to the fictive temperature for a cooling rate of about 5 $Kmin^{-1}$

$10^{6.6} Nsm^{-2}$ softening point, at which the melt becomes macroscopically deformable by low stresses

$10^{3} Nsm^{-2}$ working point, at which the glass is soft enough for normal working and moulding.

Few glasses are used at temperatures approaching even the strain point, but their behaviour as viscous melts is important in determining shaping, annealing and use temperatures. In addition, if they are held at a temperature

Figure 2.2.27
(a) The effect of cooling rate on specific volume of a glass, and (b) the definition of fictive temperature and the effect on linear dimensions of long-term holds at temperatures below the annealing temperature.

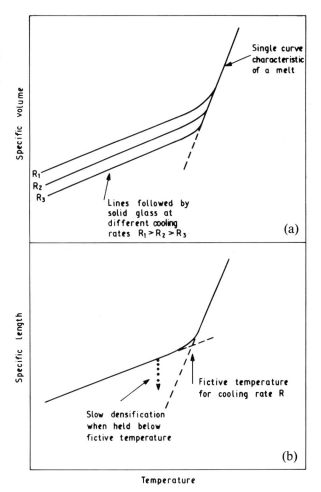

near or a little below the strain point, densification occurs as the structure tries to achieve equilibrium as a liquid, i.e. it tries to achieve a lower fictive temperature characteristic of a slower cooling rate. This has implications in joints made to other rigid materials; the mismatch strain becomes more tensile and may limit the life of the joint when held at elevated temperatures. At room temperature most glasses do not undergo such changes at a detectable rate, except under the influence of ionizing radiation which promotes the same slow densification process.

Glasses have no obvious ordered structure, and unless they contain processing defects such as bubbles, striae of non-uniform composition, or some foreign matter such as a fragment of refractory, generally have featureless microstructures.

The properties of a glass are strongly determined by its composition. The majority of technical and domestic glasses are based on silicates or borates, and have compositions designed to achieve the required properties, such as refractive index, spectral transparency, chemical durability, etc., in combination with suitable melting, shaping, and cost characteristics. This Handbook is not intended to cover technical glasses in detail, but for comparison purposes properties of some of the important compositions for technical uses are described. Their compositions in oxide terms are given in Table 2.2.2.

Table 2.2.2 Typical compositions of some technical glasses

Glass type	Composition, weight%						
	SiO$_2$	Al$_2$O$_3$	Na$_2$O	B$_2$O$_3$	CaO	MgO	FeO
Silica	99.8	—	—	—	—	—	—
Vycor	96	—	—	3	<1	—	—
Borosilicate (e.g. 'Pyrex')	60–80	1–4	low	10–25	—	—	—
Soda lime (e.g. flat glass, bottle glass)	70–75	0.5–3	12–17	—	4.5–12	0–3	<1

Pure silica in the glassy state falls into a special category. This has various names depending on how it is made. *Fused silica* is made by electrically fusing quartz sand to a translucent state, but not refining it sufficiently to remove small bubbles. This type of material is used for technical applications that require good thermal shock resistance or corrosion resistance, but not optical properties. *Fused quartz* is transparent and relatively free of bubbles, and is produced from selected quartz crystals by melting using a variety of electrical or flame-heated methods. This type of product is used for high quality tubing. *Synthetic vitreous silica* is made by what is essentially a c.v.d. process, namely by the oxidation of silicon tetrachloride in a gas or plasma flame. This type of product is generally free of bubbles and is preferred for high-quality optical components. The flame-oxidized material has a high water content, and the plasma-produced material is preferred for optical transmission in the infra-red region where water produces absorption peaks. *Sintered fused silica* is a product produced from granular fused silica or fused quartz. In the sintering process, some crystallization to cristobalite occurs, and this is detectable in thermal expansion behaviour. It is sold in block form as a machinable ceramic, and in precision-moulded shapes as cores in the casting of gas turbine blades (Figure 2.2.28).

Figure 2.2.28
An injection-moulded sintered fused silica core about 150 mm wide for casting an aero engine nozzle guide vane. (Courtesy Doulton Industrial Products Ltd.)

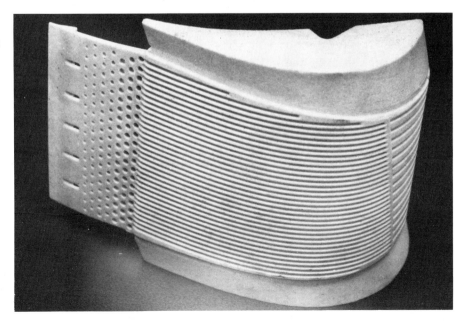

2.2.4.2 Phase-separated glasses

These are glasses in which on cooling from the melt a lower energy state can be achieved by unmixing into two glassy phases of differing composition. This occurs between the normal melting temperature and the strain point. The result is usually droplets of one composition in a matrix of the other, e.g. as in an opal glass, but under carefully controlled conditions of cooling or heat-treatment some compositions can be made to give a structure comprising two interconnected glassy phases. This latter usually occurs on a very fine scale (often sub-micron) which can be controlled by the temperature schedule of heat-treatment.

Phase separation is considered to be a prerequisite for fine-scale crystallization in some opal glasses and glass-ceramics (see below), but is also exploited in the manufacture of micro-porous glasses for chemical purposes in which one of the interconnected phases is removed by leaching. The same principle is used for the manufacture of high-silica glass, such as 'Vycor'. Phase separation leaves one of the phases high in silica and resistant to the leaching treatment. After leaching out the more soluble phase (which is high in boron and sodium), the porous structure is densified by heat treatment to give a high-silica glass with some residual porosity, but one which can be made without recourse to a very high temperature fusing operation that would be required to make the final product directly, or to make pure vitreous silica (see Section 3.2.5.5).

2.2.4.3 Glass-ceramics made in bulk

Whereas glasses for applications requiring transparency have compositions designed to be resistant to crystallization during the shaping process, any glass can be made to crystallize eventually within the temperature range between about 50°C below the glass transformation range and the liquidus temperature. If the composition is such that crystallization can occur fairly readily, and with the addition of suitable components can be made to occur on a micron or sub-micron scale, then the product is known as a glass-ceramic. The microstructures of glass-ceramics are generally very complex and multiphase, comprising mixtures of silicate phases, frequently with an identifiable glassy phase surrounding each crystal (Figure 2.2.29).

Small changes in composition and heat treatment can produce large changes in microstructural appearance, and hence in properties. In the main glass-ceramics find applications which require properties not possessed by any other form of sintered ceramic or transparent glass, and therefore tend to be highly specialized. Some large-volume applications have been found such as cooking ware, cooker tops and telescope mirrors.

One of the principal assets of glass-ceramics as a class is 'tailorability'. Because of the wide range of properties of the silicates that can be crystallized from silicate glasses, particularly expansion coefficient, materials can be produced to have specific properties to suit particular applications. One example is matching of thermal expansion to metals to which they may be joined by direct fusion of the precursor glass. Another is the production of materials of nearly zero expansion coefficient over a temperature range near ambient. These have optical applications as well as excellent thermal shock resistance. Other applications exploit their thermo-setting nature, crystalliz-

Figure 2.2.29
Microstructure of a
commercial lithium aluminosilicate glass-ceramic showing
the fine uniform grain size and
an intergranular glassy phase;
(a) replicated polished and
etched surface and
(b) by transmission electron
microscopy.

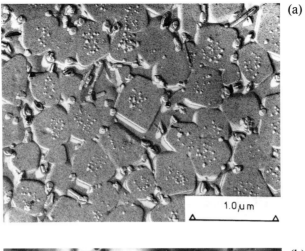

(a)

1.0 μm

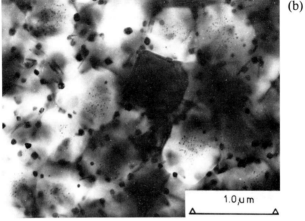

(b)

1.0 μm

ation raising the refractoriness of the precursor glass. In view of the wide range of possible compositions that can be made, and the specialist nature of many of the applications, some general points only will be made in this Section. Points relating to manufacture and subsequent processing and heat-treatment are discussed in Section 3.2.5.7.

Transparent materials

Transparency in a polycrystalline material is achieved either by elimination of porosity and impurities at grain boundaries or by ensuring that all phases have the same refractive index or by reducing the grain size to approach the wavelength of light to reduce scatter at grain boundaries. This last is most readily achieved in a glass-ceramic by limiting the crystallization to a very fine scale, usually 0.2 μm or less, with any secondary phases, such as nucleation additions, on an even finer scale. Transparent materials are often based on Li_2O-Al_2O_3-SiO_2 compositions, but can be made with other components if suitable control over nucleation and crystallization can be achieved. The range of commercially available materials is small, but combined with a very low coefficient of expansion large-scale applications have been established, such as in telescope mirrors and interferometer equipment where thermal stability would be a problem with other materials.

Translucent materials

Increasing the maximum temperature during heat-treatment will cause an increase in crystal size. At a grain size of around 0.3 μm, the crystal morphology becomes clearly visible by transmission electron microscopy. Materials designed to have little or no glassy phase at grain boundaries show grain growth phenomena typical of other ceramic or metal systems. Materials with significant amounts of intercrystalline glassy phase tend to behave rather differently, and in ways depending on the distribution of the glass. In some materials, the glassy phase may be in isolated pockets at grain junctions, while in others it may surround all grains. Grain growth tends to be inhibited in this latter case since transport of material across the glassy zones requires more of a driving force than simply moving a grain boundary in the solid state. Translucent glass-ceramics tend to result if the grain size is in the region 0.5–1.0 μm and there is little or no heavy metal oxide content to cause large variations of refractive index at grain boundaries.

Opaque materials

Materials which contain significant amounts of heavy metal oxides, or high valency oxides, tend to result in crystalline phases of high refractive index, and when combined with low refractive index phases lead to opacity and a matt appearance. Grain size above about 1 μm tends to result in opacity in most systems.

Machinable glass-ceramics

This name is given to a class of glass-ceramics which have been formulated to result in the crystallization of synthetic fluorine-based mica-type phases (e.g. fluorophlogopite mica) of fairly large size, typically 5–50 μm. Since the mica phases possess easy cleavage, such glass-ceramics are rendered machinable by a cleaving and chipping process using steel or, preferably, tungsten carbide tipped tools. Materials of this type are valuable for small-quantity or prototype work requiring complex shapes which are not subjected to exacting conditions. They do not require firing after machining as they are fully dense and impervious in the machined state.

Colour

As with some oxide ceramics, coloration can be produced by suitable additions of small amounts of transition metal oxides. Some materials may have a natural coloration due to their basic composition. For example, materials containing TiO_2 as a nucleation addition may be blue, particularly if heated in reducing conditions. Some transparent materials have a brownish cast, and a black cooker hob material is available.

Control of properties

Control of properties in glass-ceramics is more difficult than for ceramics or glasses because not only is composition important, but also the microstructure developed can be highly sensitive to the heat-treatment schedule employed, in particular the conditions of nucleation of the crystalline phases. Material development usually commences by definition of the required properties in terms of final expansion coefficient and the constraints applied by the mode in which the material is to be used, such as the conditions under which it is to be sealed to a metal component. This makes it possible to choose a glass-forming system to achieve crystalline phases which produce the required expansion coefficient. Then, experience and scientific understanding of the typical behaviour of glass-ceramics during heat-treatment are required to pin-point precise compositions which meet the target requirements. For example, the composition of any residual glassy phase is important in determining the effective setting point of the glass-ceramic when sealed to a metal. The proportion and type of nucleating agent required to produce crystallization on a fine and reproducible scale must be established. The working properties of the precursor glass, important in determining for-mability of shapes, may need to be modified to lengthen the working range or prevent crystallization during shaping. Thus, for novel applications, glass-ceramic development is a many-stage process, and a successful outcome may require considerable effort. Organizations which specialize in such work should be consulted at the earliest possible stage since their practical experience may make it possible to short-circuit some of the development stages.

2.2.4.4 Glass-ceramics in sintered form

Another class of glass-ceramic is made by sintering a precursor glass powder of suitable composition. In this case a nucleating agent may not be required because crystallization can generally take place after sintering by nucleation from the original glass particle surfaces. Thus, if the glass powder particle size is small, a fine-grained microstructure will be produced. Whereas bulk glass-ceramics are usually free from porosity, sintered materials can be expected to have 1–5% porosity, determined by how far the sintering process can progress before it is halted by crystallization.

Applications for this type of material tend to be restricted to sealing or joining, in which the technology is similar to that of using fritted glazes, except that true glazing is usually prevented by the crystallization process. An alternative term used is 'devitrifying frit'. The face-plate of a colour television tube is sealed with such a material, so that the seal is made at low temperature to avoid degrading the phosphors on the screen, but the sealed tube is then capable of being baked out at a higher temperature during evacuation. The thermo-setting nature of glass-ceramics makes this possible. Monolithic shapes can also be made with compositions in which the onset of crystallization is delayed just enough to allow sintering to the required density, but not enough to allow excessive viscous slumping.

2.2.4.5 Fusion-cast ceramics

The freezing of a melt usually allows no effective control over grain size. In the case of a glass-ceramic, the material is cooled rapidly as an unstable glass, which is then controllably crystallized. If the starting composition cannot be cooled to a glass, then usually the thermal strains produced by temperature gradients through a block, or by differential thermal expansion coefficients between the different crystalline phases, cause unacceptable cracking. There are exceptions, however, such as the fusion-cast blocks of refractory material used in the construction of large glass tanks. They are based on ZrO_2-Al_2O_3-SiO_2 compositions, and have low levels of porosity which restrict penetration of molten glass. Such materials are outside the scope of this Handbook. Fused cast basalt is made in large quantities for lining of ore-chutes and mineral processing plant. Slag-based materials are also made, especially in the USSR and are under development in the UK. In this case, extra components are usually added to improve the nucleation of crystals.

2.2.4.6 Flame-sprayed ceramics

Dense layers of a variety of ceramic materials can be made by flame-spraying, a technique by which ceramic powders are fed into a high-temperature gas or plasma flame, are fused, and are essentially splat-cooled on a substrate at a suitable temperature. Ceramics can be sprayed with or without a metal binding phase, and free-standing, thin-walled articles can be built up by prolonged spraying onto a mandrel which is subsequently removed. The technique is limited to materials which fuse without decomposing, and is therefore not applicable to silicon nitride or silicon carbide unless they are co-sprayed with a metal melting at a temperature below the decomposition temperature of the ceramic. Some other non-oxides may not be sprayed satisfactorily if there is a strong tendency to oxidize in the flame conditions, and it may be necessary to operate under reducing conditions in this case.

Microstructures vary with spraying conditions, but are generally anisotropic with some flattening of grains in the direction of spraying. There is usually considerable porosity. Some manufacturers recommend a high-temperature sintering process to consolidate the material, especially in thick layers, but this can lead to cracking if the deposition conditions vary through the thickness of the layer. Each case has to be treated on its own merits.

2.2.5 Single-crystal materials

By definition, single-crystal materials should not have grain boundaries or porosity typical of polycrystalline aggregates. Microstructures should show no gross features. However, since the growth of single crystals either from the melt or hydrothermally relies on nucleation of one crystal and maintenance of the same crystal orientation throughout the process, there are usually limitations to the size to which it is possible to avoid nucleation of secondary crystals or variations in composition. Secondary crystals may nucleate on the edges of the primary due to dirt or interruptions in the process. Sometimes the orientation of the secondaries is crystallographically related to the primary, for example 'twins' may develop. In transparent materials such secondaries are readily recognized if the crystal is examined under crossed polars. Twinning may not be important for some applications where the principal properties being used are not affected. In others, particularly optical applications, twinning has to be avoided. Much depends on the individual type of material. Compositional variation, particularly in instances where a material is deliberately doped with a low level of an impurity, may not change the single-crystal habit, but does change the properties that depend on the level of dopant, particularly electrical properties and colour.

Other microstructural defects can arise during growth. These are generally small and are related to the ordering of the atomic planes as the crystal grows. Defects such as stacking faults and dislocations are observable by transmission electron microscopy, but do not in general affect the macroscopic properties of the crystal.

From the engineering viewpoint, the only advantages of single-crystal ceramic materials are highly specific ones resulting from the uniform structure. For example, transparency, refractoriness, and hardness are advantageous properties of single-crystal alumina (corundum or sapphire, or when doped with a trace of chromium, ruby, see Section 2.2.2.1), but thermal, elastic and optical anisotropy, and strength may not be improved compared with a polycrystalline aggregate of the same material.

2.2.6 Machinable ceramics

The vast majority of ceramic and glass materials cannot be machined in the same sense as metals and alloys. They require grinding with an abrasive wheel, usually diamond-impregnated but occasionally silicon carbide. However, some materials are manufactured to be machinable by ordinary machine-shop tools to engineering tolerances and to be used in the machined state.

Machinable ceramics fall into two broad types: those that have platy structures which can be readily cleaved, and those that are not platy but consist of particles that are only weakly bonded together so that they can be readily chipped apart. These categories should not be considered exclusive.

Materials with platy structures include boron nitride, graphite, natural minerals quarried in block form such as talc and pyrophyllite, and materials based on mica such as some glass-bonded micas and machinable glass-ceramics based on fluorine-substituted micas. All these can be turned, drilled or milled, preferably with carbide tipped tools, and can be used in the machined state. The natural minerals can be fired subsequent to machining to give a stronger ceramic body, free of combined water, but some dimensional change can be expected and this may be anisotropic and depend on the firing temperature. See the relevant sections in Part 2 for detail. Some comments on the microstructure of pyrophyllite are made in Section 2.2.1.8, and on talc in Section 2.2.1.2. The problem of anisotropy is circumvented in some products by crushing and recompacting the natural mineral, although the original density is unlikely to be achieved. Some glass-bonded micas, such as 'Mycalex' are not intended as machinable materials because of high glass contents, but are for hot injection moulding. Machinable glass-ceramics are useful in the sense that they are dimensionally stable to high temperature, are relatively strong, and have no significant porosity. The machinability depends on the type, flake size and volume fraction of the fluorine mica grown in the precursor glass (see Section 2.2.4.3).

Materials that can be machined by chipping weakly bonded particles include so-called machinable aluminas, many carbon and carbon-bonded products, and some weakly sintered glasses such as sintered fused silica. Some products are sold for use in the machined state. Others need to be refired to consolidate the shape, and obviously an allowance for shrinkage must be made at the machining stage. This technique is sometimes employed in ceramic manufacture when the pressed blank is fired to a temperature sufficient to bond the particles together weakly. It can then be machined to shape and refired to final density with a lower allowance for firing shrinkage than would be needed if machining were done in the green state. Some comments on machinable alumina are made in Section 2.2.2.1.

2.3

Density and porosity

2.3.1 Definitions

The density of ceramic materials is dependent on the crystal phases present, of which there is an enormous variety. Most ceramics in common use do not contain heavy metal species, while some contain only a small proportion, e.g. the barium content of low-loss steatite. Most products therefore have densities lying in the range 2.2–4 Mgm^{-3}. Materials based on compounds of heavy metals, such as Zr, Ta, Y, La, Ba, Th, and W, are much denser, up to 12 Mgm^{-3}.

Unlike most other materials, an important additional factor with ceramics is the porosity or void content which is nearly always significant as a result of the incomplete densification of the material during the firing process. As indicated at the beginning of Section 2, the definitions of density and porosity should be noted:

BULK DENSITY:
The mass of the material divided by its bulk volume, i.e. its total volume including internal pores.

TRUE DENSITY:
The mass of the material divided by the volume of solid material excluding open porosity (see below). This is equivalent to the theoretical density of pore-free material, or to the bulk density in materials with no open porosity.

THEORETICAL DENSITY:
The density of the material excluding all forms of porosity, being a weighted average of the densities of the individual crystalline and glassy phases.

TOTAL POROSITY:
The volume of void space within the material divided by the bulk volume, expressed as a fraction or a percentage. Some of this void space may be as isolated voids and some as interconnected voids with access to a free surface.

OPEN POROSITY:
The volume of void space within a material accessible from the exterior, divided by the bulk volume.

CLOSED POROSITY:
The volume of void space within the material inaccessible from the exterior, divided by its bulk volume.

Open porosity is generally an undesirable feature for many technical applications since it offers a large internal surface area for absorption of dirt and attack by corrosive liquids, and of course results in non-hermetic properties. Most Standard specifications put a low or zero limit on open-porosity levels for the majority of materials to avoid these disadvantages. However, it is sometimes difficult to eliminate all open porosity in manufacture because of the nature of the material, e.g. in reaction-bonded silicon nitride, or in pressed porcelains. In some cases a component may appear to be closed-porous, but this may only be by virtue of an impermeable skin, e.g. in glazed pressed porcelain or in some stonewares.

Controlled high levels of mainly open porosity are desirable, on the other hand, for optimizing thermal shock damage resistance, for filter media, for catalyst supports, and for friable or crushable materials. The ability to control porosity levels gives ceramics one of their advantages over other types of material.

The presence of residual *closed porosity*, typically 1–5%, is broadly disadvantageous for mechanical properties, resistance to dielectric breakdown, and surface finish quality, which are more sensitive to it than most other properties. Some closed porosity is usual in most ceramics, except some hot-pressed types, and has to be accepted.

Closed pores take the form of irregular sealed holes, usually between grains, and can take a range of sizes and shapes depending on the nature of the processing route. If they occur as a result of a processing defect, such as a delamination in pressing, they may be as large as a few mm., but these are usually isolated and in addition to a generally uniform distribution of smaller pores typically of a size similar to or smaller than that of the largest grains in the material.

During firing, a closed-porous body is generally obtained if the density achieved is better than about 91–93% of theoretical. Manufacturers have an indirect check on fired density through the shrinkage of a component on firing, which is typically 15–18% for many materials. The green body is known to shrink normally by a given amount on firing, and this figure is used to obtain the appropriate green dimensions for given fired dimensions. If the fired body is within normal tolerance, the fired density should then be correct and the body should have a sufficiently low level of open and/or closed porosity.

It is advantageous for mechanical properties to remove as much of the residual porosity as possible by improved processing, for example by the use of more uniform, finer powders, or by hot-pressing. It is expected that in the near future more high-quality commercial products with very low levels of porosity will become available.

2.3.2 Measurement methods

The method of measuring the density of a piece of ceramic material usually described in Standards is based on the Archimedes principle, recording the mass in air and then immersed in water. However, it is usual to measure open porosity levels at the same time by ensuring that during immersion water can penetrate all parts of the specimen through the open porosity. (Some Standards require a certain minimum fraction of fracture surface on fragments to ensure that open porosity is measured on bulk material and not on the possibly sealed as-fired surface of a component.) Typical procedures are:

1. Dry specimen(s) in air at 110°C, store in a desiccator, weigh when cold (mass W_1).
2. Boil in distilled water for a period, typically 30 mins.
3. Weigh immersed in water (W_2).
4. Remove, lightly dab the surface with a damp cloth to remove surface moisture without drying the interior, and reweigh (W_3). This step is tricky and requires some practice but can be reasonably reliable.
5. Repeat procedure to check on constancy of weighings, particularly W_3, if necessary.
6. Calculations:

True volume of test-piece $= \dfrac{W_1 - W_2}{\varrho_0}$

where ϱ_0 is the density of water at the temperature of weighing.

True density of test-piece $= \dfrac{W_1 \varrho_0}{W_1 - W_2}$

Volume of open porosity $= \dfrac{W_3 - W_1}{\varrho_0}$

Bulk volume $= \dfrac{W_1 - W_2}{\varrho_0} + \dfrac{W_3 - W_1}{\varrho_0} = \dfrac{W_3 - W_2}{\varrho_0}$

Bulk density $= \dfrac{W_1 \varrho_0}{W_3 - W_2}$

Volume fraction open porosity $= \dfrac{W_3 - W_1}{W_3 - W_2}$

This method does not estimate closed porosity levels which are much more difficult to measure. Recourse has to be made to grinding the material to a powder finer than the smallest inter-pore distance and comparing the powder density with the bulk density. However, fine powders tend to trap bubbles during immersion in liquid, and are more difficult to handle without loss than large fragments. It may be more appropriate to estimate porosity levels by comparing the bulk density with the theoretical value if this is known. Alternatively, the total porosity can be estimated by a line intercept or area counting method on carefully prepared polished cross-sections. Care is especially required to ensure that no grain tear-out in polishing is counted as porosity, and that a sufficiently large area is used so that counting is representative of the true figure. It is always worthwhile checking that extra polishing stages do not lead to a reduction in apparent porosity, and that measured values are in keeping with the ratio of bulk density to theoretical density.

Pore-size distributions in open-porous materials are usually measured by mercury porosimetry, whereby the volume of mercury admitted to the test sample is measured as the applied pressure is increased. The pore size is then related to the known surface tension of mercury and the applied pressure. However, this presumes that all pores are intruded at the relevant pressure,

Table 2.3.1 Density and porosity for common engineering ceramics

Material (IEC class)	Density, Mgm^{-3}			Porosity, %		
	IEC min.	Practical, range	Theoretical	Closed, range	Open, range	Open, IEC max.
Clay-based materials:						
Siliceous porcelain (C-110)	2.2	2.26–2.42	2.42–2.50	2–8	0	0
Pressed porcelains (C-111)	2.2	2.2–2.3	2.42–2.50	5–10	0–3	3
Cristobalite porcelain (C-112)	2.3	2.3–2.35	2.35–2.45[1]	2–8	0	0
Aluminous porcelain (C-120)	2.3	2.3–2.8	2.5–3.0	2–8	0	0
Aluminous porcelain (C-130)	2.5	2.6–3.3	3.0–3.4	2–8	0	0
Steatite, low-voltage (C-210)	2.3	2.3–2.5	2.8	2–10	?	0.5
Steatite, normal (C-220)	2.6	2.6–2.65	2.8	2–8	0	0
Steatite, low-loss (C-221)	2.7	2.7–3.1	2.9–3.2	2–8	0	0
Steatite, porous (C-230)	1.8	1.8–2.2	2.8	?	20–35	35
Forsterite, porous (C-240)	1.9	1.9–2.5	3.1–3.2	?	20–30	30
Forsterite, dense (C-250)	2.8	2.8–3.0	3.1–3.2	2–8	0–1	0.5
Cordierite, dense (C-410)	2.1	2.2–2.5	2.5–2.6	2–8	0–1	0.5
Celsian, dense (C-420)	2.7	2.7–2.9	3.0–3.2	2–8	0–1	0.5
Lithia porcelain	—	2.4	2.6	2–8	?	—
Zircon porcelain	—	3.4–3.8	3.6–3.9	2–8	0–1	—
Mullite ceramics (C-610)	2.6	~ 2.7	2.7–2.9	2–8	0	0
Mullite ceramics (C-620)	2.8	~ 2.8	2.8–3.0	2–8	0	0
Porous electrical refractories:						
Aluminosilicate (C-510)	1.9	1.9–2.4	2.5–3.3	?	?	30
Cordierite-containing (C-511)	1.9	?	2.5–2.8	?	?	20
Cordierite-containing (C-512)	1.8	?	2.5–2.6	?	?	40
High-cordierite (C-520)	1.9	1.9–2.1	2.5–3.0	?	?	20
High-alumina (C-530)	2.1	2.1–2.8	2.8–3.6	?	?	30
Chemical wares:						
Chemical stoneware	—	2.0–2.4	—	?	~ 1	—
Chemical porcelain	—	2.2–2.8	—	?	0	—
Oxides:						
Alumina 99% (C-799)	3.7	3.65–3.93	3.97	1–8	0	0
Alumina 95% (C-795)	3.5	3.55–3.76	3.86	2–8	0	0
Alumina 90% (C-786)	3.4	3.45–3.60	3.73	2–8	0	0
Beryllia BeO (C-810)	2.8	2.8–2.9	3.008	2–8	0	0
Chromic oxide Cr_2O_3	—	4.2–4.4	5.2	?	10–20	—
Magnesia MgO hot-pressed	—	> 3.55	3.58	< 1	0	0
Magnesia MgO porous (C-820)	2.5	2.5–3.2	3.58	?	10–30	30
Spinel $MgAl_2O_4$	—	2.8–3.2	3.59	0–10	0–20	—
Thoria ThO_2	—	9.2–9.6	10.0	0–10	?	—
Tin oxide SnO	—	6.0–6.7	7.0	?	0–20	—
Titania TiO_2 (C-310)	3.5	3.5–4.0	4.0–4.2	2–8	0	0
Urania UO_2	—	?	10.96	?	?	—
Zircon $ZrSiO_4$	—	3.5–4.5	4.68	?	0–20	—
Zirconia ZrO_2 (CaO, MgO stab.) (C-830)	5.0	5.0–5.8	5.5–5.8[2]	2–8	0	0
Zirconia ZrO_2 (Y_2O_3 stab.)	—	5.2–5.9	5.6–5.9[2]	2–8	0	0
Zirconia (tetragonal phase)	—	—	6.1	—	—	—
Zirconia (monoclinic phase)	—	—	5.56	—	—	—
Non-oxides:						
Silicon nitride (reaction-bonded)	—	1.9–2.8	3.19	?	15–40	—
Silicon nitride (hot-pressed)	—	3.1–3.2	3.19–3.25	0–1	0	—
Silicon carbide (clay bonded)	—	2.5–3.0	2.8–3.1	2–8	0–20	—
Silicon carbide (nitride bonded)	—	2.2–2.7	3.21	?	15–30	—
Silicon carbide (sintered)	—	3.0–3.2	3.208	1–6	0	—
Silicon carbide (coarse, sintered)	—	2.2–2.7	3.208	0–1	20–40	—
Silicon carbide (hot-pressed)	—	3.0–3.2	3.21	0–5	0	—
Silicon carbide (reaction-bonded)	—	3.0–3.15	3.0–3.15	< 1	0	—

Table 2.3.1 (*contd*)

Material (IEC class)	Density, Mgm^{-3}			Porosity, %		
	IEC min.	Practical, range	Theoretical	Closed, range	Open, range	Open, IEC max.
Non-oxides (*contd*)						
Boron carbide (hot-pressed)	—	2.3–2.5	2.52	0–10	0	—
Boron nitride (hot-pressed)	—	1.9–2.1	2.27	?	0	—
Boron nitride (pyrolytic)	—	~ 2.1	2.27	0–5	0	—
Boron nitride (cubic form)	—	—	3.48	—	—	—
Graphite	—	1.6–1.9	2.26	0–20^3	0–30	—
Vitreous carbon	—	2.0–2.2	—	10–20	0	—
Pyrolytic graphite	—	2.15–2.23	2.26	0–1	0–5	—
Silicon	—	—	2.33	—	—	—
Tungsten carbide (no metal)	—	—	15.8	—	—	—
Molybdenum disilicide	—	—	6.26	—	—	—
Glasses:						
Soda-lime (float or bottle)	—	—	2.49–2.50	0	0	—
Borosilicate (e.g. 'Pyrex')	—	—	2.24–2.30	0	0	—
Vitreous silica (all types)	—	—	2.20	0	0	—
'ULE' silica (Corning 7971)	—	—	2.21	0	0	—
Glass-ceramics:						
'Pyroceram 9606' (Corning)	—	—	2.60	0	0	—
'Pyroceram 9608' (Corning)	—	—	2.50	0	0	—
'EE1087' (GEC Power Eng)	—	—	2.40	0	0	—
'Zerodur' (Schott)	—	—	2.52	0	0	—
Machinable ceramics:						
Pyrophillite unfired	—	2.8–2.9	—	?	?	—
fired	—	2.3–2.5^4	—	?^{4}	?^{4}	—
'Macor' machinable glass-ceramic	—	2.52	—	0	0	—
Block talc unfired	—	2.6–2.8	—	—	—	—
fired	—	2.4–2.7^4	3.1–3.2	?^{4}	?^{4}	—
Machinable alumina	—	2.0–2.7	3.7–3.9	?	30–50	—
Sintered fused silica	—	1.5–2.0	2.20	—	10–30	—
Single-crystal materials:						
Alpha-quartz	—	—	2.65	0	0	—
Sapphire	—	—	3.99	0	0	—

[1] Assuming no added alumina. With increasing alumina content, densities increase.
[2] Density depends on stabilizer type and content. With CaO and MgO, theoretical density decreases with increasing stabilizer content. With Y_2O_3, the fall is less marked.
[3] Many graphites and carbons are impregnated to reduce open porosity.
[4] Depends on firing conditions and degree of vitrification.

which is clearly not the case if large pores are connected by narrow channels. Nevertheless, this technique gives valuable data on materials of high porosity which would be difficult to characterize from polished sections. For materials with only closed porosity, there is no alternative but to use polished sections and a line intercept or area counting method to deduce pore sizes.

2.3.3 Data tables

Table 2.3.1 gives data for the most common types of material as typical ranges obtained on commercial products, comparing these figures with theoretical full density where this is known, and with minimum figures for density and maximum figures for open porosity quoted in the draft IEC classification scheme.

Table 2.3.2 Theoretical densities of less-common materials

Phase	Theoretical density Mgm^{-3}
Oxides:	
Aluminium titanate Al_2TiO_5	3.68
Magnesium titanate $MgTi_2O_5$	3.66
Hafnia HfO_2 (monoclinic)	9.68
(tetragonal)	10.01
Lanthana La_2O_3	6.51
Lanthanum chromite $LaCrO_3$	6.65
Yttria Y_2O_3	5.03
Non-oxides:	
Titanium nitride TiN	4.92
Zirconium nitride ZrN	7.35
Titanium carbide TiC	4.92
Tantalum carbide TaC	14.50
Chromium carbide Cr_3C_2	6.68

2.4

Thermal properties

2.4.1 Importance

The thermal properties of ceramics are probably of greater importance when considering engineering applications than are those of metals and alloys. The reason for this is that ceramics are brittle and cannot tolerate large internal strains imposed by thermal expansion mismatch or thermal transients. Thus a knowledge of thermal properties becomes important in any application involving heat flow or high temperatures, not only in use but also in assembly of components, particularly in joining to other materials.

Almost invariably, *all thermal properties are functions of temperature*, and this should be considered when undertaking any calculation. Temperatures or temperature ranges should be quoted against data at all times.

2.4.2 Specific heat and heat content

2.4.2.1 Definitions

Specific heat is the rate of change of heat content of unit mass with temperature. It is normally measured at constant pressure in units of $Jg^{-1}K^{-1}$. (Note: In some source books of thermodynamic data, specific heat or heat capacity is commonly quoted in terms of $cal.mole^{-1}K^{-1}$ for single phase materials. To convert to $Jg^{-1}K^{-1}$, it is necessary to multiply by 4.182/(molecular weight).) The total heat content, Q, of a mass, m, is thus:

$$Q = \int_{T_2}^{T_1} mC_p.dT$$

over the temperature range T_1 to T_2, where C_p is the specific heat at temperature T. A mean specific heat can also be defined as:

$$\overline{C}_p, (T_1 \text{ to } T_2) = \frac{Q}{m(T_2 - T_1)}$$

the numerical value of which is different to C_p above because specific heat is always a function of temperature.

The factor that primarily determines specific heat is the phase content of a material. Generally speaking, low atomic number species contribute more to specific heat than high atomic number species. Thus beryllia has a much higher specific heat than thoria, but when density is taken into account, the specific heat per unit volume is not very different. In a multiphase material, the net value is approximately equal to the weighted sum of the individual components, i.e.

$$C_p = m_1 C_{p1} + m_2 C_{p2} \ldots\ldots + m_i C_{pi}$$

where m_i and C_{pi} are the mass fraction and specific heat of the ith component. C_p is not strongly dependent on microstructure, strain effects due to thermal expansion mismatch between phases or due to phase changes being second order effects.

Single-phase crystalline materials generally show slowly increasing specific heat with increasing temperature, tending to a plateau value at temperatures above 1500°C. Small discontinuities are shown by materials that exhibit phase changes. Instances to note are:

quartz: in single-crystal applications and in some porcelains.

cristobalite: developed in many clay-based products, some porcelains, some glass-ceramics, and clay-bonded silicon carbide. It is also an oxidation product in silicon carbide and silicon nitride.

zirconia: of note in partially or unstabilized materials, or materials in the process of destabilizing.

In such cases, the latent heat of any phase conversion should be added to the total heat contents calculated.

2.4.2.2 Methods of measurement

There are two principal techniques by which specific heat is normally measured. For temperatures up to 700°C, differential scanning calorimetry (DSC) is frequently used. In this method, the test sample in the form of powder or a small disc or fragments is heated or cooled at the same time as a reference material, normally alpha-alumina. The temperature difference between the test sample and the reference during heating is then a measure of the difference in heat content between the two. Equipment to undertake such measurements directly is available commercially. The result is usually expressed as a specific heat at temperature T, i.e. C_p. For higher temperatures, DSC is not appropriate because the errors due to electrical noise and radiation become too high. The normal technique is then so-called drop calorimetry, in which a test sample is heated to a known temperature and then rapidly removed to a cold enclosure. The rise in temperature of the cold enclosure is then a measure of the heat content change on cooling the test sample. The specific heat calculated is a mean value, $\overline{C}_p$, over the temperature range of the drop. The actual specific heat, C_p, can be derived from a series of such experiments using different initial temperatures, followed by curve-fitting and estimation.

The accuracy of these techniques depends on experimental care. For DSC, at up to 400°C, an accuracy of about 1% can be achieved, but for drop calorimetry, accuracy is lower, up to 3–5%, especially at very high initial temperatures, due to possible errors in estimating heat losses.

2.4.2.3 Specific heat and heat content data

The specific heat and heat content data for a variety of ceramic phases are shown in Tables 2.4.1 and 2.4.2 respectively. By using the addition rule, values for multiphase materials can be estimated with a reasonable degree of certainty. The estimated accuracy of the data is $\pm 2\%$ for specific heat data and $\pm 5\%$ for heat content.

It will be noted that differences between the various aluminosilicate phases listed are small. To a first approximation, errors arising from the use of assumed figures for minor components such as glassy phases are quite small unless a heavy metal species is also involved.

Table 2.4.1 Specific heat of single-phase materials

Formula, mineral name, transition temperature, °C, (latent heat, Jg^{-1})		Specific heat, Jg^{-1}, at temp., °C					
		-50	25	100	500	1000	1500
Oxides:							
Al_2O_3	corundum	0.54	0.78	0.92	1.16	1.25	1.32
$Al_6Si_2O_{13}$	mullite	—	0.76	0.88	1.16	1.26	1.32
BeO	beryllia	0.69	1.02	1.28	1.84	2.23	2.58
CaO	calcia	0.67	0.77	0.83	0.93	0.98	—
MgO	periclase	0.74	0.94	1.01	1.17	1.28	1.37
$MgAl_2O_4$	spinel	—	0.81	0.94	1.18	1.30	1.40
$MgCr_2O_4$	chrome spinel	—	0.66	0.75	0.90	1.30	1.40
$Mg_2Al_4Si_5O_{18}$	cordierite	0.62	0.73	0.88	1.13	1.25	—
SiO_2	quartz 573 (20.2)	0.60	0.74	0.86	1.11	1.18	—
SiO_2	cristobalite 250 (14)	0.61	0.75	0.86	1.11	1.18	1.25
SiO_2	vitreous silica	0.60	0.74	0.85	1.09	1.24	1.38
SnO_2	tin oxide	—	0.35	0.41	0.52	0.57	—
ThO_2	thoria	0.20	0.23	0.25	0.28	0.30	0.32
TiO_2	rutile	0.57	0.69	0.78	0.91	0.94	0.96
UO_2	urania	—	0.24	0.26	0.31	0.33	0.34
ZrO_2	zirconia 1200 (48) (unstabilized)	0.38	0.45	0.51	0.59	0.64	0.60
$ZrSiO_4$	zircon	—	0.54	0.62	0.76	0.82	0.87
Non-oxides:							
AlN	aluminium nitride	—	0.80	0.86	1.17	1.57	—
BN	boron nitride	0.58	0.78	1.02	1.59	1.95	2.14
Si_3N_4	silicon nitride	—	0.68*	0.80*	1.06*	1.30	1.55
C	carbon/graphite	—	0.70	0.90	1.60	1.90	2.10
B_4C	boron carbide	—	0.95	1.13	1.92	2.21	2.44
SiC	silicon carbide	0.48	0.67	0.84	1.12	1.26	1.36
WC	tungsten carbide	—	0.18	0.21	0.25	0.26	0.28
$MoSi_2$	molybdenum disilicide	—	0.42	0.45	0.51	0.55	—
Si	silicon m.p. 1400 (427)	—	0.71	0.78	0.89	0.95	0.91
TiB_2	titanium diboride	—	0.63	0.77	1.03	1.17	—
ZrB_2	zirconium diboride	—	0.43	0.50	0.61	0.67	0.71
Glasses:							
Soda-lime (flat, bottle)		—	0.83	0.91	1.21	1.35	—
Borosilicate (e.g. 'Pyrex')		—	0.77	0.88	1.13	—	—
Complex ceramics:							
Quartz porcelain		—	0.76	0.87	1.16	1.26	—
'Pyroceram 9606' (Corning) (cordierite base)		—	0.78	0.89	1.12	1.30	—
'Pyroceram 9608' (Corning) (spodumene base)		—	0.80	0.92	1.18	—	—

Sources:
(1) MT data bank, NPL; (2) Kubaschewski, Evans, Alcock, *Metallurgical Thermodynamics*, Plenum Press, Oxford, 1970. (3) *NPL measurements. Specific heat data on complex silicate phases can be found in NPL report CHEM 21, Spencer, P J, 1973.

Table 2.4.2 Heat contents from 25°C

Phase	Heat content, Jg^{-1}, from 25-T°C			
	T = 100	500	1000	1500
Oxides:				
alumina	64	494	1100	1740
mullite	62	482	1090	1740
beryllia	87	730	1750	2960
calcia	58	403	868	—
magnesia	73	516	1130	1790
spinel	66	502	1124	1800
chrome spinel	53	390	855	1340
cordierite	61	478	1075	—
quartz	60	506	1080*	—
cristobalite	62	491*	1065*	—
vitreous silica	60	458	1040	1700
tin oxide	29	220	492	—
thoria	17	122	264	416
rutile	55	403	869	1346
urania	19	135	293	460
zirconia (unstabilized)	36	260	568	927*
zircon	44	326	722	1145
Non-oxides:				
aluminium nitride	61	467	1150	—
boron nitride	68	608	1900	2460
silicon nitride	55	417	1030	—
carbon	66	618	1476	2445
boron carbide	86	763	1800	2960
silicon carbide	57	464	1060	1720
tungsten carbide	15	263	583	927
molybdenum disilicide	35	226	490	—
silicon	54	384	834	1720*
titanium diboride	53	464	975	—
zirconium diboride	35	263	583	927
Glasses:				
soda-lime	63	490	1140	—
borosilicate	60	450	—	—
Complex ceramics:				
Quartz porcelain	62	480	1090	—
'Pyroceram 9606'	61	478	1075	—
'Pyroceram 9608'	65	500	—	—

Sources:
Mainly Kubaschewski et al. (see Table 2.4.1), data based on fitted equations to C_p data.
*Including latent heat of phase change.

2.4.3 Thermal expansion

2.4.3.1 Definition

Data quoted for linear thermal expansion of solids are confusing if care is not taken over the definition. The *linear expansion coefficient* is strictly the fractional increase in length, *l*, per degree rise in temperature *at a particular temperature*, T, and is also known as *expansivity*:

$$\alpha(T) = \frac{1}{l}\frac{dl}{dT}$$

It is usually dependent on temperature. However, for engineering purposes, the expansion resulting from a change in temperature ΔT is more often required than the slope of the expansion versus temperature curve. Thus, more commonly, a *mean expansion coefficient* between two temperatures is quoted, i.e.:

$$\bar{\alpha} = \frac{1}{l_0}\frac{\Delta l}{\Delta T}$$

where Δl is the change in length from l_0 at temperature T_0 as a result of changing the temperature by $\Delta T = T - T_0$.

In this Handbook, in order to be as flexible as possible, the comparative information in Part 1 is expressed in terms of mean linear coefficients from 25°C. In Part 2, both fractional increase in length ($\bar{\alpha}\Delta T$,), usually expressed in parts per million for convenience, and mean linear coefficient are quoted at 100°C intervals from 25°C.

To obtain the true linear expansion at temperature T, the fractional increase in length should be curve-fitted and the slope calculated at temperature T.

2.4.3.2 Measurement

Thermal expansion is normally measured by some form of mechanical dilatometer, recording the displacement between the ends of the specimen as a function of temperature. The apparatus needs to be calibrated with certified standards that have been measured by rather more accurate methods, such as interferometry.

For many purposes, mechanical dilatometry is adequate if proper calibration procedures are followed. All NPL data reproduced in this Handbook were obtained using such methods, employing calibration with National Bureau of Standards vitreous silica and sapphire certified standards. In most cases, the data were obtained by averaging the results for heating and cooling the test sample. In performing tests in this manner, rather than simply relying on heating alone, there are checks on mechanical drifts and on the reproducibility of specimen behaviour. The overall accuracy of the results for the equipment used is considered to be:

25 – 200°C:	$\pm$ 30 ppm in $\bar{\alpha}\Delta T$, or $\pm 0.2 \times 10^{-6}$ K^{-1} in $\bar{\alpha}$
25 – 800°C:	$\pm$ 40 ppm in $\bar{\alpha}\Delta T$, or $\pm 0.1 \times 10^{-6}$ K^{-1} in $\bar{\alpha}$
25 – 1400°C:	$\pm$ 100 ppm in $\bar{\alpha}\Delta T$, or $\pm 0.1 \times 10^{-6}$ K^{-1} in $\bar{\alpha}$

No estimate of accuracy is placed on data abstracted from the scientific literature.

For some purposes, mechanical dilatometry cannot be sufficiently accurate because of limitations of the method in terms of mechanical instability, electronic sensitivity of the measuring device, temperature inhomogeneity and calibration errors. For example, if precise matching of expansion characteristics or accurate correction to optical path lengths or optical figure is required, then mechanical dilatometry is inadequate. In such cases alternative methods should be sought.

Accurate absolute measurement may be required, for example for materials with coefficient of expansion near zero. Interferometric methods are available, but are slow and expensive compared to the simple mechanical methods. Generally speaking, it is necessary to polish parallel optical flats on two opposing faces of a rigid test block, and to take measurements of displacement after several hours' stabilization of temperature. The accuracy of the results is basically limited by uncertainty in temperature uniformity, especially in poor thermal conductors, but can be ± 2ppm in $\bar{\alpha} \Delta T$, or $\pm 0.01 \times 10^{-6}$ K^{-1} in $\bar{\alpha}$ over the temperature range 25–200°C. The requirement for an optical flat limits direct measurement to dense materials. For porous materials, or those which cannot have optical flats prepared on them, a separate optical flat can be placed on top of the specimen, but the accuracy tends to be lower because of increased mechanical instability. The technique is of course unsuitable for thin bars or rods.

For glasses, optical methods can be used, such as the thin sandwich seal technique whereby the difference in expansion coefficient between a glass and a known reference can be observed by measuring stress birefringence and calculating the thermal mismatch strain on cooling from the setting point of the glass. This technique is particularly suitable for estimating thermal expansion mismatch between a glass and the material to which it is to be joined as a seal or glaze by taking into account the setting characteristics of the glass. If reliance were placed solely on the difference of separately measured expansion characteristics, the setting behaviour and the effects of subsequent annealing procedures could not be adequately allowed for.

2.4.3.3 Factors affecting the thermal expansion of ceramics

Solids expand on heating because of a change in mean inter-atomic spacing resulting from thermal motion of the atoms. The extent of the expansion depends on the nature of the bonding between atoms and on their spatial arrangement, i.e. on the crystal structure. Each crystal type behaves in a different manner, and expansion is different in different crystallographic directions, unless the crystal has cubic symmetry, in which case the expansion is isotropic. Thus if large single crystals are being used in a situation where thermal expansion is important, allowance may have to be made for the anisotropy.

In a dense polycrystalline material comprising a single phase of fine grain size, the anisotropy of individual grains is swamped unless the grains have some preferred orientation or texture. The net apparently isotropic expansion is then an average of the expansions in the different crystallographic directions, weighted according to the associated elastic anisotropy. In a dense multi-phase material of fine grain size, again the net expansion is a weighted average, this time of all the phases present. There is a variety of formulae for predicting the expansion of mixtures, Turner's formula being fairly close to experimental results for isotropic materials:

$$\bar{\alpha} = \sum_i \frac{\alpha_i v_i K_i}{v_i K_i}$$

where α_i, v_i, K_i are the linear expansion coefficient, volume fraction and the bulk modulus of the ith component, respectively. Having zero bulk modulus, a pore phase does not affect the net thermal expansion, except in coarse-grained, highly porous materials of crystallographically anisotropic expansion characteristics, where the constraint of one grain on the next may be reduced (see below).

In cases where the method of manufacture of a polycrystalline material introduces some preferred orientation of the component crystallites, expansion anisotropy of the crystallites is reflected in the expansion anisotropy of fired components. Examples of this are:

1. Extruded or pressed materials, particularly when platy raw materials such as clays are used: porcelains, steatites, some aluminas, some beryllias, graphite.
2. Hot-pressed materials: boron nitride, to some degree in silicon nitride.
3. Natural minerals: pyrophillite, block talc.
4. Fibre-reinforced materials: carbon/carbon composites.

In instances where the crystallite expansion anisotropy is moderate or high, the mismatch between adjacent grains may generate sufficient local elastic energy to cause grain boundary fracture on cooling from the firing temperature (bearing in mind that stress relief by plastic flow is not possible in ceramics). Shrinkage along high expansion coefficient directions causes loss of contact, and these no longer contribute to the polycrystalline average. The net value of the expansion coefficient is then reduced, and an expansion hysteresis loop may become evident during heating and cooling. If internal cracking is significant, strength and stiffness will be reduced substantially. Materials in which expansion hysteresis may be detected are, in the main, medium- to coarse-grained, but in some cases expansion anisotropy is so extreme that the upper limit of grain size for avoiding internal fracture may be as low as 1 or 2 μm. Examples of medium- to coarse-grained products include beryllia and cordierite, while fine-grained products include lithium-containing spodumene and eucryptite ceramics and glass-ceramics, and magnesium or aluminium titanate.

Phase changes can also introduce internal cracking. Of note are those associated with the various forms of crystalline silica, evident in many clay-based products, porcelains, some glass-ceramics and some silicon carbides, and in zirconia in the unstabilized or partially-stabilized forms. Again if crystallite sizes are sufficiently small, internal cracking is avoided and the transformation introduces marked discontinuities into the expansion curve. If crystallite sizes are large or the volume change associated with the transition is large, then internal cracking will occur and lead to a less marked effect on net thermal expansion.

The nature of the hysteresis will depend on the temperature range over which expansion measurements are made. The extent of the effect will be seen only if both heating and cooling measurements are made, a practice not commonly adopted but essential for studying hysteresis and phase

Figure 2.4.1
Thermal expansion hysteresis demonstrated by porous sintered cordierite glass-ceramics of different starting particle size fractions, demonstrating that as the resulting crystallite size is increased the mean coefficient of expansion on heating decreases, but the hysteresis increases.

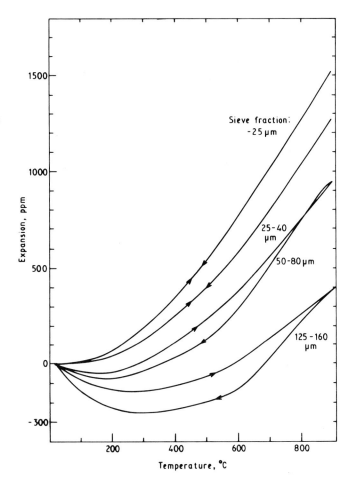

Figure 2.4.2
A schematic thermal expansion trace of a glass heated to above the annealing temperature, showing the effect of setting on the correct mismatch to a solid to which it is joined.

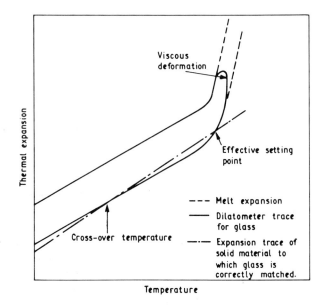

changes. Each material should be tested on its own merits. Figure 2.4.1 shows an example of hysteresis as a function of starting glass particle size in a sintered cordierite glass-ceramic.

The thermal expansion of glasses is complicated by the fact that the 'phase change' from rigid solid to viscous liquid occurs over a range of temperature. Very often the information required is the effective mismatch between a glass and a rigid solid to which it is joined. The low-temperature expansion coefficient is not appropriate because it is necessary to take the setting behaviour of the glass into account. As demonstrated by Figure 2.4.2, the solid expansion coefficient of the glass must be lower than that of the other material in order to avoid a joint which stresses the glass in tension. Typically the difference in coefficient has to be no more than $1 \times 10^{-6} K^{-1}$. Since the effective setting point cannot be measured using a dilatometer, mismatch in joints has to be measured in alternative ways, e.g. photoelastically, or, for glazes, by monitoring the changes in curvature of a strip glazed on one side only as it is heated and cooled. Such techniques can also be used to monitor the changes in stress level produced by the phenomenon of densification when the glass is held near to but below the strain point (see Section 2.2.4.1).

2.4.3.4 Data tables

Typical linear thermal expansion coefficient data are given in Table 2.4.3. In many cases a band or range is quoted because commercially available products are not identical in composition or phase content. Many products contain a number of phases, but are classified by the name of their primary component, such as 'high-alumina' or 'titanium diboride'. Many of the more exotic refractory materials not in regular production are made primarily by hot-pressing with substantial amounts of other components, which produce some variation in thermal expansion characteristics. Data for such products, Table 2.4.4, must be considered tentative.

In high-alumina ceramics, small variations in expansion data can be expected as a consequence of differing amounts of different bonding phases, with deviations increasing with decreasing alumina content. A degree of anisotropy may be introduced in fine-grained extruded products as a consequence of preferred orientation of the grains. The effect is small but may be of significance in some applications.

The generalization of expansion data in the case of clay-based products reflects the fairly broad bands allowed by the draft IEC classification scheme. Expansion characteristics are dependent on raw materials, composition, grain size, and firing temperature, the microstructure depending on the extent of reaction.

Few data are quoted for glasses, because in principle the expansion coefficient can be varied continuously by varying composition. There are limits defined by glass stability against crystallization, by durability and by workability, but even so it is often possible to develop a glass with specified expansion characteristics combined with other particular properties. In Table 2.4.3 some data are quoted for some well-known 'standard' types of glass, but many glasses are commercially available with expansion coefficients in the range $1-15 \times 10^{-6} K^{-1}$ ($25-300°C$). Materials of higher expansion coefficient tend to be unstable with respect to water. Generally, it is important

Table 2.4.3 Typical thermal expansion coefficients for common types of ceramic*

Material (IEC class) (where appropriate)	Mean linear thermal expansion coefficient ($10^{-6}K^{-1}$) over temperature range from 25°C to:					
	−50°C	100°C	500°C	1000°C	1500°C	2000°C
Porcelains and clay-based products:						
Siliceous porcelains (C-110, 111)	2–6	3–6	4–7	5–8	—	—
Cristobalite porcelains (C-112)	—	6–8	6–8	6–8	—	—
Aluminous porcelains (C-120)	—	3–6	6–8	6–8	—	—
Aluminous porcelains (C-130)	—	4–7	4–7	5–8	—	—
Steatites (C-210, 220, 221)	—	6–9	6–9	6–10	—	—
Porous steatites (C-230)	—	8–10	8–10	—	—	—
Porous forsterite (C-240)	—	8–10	8–10	8–10	—	—
Dense forsterite (C-250)	—	9–11	9–11	9–11	—	—
Cordierite (C-410)	—	1–3	2–4	2–4.5	—	—
Celsian (C-420)	—	3–5	3.5–6	4–7	—	—
Zircon	—	—	—	4.5–6	—	—
Porous electrical refractories (C-510, 511, 512, 520, 530)	—	1.5–3.5	2–4	2.5–4	—	—
Mullite ceramics (C-610, 620)	—	5–6	5–7	5–7	—	—
Oxides:						
Alumina 99% (C-799)	4.5	5.9	7.4	8.0	9.0	—
Alumina 95% (C-795)	—	5.6–5.9	7.0–7.6	8.0–8.3	—	—
Alumina 90% (C-786)	—	5.0–6.0	6.8–7.4	8.0–8.3	—	—
Beryllia (C-810)	—	5–7	8.4–8.6	8.8–8.9	—	—
Cordierite	~ −1	0	1.0–1.5	1.8–2.5	—	—
Magnesia (C-820)	—	8–9	10–12	11–13	14–15	16–17
Mullite	—	3.2	4.6	5.2	—	—
Spinel	—	5.6	7.6	8.4	10.2	—
Thoria	—	—	—	9.2	11.7	12.7
Titania (C-310)	—	5–7	7–8	8–9	—	—
Urania	—	—	8–9	10–11	11–12	12–13
Zircon	—	5	6	6	—	—
Zirconia (stab.) (C-830)	—	8–9	9–10	11–13	12–13	13–14
Zirconia (partially-stabilized[1])	—	7–8	8–9	9–10	—	—
Non-oxides:						
Silicon nitride[2]	—	1.5	2.7	3.3	3.6	—
Sialons, sintered silicon nitrides	—	1.5–1.7	2.7–3.0	3.3–3.7	—	—
Silicon carbide[3]	—	2.8	3.9	4.6	6.6	—
Boron carbide	—	3.3	4.5	5.8	—	—
Boron nitride:						
// hot-pressing direction	0–2	0–2.5	0–3	2–6	3–7	—
⊥ hot-pressing direction	~1	0–1	0–1	1–2	1–2	—
pyrolytic, // deposition	—	—	~25	~25	—	—
pyrolytic, ⊥ deposition	—	−2	−0.4	~1.4	~2	—
Carbon, vitreous	—	2.0–2.2	2.8–3.0	3.0–3.2	—	—
Carbon, graphite[4]	—	1–3	2–4	3–5	—	—
Tungsten carbide[5]	—	4.7	5.0	—	—	—
Glasses:						
Soda-lime sheet	6.4	7.8	—	—	—	—
'Pyrex' borosilicate	—	2.5–3.5	2.5–3.5	—	—	—
Vitreous silica[6]	0.60	0.55	0.52	0.50	—	—
'ULE' silica (Corning 7971)	~ −0.06	0.013–0.067	—	—	—	—

Table 2.4.3 (*contd*)

Materials (IEC class) (where appropriate)	Mean linear thermal expansion coefficient ($10^{-6}K^{-1}$) over temperature range from 25°C to					
	−50°C	100°C	500°C	1000°C	1500°C	2000°C
Glass-ceramics:						
'Pyroceram 9606' (Corning)	~1.0	6.5	4.8	4.5	—	—
'Pyroceram 9608' (Corning)[7]	—	0.7–2.0	1–3	1.5–4	—	—
'EE 1087' (GEC Ceramics Ltd.)	—	—	10–11.5	—	—	—
'Zerodur' (Schott)	0.05	0.03	—	—	—	—
Machinable materials:						
'Macor' machinable glass-ceramic (Corning 9658)	—	~8	~10	~13	—	—
Pyrophillite (unfired)	—	~8	~8	—	—	—
Pyrophillite (fired 1250°C)	—	2–3	3–4	3–4	—	—
Pyrophillite (fired 1350°C)	—	3–6	4–6	5–6	—	—
Talc (fired 1000°C)	—	~11	—	—	—	—
Sintered fused silica	—	0.6	0.6	0.6	—	—
Single-crystal materials:						
Sapphire // c-axis	—	6.9	8.33	9.03	—	—
⊥ c-axis	—	5.3	7.70	8.31	—	—
Quartz // c-axis	6.17	7.57	12.8	transforms to β-quartz at 573°C.		
⊥ c-axis	11.03	13.79	22.2	Over range 600–1000°C, $\bar{\alpha} \approx 0$.		

* Figures underlined refer to the range given in IEC 672: 1980.
[1] Partially-stabilized zirconia shows some variation depending on tetragonal phase content, grain size and temperature range of measurement.
[2] Reaction-bonded and hot-pressed forms show similar behaviour.
[3] Most forms of SiC product show similar behaviour except after oxidation.
[4] Graphite-containing products can be considerably anisotropic.
[5] Typical of low metal content hardmetal.
[6] All types show similar expansion behaviour.
[7] Depending on heat treatment.

Table 2.4.4 Thermal expansion coefficients of some less-common materials

Material	Mean linear thermal expansion coefficient ($10^{-6}K^{-1}$) over temperature range (°C)					
	−50–25°C	25–100°C	25–500°C	25–1000°C	25–1500°C	25–2000°C
Oxides:						
Aluminium titanate	(anisotropic, shows hysteresis)					
Chromium oxide	—	8.0	8.0	8.0	—	—
Lanthanum oxide	—	8.0	10.5	12.0	—	—
Lanthanum chromite	—	7.6	7.6	8.0	—	—
Magnesium titanate	(anisotropic, shows hysteresis)					
Tin oxide	—	3.0	4.2	5.2	—	—
Yttria	6.9	7.2	7.6	8.4	8.7	—
Non-oxides:						
Zirconium diboride	—	5.4	6.1	6.9	7.4	7.7
Titanium diboride	—	5.7	6.7	7.6	8.3	8.8
Hafnium diboride	—	6.0	6.5	7.0	7.4	7.6
Titanium carbide	—	6.5	7.0	7.6	8.2	8.9
Tantalum carbide	—	5.9	6.1	6.5	6.9	7.3
Aluminium nitride	2.1	3.6	4.5	5.3	—	—
Boron nitride, cubic	—	1.8	3.4	4.6	—	—
Molybdenum disilicide	—	6.9	7.9	8.5	8.8	—

to consider the glass transformation temperature and other relevant properties as well as the expansion coefficient.

The same comments are true for glass-ceramics. Special formulations can be made, crystallizing to give the expansion coefficient required, for example, for matching to other materials. The range of coefficients is wider than for glasses, typically -3 to $18 \times 10^{-6} \mathrm{K}^{-1}$ ($25 - 300°\mathrm{C}$), because of the wider range of expansion coefficients of crystalline silicate phases than of glasses.

For detailed data on individual types of product, see the relevant Data Sheet in Part 2.

2.4.4 Thermal conductivity and thermal diffusivity

2.4.4.1 Definitions

THERMAL CONDUCTIVITY, (λ), is defined as the heat flow per unit area developed under unit temperature gradient:

$$\lambda = -\frac{1}{A} \frac{dQ}{dt} \frac{dl}{dT}$$

where dQ/dt is the rate of heat flow across area A, and dT/dl is the temperature gradient. λ is normally a function of temperature, and in anisotropic materials, of direction. The technical literature uses a wide range of units, but in this Handbook, the S.I. units of watts per metre per kelvin ($\mathrm{Wm}^{-1}\mathrm{K}^{-1}$) are used throughout.

THERMAL DIFFUSIVITY, (D), is the equivalent of a diffusion coefficient in the Fourier equation for heat flow, and is a measure of how fast a heat pulse is transmitted through a solid. It is related to the thermal conductivity through the relationship:

$$D = \frac{\lambda}{\varrho C_p}$$

where ϱ is the density and C_p is the specific heat. Since it is related to λ, D is usually also a function of temperature, and has units of (metre)^2 second^{-1} ($\mathrm{m}^2\mathrm{s}^{-1}$).

2.4.4.2 Measurement methods

The best technique for measurement of thermal transport properties depends on the thermal conductivity value in question. Direct steady-state thermal conductivity measurements on high-conductivity materials are generally made by various bar methods while those on low-conductivity materials are made by short cylinder or comparator methods (sandwiching the specimen between reference materials of known thermal conductivity and noting the relative temperature gradients). Of all physical property measurements, those of thermal conductivity are probably subject to the greatest inaccuracies unless very great care is taken over design and operation of apparatus. Overall accuracy is seldom better than 5%, particularly at higher temperatures. In practice it is quicker and more accurate to measure thermal diffusivity and density and, with knowledge of the specific heat, calculate the thermal conductivity.

Thermal diffusivity may also be measured in various ways, but under conditions of transient heat flow. One of the most popular methods is the heat pulse method where a heat pulse is applied to one side of a disc or short cylinder and the time taken for the temperature of the opposite face to reach one-half its final value is recorded. A simple relationship between thermal diffusivity, this time, and the specimen thickness is then used to calculate D. The heat pulse is commonly provided by a power laser flash. An alternative technique is the so-called Ångström method in which the temperature of one face of a specimen is cycled and the phase lag in the cycle at the opposite face is recorded. This lag is inversely related to the thermal diffusivity. Thermal diffusivity measurements are usually more accurate than thermal conductivity measurements, typically to the level of 2–3% for the laser flash method when corrections are made for radiation losses at high temperatures. However, care should be exercised with coarse-grained materials, as the usual test thickness may be smaller than the thickness required to ensure the test sample is representative of a larger component, and with optically- or infrared-transparent materials, where the result depends on the type of coating, surface finish and specimen thickness.

Most thermal conductivity data in this Handbook have been gleaned from literature sources. Some data have been converted from thermal diffusivity measurements made by the laser flash or similar methods. Some of the NPL data on thermal diffusivity quoted in this Handbook were obtained at UMIST Department of Metallurgy in a sponsored programme.

2.4.4.3 Factors affecting thermal transport properties

Thermal conduction in solids occurs by two parallel processes: by the transfer of energy as lattice vibrations (phonons) and by electromagnetic radiation (photons). The latter becomes of significance above about 600°C, but then only for materials that are transparent to the radiation in the thickness in which they are used. Materials with the highest phonon conductivity are the well-ordered low atomic weight materials, BeO, SiC, C (diamond and graphite), MgO, Al_2O_3, and a number of non-oxides of heavy metals. For these materials, thermal conductivity is usually highest at a few tens of kelvins (~ -250°C), falling off at higher temperatures approximately in proportion to reciprocal temperature. Other more complex structures, especially glasses, complex silicates, and oxides of some heavy metals, have rather lower thermal conductivities, and frequently have rather less dependence on temperature.

Microstructure is also important in determining thermal conductivity because the types of phase and their distribution within a material can be so varied. Porosity and minor phases at grain boundaries influence thermal conductivity owing to their scattering effect on phonons and radiation. If a high-conductivity phase, such as alumina, is bonded with a low thermal conductivity glass, the net result will depend on the proportion of glass-free boundaries between the crystals giving a high-conductivity path, and this in turn will depend on the composition and thermal history of the product. The effect of porosity depends on its geometry and distribution. Small closed spherical pores occupying less than 3–5% of total volume have relatively little effect, but clearly as the level of porosity increases, the degree of interconnectedness of the crystalline material decreases and the thermal conductivity falls. Various formulae for the effect of porosity on thermal conductivity have been proposed, but correlation equations are found to depend on pore shape and distribution. For open-porous materials with more than about 15% total porosity, each case should be treated on its own merits. Equations are typically of the form:

$$\lambda = \lambda_o \left\{ \frac{1-v}{1+av} \right\}$$

where v is the volume fraction of pores, λ_o is the thermal conductivity of fully dense material, and a is the correlation constant that may vary between 0.5 and 20. This type of formula does not necessarily apply to materials in which internal cracking occurs due to phase changes or to thermal-expansion mismatch or anisotropy in the constituent phases.

An additional factor that should not be ignored in estimating thermal transport in components and systems is the effect of contact between materials at joints. Unless contact involves chemical bonding between the mating surfaces, as in a metallized and brazed joint, there will be a contact thermal resistance which will influence temperature distributions. Thus in design, one needs to consider heat transfer coefficients as well as thermal conductivity (see also Section 2.6.2.2).

2.4.4.4 Data tables

The data tables give thermal conductivities typical of dense single phase materials (Table 2.4.5), and of commercial products (Table 2.4.6) which usually comprise two or more phases. The data are subject to considerable variation at temperatures below 200°C, both from source to source on the same material and from one commercial product to the next. This arises because in many instances thermal conductivity is a strong function of temperature in this temperature regime, and also because, particularly for materials of higher thermal conductivity, microstructural features can play a major role in controlling phonon interactions. At higher temperatures such variations tend to be smaller, thermal conductivity values being less temperature-dependent, and quoted results show greater consistency. No estimates of error can be placed on these data since strictly each product should be considered on its own merits. The data should be considered only as a band of typical values.

Thermal diffusivity data for commercial products are given in Table 2.4.7. The relationship between density, specific heat, thermal conductivity and thermal diffusivity should be borne in mind, so if either the conductivity or the diffusivity are known, the other can be readily calculated.

Table 2.4.5 Thermal conductivity of dense polycrystalline single-phase compounds in fine grain size

Phase formula	Thermal conductivity, $Wm^{-1}K^{-1}$, at temperature					
	$-50°C$	$25°C$	$100°C$	$500°C$	$1000°C$	$1500°C$
Oxides:						
Al_2O_3	~50	38	35	11	7	6
$Al_6Si_2O_{13}$	—	—	6.1	4.5	4.0	—
BeO	~500	~300	~220	~70	18	14
CaO	—	—	15	8.7	7.8	—
$LaCrO_3$	—	~6	~5	~4	~3.8	~3.6
MgO	~70	~40	~35	16	7	6.5
$MgAl_2O_4$	—	16	15	9	6	—
SiO_2 (vitreous)	—	1.6	1.7	2.1	5.0[1]	—
SnO_2	—	~35	~25	~10	6	—
ThO_2	~17	14	—	6	2	2
TiO_2	—	—	9.2	4.5	3.3	—
UO_2	—	12	8	4.5	3.2	—
Y_2O_3	~25	~18	~15	~5	~3	—
ZrO_2 (stabilized)	—	1.8	1.8	2.0	2.2	2.4
$ZrSiO_4$	—	8	5.8	4.8	4.2	—
Non-oxides:						
AlN (// hot-pressing direction)	—	36	33	23	—	—
BN (see Table 2.4.6)						
Si_3N_4 (hot-pressing 1% MgO)	—	30	28	21	14.5	13
B_4C	—	30	25	21	17	15
Si	—	150	110	45	26	—
SiC	—	110	90	65	45	40
$MoSi_2$	—	60	54	33	—	—
TiC^2	—	~30	~32	~36	~40	~45
WC^2	—	~40	—	—	~45	~50

[1] This increase at higher temperatures is due to increasing direct transmission of radiation.
[2] Depends on the metal/carbon ratio.

Table 2.4.6 Thermal conductivity of commercial products

Material (IEC class)	Thermal conductivity, $Wm^{-1}K^{-1}$, at temperature						IEC 20–100°C
	−50°C	25°C	100°C	500°C	1000°C	1500°C	
Porcelains, clay-based materials:							
Siliceous (C-110, C-111)	—	1.7–2.1	1.7–2.0	1.8–2.0	1.9–2.0	—	1–2.5
Cristobalite (C-112)	—	—	—	—	—	—	1.4–2.5
Aluminous (C-120)	—	—	—	—	—	—	1.2–2.6
Aluminous (C-130)	—	—	—	—	—	—	1.5–4.0
Steatite, low-voltage (C-210)	—	~2.5	~2.4	~1.9	~1.9	—	1–2.5
Steatite, normal (C-220)	—	5.5–6.0	—	2.8–3.7	—	—	2–3
Steatite, low-loss (C-221)	—	—	—	—	—	—	2–3
Steatite, porous (C-230)	—	—	—	—	—	—	1.5–3
Forsterite, porous (C-240)	—	—	4	2	1.7	—	1.4–2
Forsterite, dense (C-250)	—	—	8	4	—	—	3–4
Cordierite, dense (C-410)	—	—	—	—	—	—	1.5–2.5
Celsian, dense (C-420)	—	—	—	—	—	—	1.5–2.5
Zircon, dense	—	7	6	4	3.5	—	—
Refractory (C-510)	—	—	—	—	—	—	1.2–1.7
Refractory (C-511)	—	—	—	—	—	—	1.3–1.8
Refractory (C-512)	—	2.4	2.3	2.1	2.0	—	1–1.5
Refractory (C-520)	—	—	—	—	—	—	1.3–1.8
Refractory (C-530)	—	—	—	—	—	—	1.4–2.0
Mullite (C-610)	—	—	—	—	—	—	2–6
Mullite (C-620)	—	—	—	—	—	—	6–15
Oxides:							
Alumina >99.5% (C-799)	~50	33	29	12	9	7	19–30
Alumina 95% (C-795)	~40	23	13	9	6	5	16–28
Alumina 90% (C-786)	~25	17	12	7	5	4	14–24
Alumina 85% (C-780)	~20	15	12	7	4	3.5	10–16
Beryllia >99.5% (C-810)	500	300	220	70	18	14	150–220
Magnesia, 30% porous (C-820)	—	10–14	5–8	—	—	—	6–10
fully dense	—	40–60	36–48	13–16	6–8	6–8	—
Cordierite (see Refractory, C-520 above)							
Spinel, dense	—	~15	~13	~8	~5	—	—
Thoria, sintered	—	8–10	6–8	3–5	2–3	—	—
Tin oxide, sintered	—	~30	22	10	6	—	—
Titania, sintered (C-310)	—	2.5–4	—	—	—	—	3–4
Urania, sintered	—	8–10	6–8	4–5	2–3	~2	—
Zircon, sintered	—	4–7	4–7	3–5	2.5–4.5	—	—
Zirconia, stabilized (C-830)	—	1.7–2.0	1.7–2.0	1.7–2.0	1.7–2.2	1.8–3.3	1.2–3.5
Zirconia, partially-stabilized	—	1.3	1.3	1.4	1.5	—	—
Non-oxides:							
Boron nitride,							
hot-pressed (// direction)	—	20	17	14	13	—	—
(⊥ direction)	—	33	31	30	27	12	—
pyrolytic (in plane)	—	150–250	150–200	130–150	—	—	—
(perp. to plane)	—	1.5–2.6	1.4–2.5	1.1–1.8	—	—	—
Silicon nitride,							
RBSN density 2.6 Mgm^{-3}	—	14	13	12	11	10	—
2.3 Mgm^{-3}	—	11	9.5	8.5	8.0	7.0	—
2.0 Mgm^{-3}	—	7	5	4.8	4.3	4.0	—
HPSN, 5% MgO	—	37–43	30	28	18	15	—
Sialons, SSNs[1]	—	—	4.5–13	4.5–11	4.5–10	—	—
Boron carbide	—	27	21	15	14	13	—
Silicon carbide,							
silicon-infiltrated	—	120–200	100–170	60–80	30–40	25–30	—
hot-pressed, 2% Al$_2$O$_3$	—	90–110	70–90	55–65	35–45	30–40	—
clay-bonded	—	20–40	20–30	10–20	10–20	—	—
nitride-bonded	—	~35	~25	~16	~15	—	—
sintered, dense	—	90–110	70–90	55–65	35–45	30–40	—
sintered, porous	—	35–50	30–40	18–25	15–20	10–15	—

Table 2.4.6 (*contd*)

Material (IEC class)	Thermal conductivity, $Wm^{-1}K^{-1}$, at temperature						IEC 20–100°C
	−50°C	25°C	100°C	500°C	1000°C	1500°C	
Non-oxides (*contd*)							
Carbon and graphite,							
diamond	700–3000	600–2000	—	—	—	—	—
carbons, graphites	—	5–90	4–80	3–50	2–40	1.5–25	—
vitreous carbon	—	4–8	—	—	—	—	—
pyrolytic graphite							
(in plane)	600–2000	400–1500	350–1200	200–500	130–300	100–250	—
(perp. to plane)	5–15	2–8	2–6	1.5–3.0	1–2	—	—
Tungsten carbide, 6% Co	—	60–80	—	—	—	—	—
Glasses:							
Soda-lime, Float[2]	—	1.2	1.5	2.1	4.8[3]	—	—
Borosilicate, 'Pyrex'[2]	—	1.1	1.1	2.0	—	—	—
Vitreous silica[2]	1.2	1.2	1.7	2.0	5.0	—	—
Glass-ceramics:							
'Pyroceram 9606'	4.5	3.6	3.6	3.3	3.1	—	—
'Pyroceram 9608'	—	2.2	2.3	2.4	—	—	—
'EE 1087'	—	—	~2	—	—	—	—
'Zerodur'	—	1.63	—	—	—	—	—
Machinable ceramics:							
'Macor' machinable glass-ceramic	—	1.3[4]	1.3	1.4	—	—	—
Pyrophillite fired 1250°C	—	0.7–1.1	0.8–1.2	1.1–1.7	1.2–1.8	—	—
Sintered fused silica	—	—	0.8	1.0	1.2	—	—
Single-crystal materials:							
Quartz, // c-axis	—	14.5	10.4	4.4	—	—	—
Quartz, ⊥ c-axis	—	8.5	6.2	3.1	—	—	—
Sapphire, // c-axis	70	40	25	11	7	—	—

Note: Ranges are given where it is known that considerable variations are shown by commercial products depending on phase content and porosity. By the same token, the single figures are representative of most products and will vary by only ±10% between products.

[1] SSN = sintered silicon nitride. Incorporation of oxides into silicon nitride generally reduces thermal conductivity.

[2] Thermal conductivity of glasses depends on infra-red and optical transmittance, which are functions of temperature and thickness. The apparent thermal conductivity increases with increasing thickness, especially above 300°C.

[3] At 1000°C, soda-lime glass is essentially a viscous liquid.

[4] Figure depends on the mica type, flake size and volume fraction.

Table 2.4.7 Thermal diffusivity of commercial products

Material (IEC class)	Thermal diffusivity, 10^{-6} m^2s^{-1}, at temperature						
	$-50°C$	$25°C$	$100°C$	$500°C$	$1000°C$	$1500°C$	Ref
Porcelains and clay-based materials:							
Siliceous (C-110, C-111)	—	—	—	0.65–0.8	0.7–0.8	—	N
Cristobalite (C-112)	—	—	~0.8	—	—	—	C
Aluminous (C-120)	—	—	~0.8	—	—	—	C
Aluminous (C-130)	—	—	~1.0	—	—	—	C
Steatite, low-voltage (C-210)	—	—	~1.5	—	—	—	C
Steatite, normal (C-220)	—	—	~2.4	—	—	—	C
Steatite, low loss (C-221)	—	—	~1.0	—	—	—	C
Steatite, porous (C-230)	—	—	~1.2	—	—	—	C
Forsterite, porous (C-240)	—	—	~0.8	—	—	—	C
Forsterite, dense (C-250)	—	—	~1.3	—	—	—	C
Cordierite, dense (C-410)	—	—	0.8	0.7	0.65	—	N
Celsian, dense (C-420)	—	—	~1.2	—	—	—	C
Zircon, dense	—	—	—	—	—	—	—
Refractory (C-510)	—	—	~0.8	—	—	—	C
Refractory (C-511)	—	—	~0.8	—	—	—	C
Refractory (C-512)	—	—	~0.8	—	—	—	C
Refractory (C-520)	—	—	~0.8	—	—	—	C
Refractory (C-530)	—	—	~0.9	—	—	—	C
Mullite (C-610)	—	—	—	0.8–1.0	0.7–0.9	—	N
Mullite, (C-620)	—	—	~3.0	—	—	—	C
Oxides:							
Alumina, >99.5% (C-799)	—	10.7	8.0	2.6	1.8	1.3	N
Alumina, 95% (C-795)	—	8.0	3.8	1.9	1.3	1.0	N
Alumina, 90% (C-786)	—	6.2	3.7	1.7	1.2	0.9	N
Alumina, 85% (C-780)	—	5.6	3.9	1.7	0.9	0.8	N
Beryllia, >99.5% (C-810)	258	105	60	13.5	2.9	1.9	C
Magnesia, 30% porous (C-820)	—	—	6	2.7	1.9	—	C
dense	—	~12	~10	~4	~1.5	—	C
Cordierite (see Refractory, C-520 above)							
Spinel, porous	—	~6	~4	~2	~1.2	—	C
Thoria, sintered	—	3.5–4.5	2.5–3.5	1.1–1.9	0.7–1.1	—	C
Tin oxide	—	~13	~8	~3	~1.5	—	C
Titania, sintered, (C-310)	—	0.9–1.5	—	—	—	—	C
Urania, sintered	—	3–4	2–3	1.2–1.5	0.6–0.9	0.6	C
Zircon, sintered	—	1.6–3.0	1.4–2.5	0.9–1.5	0.7–1.2	—	C
Zirconia, stabilized, (C-830)	—	0.7	0.7	0.6	0.5	0.6	C
Zirconia, part.-stab.	—	—	0.8	0.55	0.45	—	N
Non-oxides:							
Boron nitride,							
hot-pressed (// hot-pressing direction)	—	11	7	3.8	2.9	—	C
($\perp$ hot-pressing direction)	—	18	13	6	6	—	C
pyrolytic (in plane)	—	90–150	70–90	40–45	—	—	C
(perp to plane)	—	0.9–1.6	0.6–1.2	0.3–0.5	—	—	C
Silicon nitride,							
RBSN density 2.6 Mgm^{-3}	—	9–12	8–10	4–5	~3	~2	NCL
2.3 Mgm^{-3}	—	6–8	6–7	3–4	~2	1.5	NCL
2.0 Mgm^{-3}	—	4–5	3–4	2–2.5	1.4–1.6	1.2	NCL
HPSN, 5% MgO	—	17–20	12–14	6–7	~4–5	3–4	NCL
Sialons, SSNs	—	—	2–5	1.8–4	1.5–3	—	NCL
Boron carbide	—	~11	~8	~3	2.5	2	N
Silicon carbide,							
silicon-infiltrated	—	75–100	50–75	15–25	9–12	8–10	NCL
hot-pressed, 2% Al_2O_3	—	45	32	16	11	8	CL
clay-bonded	—	10–20	9–13	3–6	3–6	—	C
nitride-bonded	—	20	11	5.5	5	—	C
sintered, dense	—	40–50	26–40	15–18	11–13	7–9	CL
sintered, porous	—	—	—	~10	~6	~5	CL

Table 2.4.7 (*contd*)

Material (IEC class)	Thermal diffusivity, 10^{-6} m²s⁻¹, at temperature						
	$-50°C$	25°C	100°C	500°C	1000°C	1500°C	Ref
Non oxides (*continued*)							
Carbon and graphite,							
diamond	—	400–1300	—	—	—	—	C
graphites	—	4.8–64	3.0–44	1.3–16	0.7–11	0.5–6	CL
vitreous carbon	—	3–5	—	—	—	—	C
pyrolytic graphite (in plane)	—	250–1000	180–600	50–150	30–75	—	C
(perp to plane)	—	2.8–5.4	1–3	0.4–0.8	0.2–0.5	—	C
Tungsten carbide, 6% Co	—	20–30	—	—	—	—	C
Glasses:[1]							
Soda-lime, Float	—	0.58	0.67	0.70	1.44	—	C
Borosilicate, 'Pyrex'	—	0.62	0.55	0.78	—	—	C
Vitreous silica	—	0.74	0.91	0.83	2.10	—	C
Glass-ceramics:							
'Pyroceram 9606'	—	1.8	1.6	1.1	0.9	—	C
'Pyroceram 9608'	—	1.1	1.0	0.8	—	—	C
'EE 1087'	—	—	~0.9	—	—	—	C
'Zerodur'	—	—	0.79	—	—	—	C
Machinable ceramics:							
'Macor' machinable glass-ceramic	—	0.7–0.8	0.6–0.7	0.5–0.6	0.5–0.6	—	NC
Pyrophillite, fired 1250°C	—	0.4–0.6	0.4–0.6	0.4–0.6	0.4–0.6	—	N
Sintered fused silica	—	—	0.55	0.54	0.57	—	C
Single-crystal materials:							
Quartz, // c-axis	—	7.3	4.5	1.5	—	—	C
Quartz, ⊥ c-axis	—	4.3	2.7	2.3	—	—	C
Sapphire	33	13	7	2.5	2.0	—	NC

[1] As with thermal conductivity, values depend on thickness, increasing with increasing thickness due to the effects of radiation.
Key to references: N = NPL/UMIST measurements, C = calculated from thermal conductivity data in Table 2.4.6 using assumed density and specific heat data, L = data direct from sources in the technical literature. Where more than one letter appears, the figures quoted represent data typical of all three sources.

2.5

Mechanical properties

Of all the factors influencing the performance of glasses and ceramics, brittleness and strength are the least well appreciated. This Section explains in some detail the meaning of mechanical property data commonly quoted in technical brochures and the scientific literature and their implications for the long- and short-term properties of real components.

2.5.1 Elastic properties

At room temperature the vast majority of brittle materials are linearly elastic up to their fracture stress. There may be exceptions to this statement but these are mainly in cases where there is considerable porosity which leads to a degree of crumbling or of densification that is non-linear with load. In materials of plate-like grain morphology, such as graphite, boron nitride, and some minerals, easy sliding on shear planes may also lead to some non-linearity and to a permanent set after unloading.

The elastic moduli of materials depend on the phase constitution and the shape and distribution of any porosity. The moduli may also vary significantly with temperature, and such variations need to be introduced into stress calculations at elevated temperatures.

2.5.1.1 Definitions

The following definitions apply to isotropic materials:

YOUNG'S MODULUS, (E) is the stress required to give unit strain in the same direction, i, without restraint in the orthogonal directions:

$$E_i = \frac{\sigma_i}{\epsilon_i}$$

2.5.1

where σ is the stress and ϵ is the strain produced.

SHEAR MODULUS, (G) is the shear stress applied to opposite faces of a body required to produce unit angular rotation of a line perpendicular to the plane of shear:

$$G = \frac{\tau}{\phi}$$

2.5.2

where τ is the shear stress and ϕ is the angular rotation in radians.

BULK MODULUS, (K) is the hydrostatic pressure p required to effect a change of volume ΔV of a body of unit volume V assumed to be homogeneous:

$$K = \frac{p}{\Delta V/V} \qquad\qquad 2.5.3$$

POISSON'S RATIO, (ν). If a body is subjected to a strain ϵ in one direction, then assuming elastic isotropy it will experience a strain $-\nu\epsilon$ orthogonal to that direction.

INTERRELATIONS. The above four basic elastic properties are related in the case of elastic isotropy by the equations:

$$E = 3K(1 - 2\nu) = 2G(1 + \nu) \qquad\qquad 2.5.4$$

Single-crystal materials which do not have cubic crystal symmetry (i.e. most ceramic materials), have anisotropic elastic properties, and therefore stresses and strains should strictly be related using tensor analysis. The above terms then do not have the same meaning, and although it is possible to define directional moduli in terms of the tensor constants, Poisson's ratio becomes especially difficult. Most polycrystalline materials are reasonably isotropic if made by dry powder processing methods, but if the grain orientation of individual anisotropic grains is not random, then the anisotropy may be reflected in the bulk properties to some extent. Examples are extruded products in which the precursor raw material has a plate-like structure, such as clay-based products and some aluminas, hot-pressed products, such as silicon nitride, and virtually all types of graphite and hexagonal boron nitride. Aspects of anisotropic elasticity are beyond the scope of this Handbook, and the reader is referred to the Bibliography for texts on the subject.

2.5.1.2 Methods of measurement

Young's modulus can be most simply (and fairly accurately) obtained by measuring the deflection of long thin beams, using transducers, strain gauges or testing-machine displacement (corrected for machine compliance). Shear modulus can be measured by the twisting of cylindrical bars. Poisson's ratio is normally obtained from the relationship given in Equation 2.5.4 from E and G, and consequently is subject to some error.

Static methods of measuring moduli give figures related to isothermal behaviour. There is an increasing tendency to measure moduli by ultrasonic pulse (time of flight) or resonance methods. In such cases the figure measured is related to adiabatic conditions and is about 0.1% higher than the isothermal figure. Since this is small in relation to the variability of materials, it is ignored in this Handbook. Ultrasonic methods have advantages for anisotropic materials since smaller test samples can be used, and these can be tested in a variety of orientations to obtain all the values of the elastic stiffness tensor. There are also advantages at elevated temperatures where anelastic effects in test jigs for static measurements may cause errors. However, it should be noted that at temperatures sufficiently high to cause any degree of anelasticity in the sample, ultrasonic measurements will always give substantially higher values of moduli than static methods. In the latter there is time for permanent deformation to occur, whereas in ultrasonic methods with rapid stress reversals no deformation takes place. Measurement by ultrasonic or resonance methods normally requires special equipment and the services of specialist test houses. The major potential error in measurements is the uncertainty of applicability of resonance formulae to the particular test-piece geometry employed.

2.5.1.3 Factors affecting moduli data

All elastic properties are influenced by the level of porosity since pores act as a second phase of zero modulus. It is generally found that porosity reduces Young's modulus according to a relationship of the form:

$$E = E_o \exp\{-av\} \qquad\qquad 2.5.5$$

where E_o is the modulus of fully dense material, v is the volume fraction of porosity, and a is a constant determined by Poisson's ratio and also by pore shape and distribution, i.e. is dependent on the microstructure. A universal relationship does not exist. Various authors have proposed equations to fit experimental data, but all depend on the above material parameters. For example, it has been shown that an equation of the form:

$$E = E_o (1 - 1.9v + 0.9v^2) \qquad\qquad 2.5.6$$

is a fair approximation for the case of small, closed, randomly distributed, spherical pores in a material of $\nu = 0.3$, and has been verified for a range of alumina ceramics of different porosities up to 50%. The majority of dense sintered materials have 2–7% porosity, giving a reduction in Young's modulus of approximately 4–13% compared to materials of theoretical density.

Multiphase materials have moduli intermediate between the values for their constituent phases, and to a first approximation, each phase contributes according to its volume fraction, V_i:

$$E = E_1 V_1 + E_2 V_2 + \ldots + E_i V_i \qquad\qquad 2.5.7$$

It is relatively common in engineering ceramics to have a high-modulus major phase bonded by a low-modulus minor phase. The modulus of the composite reduces rapidly as the minor-phase content increases.

Moduli are also affected by temperature. Increasing temperature tends to lead to a decreasing modulus, although this is not always the case. Some glasses and complex glass-ceramics become stiffer as the temperature is raised. In this Handbook, the temperature coefficient of modulus is defined as the fractional increase in modulus for each kelvin rise in temperature:

$$E_T = E_{25}\{1 + \eta_E(T - 25)\}$$

$$\qquad\qquad 2.5.8$$

$$G_T = G_{25}\{1 + \eta_G(T - 25)\}$$

for Young's and shear modulus respectively, where η_E and η_G are the respective temperature coefficients which are assumed to be averages over the temperature range considered, and T is the temperature in °C. In general, these coefficients are negative.

2.5.1.4 Elastic moduli data

The data table, Table 2.5.1, gives approximate values of the elastic moduli of commonly available materials, together with temperature dependence. In Figure 2.5.1, Young's modulus is plotted against Al_2O_3 content for a range of high-alumina ceramics. These all contain between 1 and 5% porosity, based on their density. The considerable spread shown by manufacturers' data probably results from several factors: variation in actual test specimen density, variation in alumina phase content as distinct from total nominal Al_2O_3 content, rounding errors, and measurement errors. Nevertheless, the trend is obvious. In Figure 2.5.2, the plot of Young's modulus against volume fraction of pores for reaction-bonded silicon nitride is shown. Here the correlation is rather better, probably as a result of a systematic series of tests within one organization. However, there are variations that can be explained on the basis of the pore morphology in the materials which can

Table 2.5.1 Typical elastic moduli data

Material, (IEC class)	Elastic moduli				
	E GNm^{-2}	$\eta_E{}^1$ $10^{-5}K^{-1}$	G GNm^{-2}	K GNm^{-2}	ν
Porcelains and clay-based materials:					
Porcelains, siliceous (C-110)	70	—	34	—	0.18
Pressed porcelains (C-111)	50	—	—	—	—
Cristobalite porcelains (C-112)	70	—	—	—	—
Aluminous porcelains (C-120)	80–100	—	—	—	—
Aluminous porcelains (C-130)	100–180	—	—	—	—
Steatite, low-voltage (C-210)	60	—	—	—	—
Steatite, normal (C-220)	80	—	—	—	—
Steatite, low-loss (C-221)	100	—	—	—	—
Steatite, porous (C-230)	~ 40	—	—	—	—
Forsterite, porous (C-240)	~ 40	—	—	—	—
Forsterite, dense (C-250)	130	—	—	—	—
Vitreous cordierite (C-410)	110	—	—	—	—
Celsian, dense (C-420)	~100	—	—	—	—
Zircon, dense	140	—	—	—	—
Electrical refractories (C–510, 511, 512, 520, 530)	Properties depend primarily on density and corundum content				
Refractory mullite (C-610)	~100	—	—	—	—
Refractory mullite (C-620)	~140	—	—	—	—
Oxide ceramics:					
Alumina, >99% Al_2O_3 (C-799)	380	−12	160	230	0.22
Alumina, 95% Al_2O_3 (C-795)	320	−12	130	180	0.22
Alumina, 90% Al_2O_3 (C-786)	260	−12	105	160	0.22
Alumina, 85% Al_2O_3 (C-780)	220	−12	90	140	0.22
Beryllia, 99% BeO (C-810)	340	—	140	—	0.23
Magnesia, dense	300	−16	124	—	0.21
Magnesia, porous (C-820)	(depends on density)				
Spinel, dense	260	−12	100	—	0.29
Thoria, dense	240	−10	95	—	0.26
Tin oxide, dense	230	—	—	—	—
Titania, dense	280	—	110	—	0.25
silicate-bonded (C-310)	90–140	—	—	—	—
Urania	200	—	80	—	0.30
Zircon	160	—	—	—	—
Zirconia, stabilized (C-830)	200	—	—	—	—
Zirconia, partially-stabilized	100 (typically)				
Zirconia, partially-stabilized, aged	200	—	—	—	—

Table 2.5.1 (*contd*)

Material, (IEC class)	Elastic moduli				
	E GNm^{-2}	η_E^1 $10^{-5}K^{-1}$	G GNm^{-2}	K GNm^{-2}	ν
Non-oxides:					
Boron nitride, hot-pressed	20–100	(anisotropic)			
pyrolytic, // plane	150	(anisotropic)			
Silicon nitride,					
reaction-bonded (Figure 2.5.2)	120–250	−3 to −7	30–80	—	0.20
hot-pressed	310	−4	120	—	0.27
Sialons, sintered silicon nitrides	300	—	—	—	0.27
Boron carbide	450	—	—	—	—
Silicon carbide,					
silicon-infiltrated	350–380	—	—	—	0.22
hot-pressed	440	—	—	—	—
clay-bonded	~ 60	—	—	—	—
nitride-bonded	~ 80	—	—	—	—
sintered, dense	400	—	—	—	—
sintered, porous	40–150	—	—	—	—
Carbon and graphite					
diamond (average)	960	—	400	—	0.20
graphites (non-linear)	3–15	—	1–6	—	~0.1
vitreous carbon	20–30	(depends on density)			
pyrolytic graphite (// plane)	30	(anisotropic)			
Tungsten carbide, 6% cobalt	600	—	240	—	0.26
Glasses:					
Soda-lime, Float	73	−13	30	—	0.22
Borosilicate, 'Pyrex'	68	—	—	—	0.20
Vitreous silica	74	—	—	—	0.16
Glass-ceramics:					
'Pyroceram' 9606 (Corning)	120	—	—	—	0.24
'Pyroceram' 9608 (Corning)	88	—	—	—	0.25
'EE 1087' (GEC Ceramics Ltd.)	92	—	37	—	0.245
'Zerodur' (Schott)	84	—	—	—	—
Machinable ceramics:					
'Macor' machinable glass-ceramic	65	−6	30	—	0.27
Pyrophyllite, fired 1250°C	~ 50	—	—	—	—
Sintered fused silica	10–30	(depends on density)			
Machinable alumina	50–150	(depends on density)			
Single-crystal materials:					
Alpha-quartz, parallel to a-axis	78	See data sheets for tensor elastic			
parallel to c-axis	105	constants			
Sapphire, parallel to a-axis	430				
parallel to c-axis	460				

[1] Temperature coefficient of Young's modulus over the temperature range up to the softening point of any of the constituent phases.

vary considerably according to processing history. Materials with uniform distributions of small pores are stiffer than those with aggregated pores giving a less well developed crystalline network. Consequently, the two types cannot have the same density correlation equation.

From the point of view of the user requiring data on a specific product, the Table should provide a guide, but because of the possible variations there is no substitute for measurements on actual products if accurate figures are required.

Figure 2.5.1
Young's modulus as a function of alumina content of high-alumina ceramics. Data are taken from manufacturers' brochures.

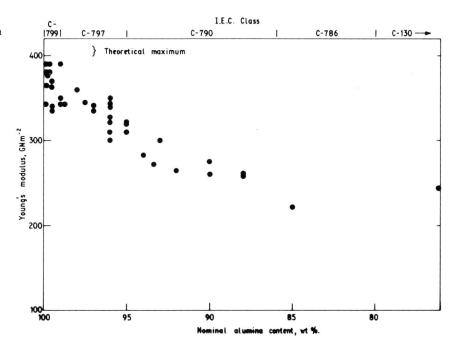

Figure 2.5.2
Young's modulus of silicon nitrides as a function of porosity, taken from Larsen, DC, (1979), 'Property screening of turbine vane materials', *Report AFML-TR-79-4188*.

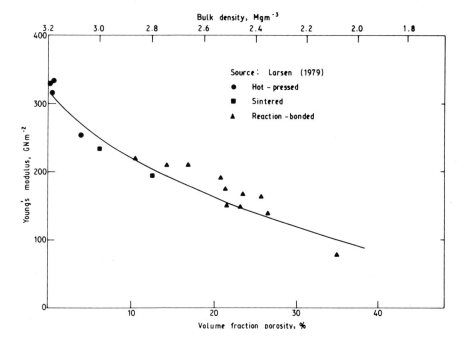

2.5.2 Brittleness and strength

Whereas many metals exhibit plasticity at room temperature, very few ceramics, and certainly none of those of practical use, do so when tested in bulk. The reasons for this are associated with the complex crystallographic structures and the strong directional bonding of oxides, carbides, etc., which means that dislocations are not easily moved except at very high temperatures. Cracks, notches and other defects in ceramics do not have a macroscopically significant plastic zone in their vicinity, which in plastic materials tends to lessen the concentration of applied stress, and thus increases resistance to propagation into a running crack. Consequently, little plastic work is done when a brittle material is broken, and the apparent fracture toughness is low.

This does imply that plastic processes do not occur in ceramic-type materials. The energy required to produce two pristine surfaces, the fracture surface energy, is always greater than the theoretical surface energy associated with broken atomic bonds. Some of the extra work done is absorbed in highly localized plastic processes. Plasticity is more significant in response to identation and machining, where local loads are extremely high. Nevertheless, at normal temperatures, most ceramics can be considered to be macroscopically brittle, and not tough in the engineering sense.

The effects of the stress-concentration at notches on the strength of brittle materials was first recognized by Griffith in 1920, who used the concept of atomically sharp notches to explain the weakness of bulk glass compared to pristine glass fibres. In particular he derived a relationship between the stress required to propagate such sharp notches, σ, and the fracture surface energy of the material. His treatment was based on an energy balance between the work done extending the specimen as a crack opens and the energy associated with the new free surface produced:

$$\sigma_f = \left\{ \frac{E\gamma_i}{Ac} \right\}^{\frac{1}{2}} \qquad\qquad 2.5.9$$

where E is Young's modulus, γ_i is the fracture surface energy for the initiation of rapid crack propagation, c is the crack length (of a surface crack, or the half-length of an enclosed elliptical crack), and A is a constant dependent on loading geometry. For plane-stress conditions (i.e. where stresses perpendicular to the applied stress across the crack face are zero), $A = \pi/2$, and for plane-strain conditions (i.e. where strains perpendicular to the applied stress are zero, or for no lateral contraction), $A = \pi (1 - \nu^2)/2$ where ν is Poisson's ratio. For more detailed discussion of the development of the Griffith criterion, the reader is referred to Davidge's book and other texts (see Bibliography).

In a glass, which has a homogenous structure devoid of porosity and grain boundaries, there is little resistance to the propagation of a crack once the stress on it is large enough. In a polycrystalline ceramic these microstructural features can act as barriers to the movement of a crack front, and more work has to be done to break the material. Glasses are therefore more 'brittle' than many polycrystalline ceramics and, as is well known, can be readily and fairly reliably broken from a scribe line, whereas ceramics cannot. It generally requires a relatively deep notch in a ceramic to control the line of a crack.

Under sufficient tensile or shear stress, ceramics fail suddenly as the criterion for propagation of a pre-existing crack or flaw is reached. Under compressive stresses, ceramics are much stronger. Failure of low-porosity materials normally occurs by propagation of cracks from defects either in shear across the specimen or radially and tangentially which reduces the specimen to a number of bent pillars. The mode of failure depends on the exact manner of loading, but typically failure occurs at 5–8 times the nominal tensile failure stress. For materials of porosity above about 10–15%, failure in compression can be a consequence of pore collapse, and the ratio of compressive to tensile strength tends to be less than 5. In materials containing microstructural features that facilitate shear sliding or cleavage, such as graphites and mica-containing products, the ratio can also be less than 5. Strength under bi- or tri-axial loading depends on the relative directions and magnitudes of the stresses.

Compressive testing is often somewhat meaningless because of the difficulties of ensuring pure uniaxial compression with no end effects. In any case failure in practice usually results from shear or tensile stress, and there are very few instances of use in pure compression. Compressive strength is reviewed in this Handbook only where it is relatively low, and thus of significance. In the majority of cases tensile strength is of far greater importance. Compressive strength may look impressive, but cannot be considered to be a useful parameter for design purposes.

The foregoing provides a brief introduction to the practical consequences of a lack of ductility. For a more rigorous discussion of fracture criteria the reader is referred to scientific texts. However, it is of note that considerable scientific work has been aimed at measuring fracture energy, γ_i, or work of fracture, γ_f, and their related parameter, the critical stress intensity factor K_{Ic}:

$$K_{Ic}^2 = 2\gamma_i E/(1 - \nu^2) \qquad\qquad 2.5.10$$

for plane-strain conditions. The widely accepted concept of stress intensity factor at the tips of cracks is used in the following Sections to describe various phenomena, and the techniques for measuring these parameters are given in Section 2.5.5.

2.5.3 Interpretation of strength data

2.5.3.1 Factors affecting a measured short-term strength

The short-term breaking stress of a ceramic material depends on a number of factors:
1. The shape, size, orientation and position of a strength-limiting defect.
2. The resistance to propagation of the defect under load, i.e. the fracture toughness of the material.
3. The stiffness of the material, i.e. Young's modulus.
4. The method of testing.

For a given material, factor 3 is essentially fixed, and factor 2 is not normally variable to any great degree by virtue of fixed microstructure and crystal types (see Section 2.2). For the majority of commercial materials, therefore, strength measured by any particular method of testing is essentially controlled by defects which are very small, and is readily estimated from

Equation 2.5.9 by inserting suitable figures. More ductile materials, being much tougher, require much larger cracks before fracture occurs. The small flaws in ceramics result from the methods by which the material is made and by which the test specimens are prepared for testing. The types of defect that may control strength include:

Internal defects

(i)   Porosity, which is a consequence of incomplete densification during sintering, is almost inevitably present in virtually all ceramic materials and some glasses (e.g. lower-quality fused SiO_2). Failure can be initiated at large pores, or groups of pores that interact locally to enhance the applied stress. Variations in porosity within a component can result from variations in green density during the initial shaping, particularly in die pressing.

(ii) Defects resulting from foreign particles entrained during powder pressing, which may oxidize or perhaps fuse during the firing process. The result is usually some discoloration, or in bad cases a fusion spot.

(iii) Defects originating from the shaping process such as delaminations and cracks.

(iv) Internal stresses, caused by local anisotropic thermal contraction or phase changes on cooling from a stress-free state at the firing temperature. Since internal crack propagation depends on the local energy available, the larger the grain size the more likely it is that cracked grains or grain boundaries will exist within the bulk and act as sharp cracks. Such cracks lower not only strength but also elastic moduli, and can result in thermal expansion hysteresis. Such effects are noted in coarse-grained beryllias, partially-stabilized zirconias, cordierites, some quartz and cristobalite porcelains, and some electrical ceramic materials such as magnesium titanate.

(v)   Exaggerated grain growth, which occurs in some sintered materials, can result in a lower local fracture toughness, and thus if associated with a mechanical defect of one of the types described above can be a source of weakness compared to the remainder of the material.

Surface defects

(vi) As-fired surfaces may be rough, or in some circumstances may have the appearance of being thermally etched and relatively free of gross defects. Even minor pickup of furnace debris or dirt can cause significant defects, and processes to clean the surface, such as rumbling or vibro-energy milling can result in a degree of additional impact damage.

(vii) Machining will completely change the surface defect distribution and will introduce damage that depends on the machining conditions.

(viii) Surface recrystallization, which may occur during subsequent heat-treatments, may also influence strength by annealing out machining damage. This can lead to increases or decreases of apparent strength depending on the type of material and machining method.

Because no ceramic except perhaps pristine fibres or whiskers can be free from defects of the types listed above, the strength of ceramic components does not approach the theoretical cohesive strength of the crystal lattice or grain boundary. Furthermore, because it is not possible to predetermine the size and location of the flaw that experiences the highest stress at its tip under the load applied to the component, there will be a distribution of apparent fracture strengths within a batch of components.

The situation is complicated by two further factors. Firstly, the measured strength of a ceramic depends on the volume under load because the greater the volume the greater is likely to be the size of the biggest strength-limiting defect. Secondly, both the chemical environment at the crack tip and the duration of loading affect a measured strength. *No ceramic material can therefore be said to exhibit a guaranteed strength in the same sense as can normally be expected of ductile metals and alloys.* Instead it is necessary to use statistical techniques to establish the spread of fracture strengths produced by the fabrication process and test method employed, and then, taking into account the effects of volume, environment and time under load, attempt to predict either a safe working level for the material, or a level at which only a tolerably small proportion of components would fail. These concepts, and that of proof-testing are expanded later.

Manufacturers often quote figures for average strength determined by short-term loading tests to one of a number of semi-standardized test procedures. Such figures should be treated with considerable caution and should not be used directly for mechanical design because they relate only to the test specimen and the test geometry. Real components made by different methods behave differently as a consequence of differences in all the factors described above.

2.5.3.2 Strength tests on test pieces

Since ceramics display no measurable bulk plasticity at ambient temperatures, stress concentrations are not reduced by macroscopic plastic flow. In a conventional tensile test, unreliable results would be produced because of the difficulties of gripping the specimen and of aligning it axially. Tensile strength figures are sometimes quoted but are suspect. It is more usual to employ a test which subjects part of the specimen to tensile stress by loading other parts in compression. These test geometries are demonstrated in Figure 2.5.3. For example, the simplest test, and the one in most common use, is the bend test where there is a gradient of tensile stress from a maximum at the convex surface to zero at the centre. Other tests include the pressurized tube or ring test which places the specimen in hoop tension, the diametral compression test which produces orthogonal tensile stress at the centre of a disc, the compression test on a ring diameter which produces maximum tensile stress on the inner surface near the points of loading, and the 'theta' shaped test in which a diametral bar across a disc specimen is subjected to tensile stress when the disc is compressed orthogonally to the bar. Each has its uses and its limitations. Generally speaking, the bend test in one of its forms is the type normally employed when otherwise unannotated strength data are given. However, there are no universally accepted test procedures to define the bend test, and as a result it is not possible to compare strength data from different tests under different conditions. The following list gives some of the reasons why this is so:

The loading geometry
The larger the specimen the greater the volume under test and the lower the average strength. In bending with three-point loading rather than four-point

Figure 2.5.3
Test methods for brittle
materials and relevant
equations for calculating the
fracture stress. Calibration
equations are required for (d)
and (f), and these are given by
Bortz and Lund, and by
Shook respectively
(see Bibliography).

(a)

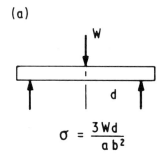

$$\sigma = \frac{3Wd}{ab^2}$$

(b)

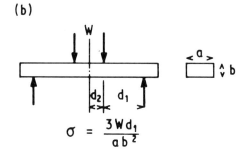

$$\sigma = \frac{3Wd_1}{ab^2}$$

(c)

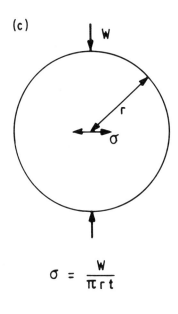

$$\sigma = \frac{W}{\pi r t}$$

(d)

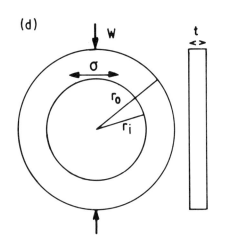

$$\sigma = \frac{W}{\pi r_0 t} \cdot K, \quad K = K(r_0, r_i)$$

(e)

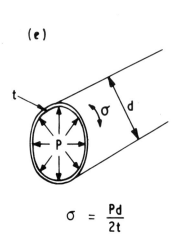

$$\sigma = \frac{Pd}{2t}$$

(f)

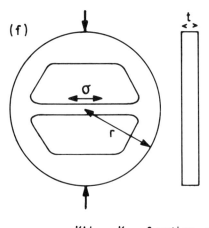

$$\sigma = \frac{KW}{2rt}, \quad K = \text{function of geometry}$$

102

of the same overall span (Figure 2.5.3), a higher mean strength will result because a smaller volume is being subjected to high stress.

Loading points

Fixed rods or knife edges supporting or loading the test specimen exert a frictional restraint on the bending of the specimen, and thus lead to higher apparent strength than if the loading point is free to rotate as the specimen bends. The difference depends on the coefficient of friction between the materials and can be as much as 10%.

External environment

The humidity level can have a marked effect on strength if this is determined by propagation of exposed defects. Similarly, strength measured while the specimen is immersed in water, aqueous solutions, and other corrosive environments will be different from that measured in dry air to an extent depending on the duration of loading.

Specimen geometry

The usual test equations used are those for the so-called thin beam geometry. If the specimen departs significantly from this elastic condition, errors of calculation result. If the specimen thickness in the direction of bending is greater than about $\frac{1}{3}$ of the span between support point and adjacent loading point (d or d_1 in Figure 2.5.3 (a) and (b)), shear stresses become significant and the strength is overestimated. If the specimen is too narrow perpendicular to the direction of bending (less than about twice the thickness) twisting can occur, and if too wide, restrictions to lateral Poisson contraction can result in significant alterations in stress distribution. Ideally, $2b \geqslant a \geqslant b/2$ (Figure 2.5.3(b)).

Since it is difficult to ensure that all loading points lie in a common plane, ideally some gimballing of them is required to take up twist or allow for non-parallel faces on test samples. This is of course overcome by the use of round-section specimens which have point contact, but here again the actual volume under test is smaller than that in a rectangular sample of the same cross-sectional area. Chamfering of the edges of rectangular specimens is sometimes done to counteract the tendency of edge damage to control the fracture load.

Since no recognized international standard exists in which not only the test technique but also specimen size and surface finish are closely and uniquely specified, strength data quoted from one source should not be compared to those from another without great care. *Small differences between the data of different manufacturers should not be treated as significant from the point of view of choosing the 'strongest'*. Furthermore, since the precise means of shaping the product may also have a strong influence on strength, the strength determined on one product made by one route may have no resemblance to that determined on another made by an alternative method. It is with particular reference to strength data that disclaimers are often included in manufacturers' data sheets. No manufacturer would guarantee that the strength figure quoted for test bars would also be produced on any particular shape of component.

2.5.3.3 Strength test results

Traditional practice as suggested by standard specifications involves testing a small number of test specimens, generally at least five. A mean nominal strength (or failure stress) under the test conditions can be calculated from the results but the figure may not be reliable. It should not be used for stress calculations or as a critical datum. It *might* be used as a quality control test to make sure that a particular batch is broadly satisfactory.

Assuming for simplicity a normal distribution of strengths, it is frequently found in testing ceramics that the standard deviation, s, of a set of N results, x, is commonly 5–15% of the mean value, $\bar{x}$, and thus the standard error of the mean:

$$\frac{s}{N^{\frac{1}{2}}} \quad \text{where } s = (\sum_{i=1}^{N} (\bar{x} - x_i)^2 / (N-1))^{\frac{1}{2}} \qquad 2.5.11$$

can also be large if N is small. Thus on the basis of a small number of tests only, large apparent differences in mean strength may not be statistically significant. Again any figures quoted should be used with caution.

If a larger number of test specimens are used, say 20 or more, the best fit to the distribution of strengths is often achieved by using the Weibull distribution. As a consequence Weibull statistics are frequently used to describe strength distributions, and the basis for the Weibull parameters is described in Inset 1. The so-called 'Weibull modulus', m, is a measure of scatter and is roughly inversely related to the coefficient of variation, C_v:

$$m \approx \frac{1.2}{C_v} \quad \text{where } C_v = \frac{s}{\bar{\sigma}} \qquad 2.5.12$$

where $\bar{\sigma}$ is the mean strength. The Weibull modulus commonly appears in relationships between different test geometries and in calculation of probabilities of failure.

It has been found that in order to achieve a reliable estimate of m from a limited number of tests, this number should exceed 20, preferably 30. Since one of the purposes of establishing a Weibull plot (Inset 1, and Figure 2.5.4) is to estimate low probabilities of failure (see also Section 3), it is noteworthy that its usefulness for this purpose increases with the number of samples tested. Extrapolations substantially beyond the limits defined by the plot are not reliable because firstly, the validity of the distribution is not guaranteed, and secondly, the defect distribution may not be statistically random. However, despite these points, the Weibull approach has some value for estimation provided that the parameters used are determined on material in an appropriate condition.

2.5.3.4 The effect of volume on strength

As mentioned earlier, the larger the test specimen, the lower the average fracture stress is likely to be. The same is probably also true for real components. Since Weibull statistics contain a volume term, it is possible to predict the effect of volume on the average strength. Correspondingly, if failure initiates at the surface, as might be the case with a glass, or with

The probability of failure S of a component of given size, surface finish, microstructure and stress conditions is given by:

$$S = 1 - \exp \left\{ -\frac{V}{V_o} \left\{ \frac{(\sigma - \sigma_u)}{\sigma_o} \right\}^m \right\} \qquad \text{I.1.1}$$

where V is the volume under consideration, σ is the (uniform) applied stress over volume V, σ_u is a (hypothetical?) lower limit of stress to produce failure, V_o and σ_o are normalizing constants, and m is also a constant, the Weibull modulus.

If a number of components, N, are tested, they can be ranked in ascending order of stress and assigned a probability of failure of approximately:

$$S_i = \frac{i}{N+1} \qquad \text{I.1.2}$$

for the ith ranked sample in a group of N.

By rearranging Equation I.1.1:

$$\ln \ln 1/(1-S) = m \ln (\sigma - \sigma_u) - m \ln \sigma_o + \ln V/V_o \qquad \text{I.1.3}$$

and by assuming that $\sigma_u = 0$ since very large flaws cannot be ruled out, a plot of ln ln $1/(1-S)$ vs lnσ has a slope of m. The Weibull modulus, m, can be calculated by a line-fitting routine, and essentially gives an estimate of the degree of scatter amongst the data, such as has been done in Figure 2.5.4.

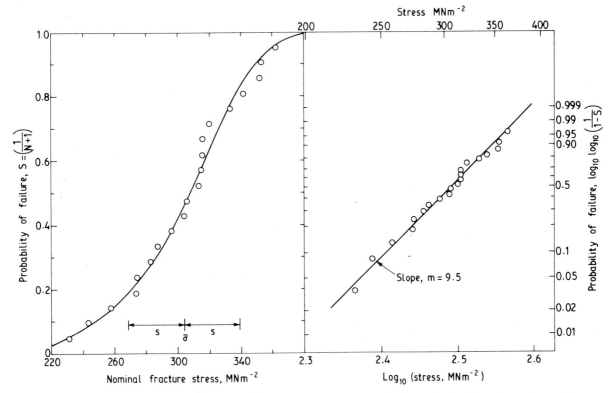

Figure 2.5.4 The fracture strengths of a batch of 95% alumina specimens tested in four-point bending at room temperature with a 320 grit ground surface finish are plotted (a) as a cumulative distribution and (b) as a Weibull plot to get a straight-line fit to the points. Using the Weibull parameters calculated, the solid line in (a) represents the Weibull distribution calculated.

many types of ceramic tested in bending, the estimation can be based on the surface area under stress and the relevant Weibull distribution contains an area term rather than a volume term. We do not intend to treat area and volume effects in detail, but merely to outline how such estimation might be done. Inset 2 shows that using a modified form of the Weibull equation, the total probability of failure can be integrated over the varying stress field within a component and then compared with that of any other component shape, size or stress distribution:

$$\frac{\bar{\sigma}_1}{\bar{\sigma}_2} = \left\{ \frac{V_2 \Sigma(V_2)}{V_1 \Sigma(V_1)} \right\}^{1/m} \qquad\qquad 2.5.13$$

where the subscripts refer to two stressed geometries and where $\Sigma(V)$ is the stress-volume integral calculated for stressed volume V. The stress-volume integral is usually a function of geometry and the Weibull modulus, m. Alternatively, for surface area under stress, the equivalent expression containing area, A, can be used for surface flaws.

Use of such an approach to estimation assumes that the flaw size distributions in the two sizes of component are the same. In reality this may not be the case, especially if different sizes of component are made in different ways, or fired to different schedules, or have different surface finishes applied. Nevertheless, used correctly such an estimation can be useful.

INSET 2

Volume Effects on Strength

It can be shown that the Weibull equation I.1.1 can be rewritten:

$$S = 1 - \exp\left\{ -\left(\frac{1}{m}!\right)^m \left(\frac{V}{V_o}\right)\left(\frac{\sigma}{\bar{\sigma}}\right)^m \right\} \qquad\qquad I.2.1$$

where V is the volume under uniform stress and $\bar{\sigma}$ is the mean fracture stress. By the choice of a reference volume V_{ref}, for example, unit volume, with an average fracture stress $\bar{\sigma}_{ref}$, the sum of all small volumes in the component with varying levels of stress can be shown to be:

$$S = 1 - \exp\left\{ -\left(\frac{1}{m}!\right)^m \left(\frac{\sigma_{nom}}{\bar{\sigma}_{ref}}\right)^m \left(\frac{V}{V_{ref}}\right)\Sigma(V) \right\} \qquad\qquad I.2.2$$

where $\Sigma(V)$ is the so-called stress-volume integral:

$$\Sigma(V) = \int_V \left(\frac{\sigma(V)}{\sigma_{nom}}\right)^m \frac{dV}{V} \qquad\qquad I.2.3$$

i.e. an integral of the variation of stress normalized by a nominal stress over the volume of the body. The nominal stress may be taken, for example, as the maximum surface stress of a beam in bending. The equivalent for area is the stress-area integral, with A substituted for V, and the integration is made over the surface area of the component. For example, for a beam in three-point bending, the bending equations can be used to show that:

$$\Sigma(V) = \frac{1}{2(m+1)^2} \qquad\qquad I.2.4$$

For equal probabilities of failure, e.g. at the mean fracture stress, Equation I.2.3 gives:

$$\bar{\sigma}_1^m V_1 \Sigma(V_1) = \bar{\sigma}_2^m V_2 \Sigma(V_2) \qquad\qquad I.2.5$$

If the mean fracture stress is known for one size of component, it can be calculated for another provided the Weibull distribution of the first is applicable to the second.

This is not the only method of dealing with the statistical effects of size or stress geometry, but is a well-known one providing a simple demonstration.

2.5.3.5 Long-term strength

It is now well recognized that many ceramics, particularly silicate-containing materials, become weaker with time under load. This phenomenon is variously described as 'static fatigue' (particularly with respect to glasses), 'stress corrosion' (a metallurgical term that is not entirely appropriate), 'stress ageing', 'delayed failure', 'slow crack growth', etc. The last of these terms essentially describes the reason for this phenomenon. Experiments on macroscopic cracks have shown that under a stress insufficient to attain the critical stress intensity factor, cracks can extend slowly at a rate that is determined by the following factors:

chemical environment
temperature
stress intensity factor.

The extension of a crack is basically a thermally activated atomic process which is driven by the applied stress, influenced by the chemical environment at the crack tip, and is fairly strongly temperature dependent.

The chemical environment may be important in two ways. Firstly, the material may be dissolved or corroded by the environment, and if penetration of the ceramic occurs, along grain boundaries for example, the material will be weakened, even under zero load. This is discussed at greater length in Section 2.9. Secondly, and relevant to this Section, the rate of extension of a sharp crack can be greatly increased if the environment in the crack lowers the fracture surface energy.

It is well documented that the OH^- ions in aqueous solutions or even adsorbed water vapour can act in this way, for example, by breaking M—O—M bonds in oxides (M = metal, O = oxygen). It has been shown that changing the pH of an aqueous solution from acid, through neutral, to alkaline greatly increases the crack growth rate in vitreous silica as a consequence of the OH^- concentration. For soda-lime glass in air of various relative humidities, it has been shown (Figure 2.5.5) that under a given stress, crack velocity increases with increasing humidity. For a given humidity level, this velocity may be controlled in certain stress regions by the ability of the environment to diffuse down to the tip of the opening crack. There is a limit to this effect determined by the crack growth rate in the absence of water, which places an upper bound on the stress regime in which environment is important. With non-oxide ceramics, water vapour may have very little effect, and thus all that can be detected is the environment-independent section close to the fracture stress. Diagrams of this type are usually obtained by observing macroscopic crack growth in plate specimens, and although they display the overall sensitivity of the crack growth process to the imposed conditions, the data may not be accurate for small flaws that control strength in real components.

In general terms, the relationship between crack velocity and stress intensity factor is shown schematically in Figure 2.5.6 as three regimes: 1–environment controlled; 2–environment limited; and 3–environment independent. Thus a crack can grow slowly at stress intensity factors less than critical.

As a crack lengthens under stress clearly the effective strength remaining decreases (since strength is proportional to (crack length)$^{-1/2}$). Under static load, the material can bear the load until the stress intensity factor at the tip of the largest crack reaches the critical value at which rapid fracture occurs. The time to failure is very sensitive to the load applied because for the

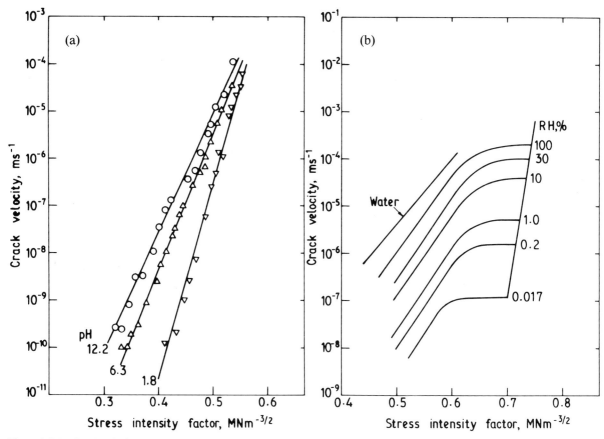

Figure 2.5.5 Crack velocity as a function of stress intensity factor for (a) silica glass in aqueous solutions of various pH, and (b) soda-lime glass under various humidity conditions. The effect of humidity on velocity at low velocities should be noted.

Figure 2.5.6
Generalized crack velocity as a function of stress intensity factor for environmentally affected subcritical crack growth.

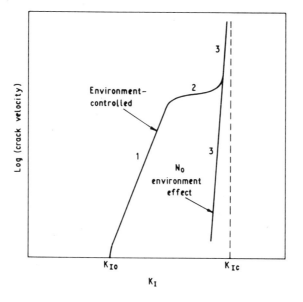

Figure 2.5.7
Generalized static fatigue curve for a brittle material subject to environment-controlled, subcritical crack growth.

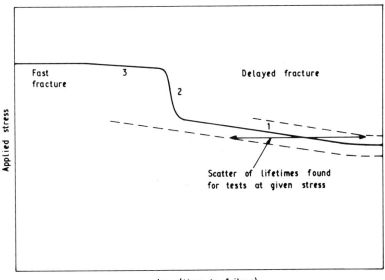

greater part of the lifetime the crack is moving slowly. 'Static fatigue' curves appear typically as in Figure 2.5.7 where at each test stress level there is a spread of lifetimes that corresponds to the spread of short-term strengths normally demonstrated by the batch of test pieces.

If a component is to be used in a high-stress environment it is clearly necessary to make an allowance for 'static fatigue' effects in assuming the tolerable stress levels for design purposes. Some fairly complex calculations are required to do this, but they end with some straightforward relationships.

As mentioned above, for the greater part of the time to failure under static load, the stress intensity factor lies on the linear part of the K_I–log (crack velocity) relationship (Figure 2.5.6). The total time to failure is given by:

$$t_f = \int_{c_i}^{c_c} \frac{dc}{v} \qquad\qquad 2.5.14$$

where c_i, c_c are the initial and critical crack lengths, and v is the crack velocity. This is expanded in Inset 3 to show that:

$$t_f \approx \frac{B}{\sigma^n} - \frac{C}{\sigma^2} \qquad\qquad 2.5.15$$

where B and C are constants, σ is the applied stress and n is the exponent in the crack velocity/K_I relationship, Equation I.3.1. Since n is generally large, greater than 10 and up to 200 or so, time to failure can be seen to be very sensitive to the applied stress.

For batches of components under different stress levels it follows that the ratio of mean times to failure is given by:

$$\frac{\bar{t}_{f1}}{\bar{t}_{f2}} \approx \left(\frac{\sigma_2}{\sigma_1}\right)^n \qquad\qquad 2.5.16$$

INSET 3

Static Fatigue Life-Time Calculation

If an empirical relationship between crack velocity v and applied stress intensity factor K_I is assumed to be of the form:

$$v = AK_I^n \qquad\qquad\qquad\qquad\qquad\qquad I.3.1$$

and that a crack of length c with stress σ applied to it gives rise to a stress intensity factor K_I such that:

$$c = \frac{K_I^2}{Y^2\sigma^2} \qquad\qquad\qquad\qquad\qquad\qquad I.3.2$$

where Y is a geometric constant, then the integral for time to failure t_f as the crack length increases becomes:

$$t_f = \int_{c_i}^{c_c} \frac{dc}{v} \qquad\qquad\qquad\qquad\qquad\qquad I.3.3$$

$$= \frac{2}{Y^2\sigma^2 A} \int_{K_{Ii}}^{K_{Ic}} \frac{dK_I}{K_I^{n-1}}$$

$$= \frac{2}{Y^2\sigma^2 A(n-2)} \left\{ \frac{1}{K_{Ii}^{n-2}} - \frac{1}{K_{Ic}^{n-2}} \right\} \qquad\qquad I.3.4$$

where the subscript i refers to the initial conditions and the subscript c refers to 'critical' conditions when rapid failure occurs. Since K_{Ic} is fixed for a given material, and K_{Ii} is proportional to σ (Equation I.3.2), Equation I.3.4 is of the form:

$$t_f = \frac{B}{\sigma^n} - \frac{C}{\sigma^2} \qquad\qquad\qquad\qquad\qquad I.3.5$$

Generally n is large, typically greater than 10, and thus a plot of log t_f vs. log σ will have a slope of approximately n. In practice of course the above analysis is simplistic and does not take into account that:
1. K_I and v may not be simply related as in Equation I.3.1
2. Real defects may not approximate to planar sharp cracks, and the local K_{Ic} may be different from the macroscopic value found by experiment on macroscopic cracks.

However, an analysis of this type does demonstrate that lifetime is sensitive to the slow crack growth characteristics, and determination of the parameter n can help estimate the sensitivity to delayed failure effects.

For some materials fatigue-like effects can be seen when making short-term strength tests at different rates. Using the same type of analysis as in Inset 3, it can be shown that:

$$\left(\frac{\bar{\sigma}_1}{\bar{\sigma}_2} \right)^{n+1} = \frac{\dot{\sigma}_1}{\dot{\sigma}_2} \qquad\qquad\qquad\qquad\qquad 2.5.17$$

in which the mean fracture strengths of two identical sets of test pieces of mean strengths $\bar{\sigma}_1$, $\bar{\sigma}_2$ are related to the (linear) rates at which the load is applied ($\dot{\sigma}_1$, $\dot{\sigma}_2$.) Simple tests can therefore give an estimate of the parameter n, which in fact may be more relevant to real components than that calculated from the growth of macroscopic cracks in plates.

Using tests of this type it is possible to set up a diagram for estimating long-term strength of a batch of material. If, say, three batches of components are tested at three different loading rates, then n can be determined, and the mean time to failure at lower stresses can be estimated using Equation 2.5.16. Estimations of this type operate on a mean value, and so with the strength variation within any batch it is desirable to include some idea of the

Figure 2.5.8
A Strength–Probability–Time diagram constructed from simple short-term bend test data by extrapolation. The plotted points are long-term delayed failure tests with stress levels corrected to a failure time of 1 sec to compare with the original short-term data from which the plot was constructed. After Davidge – see Bibliography.

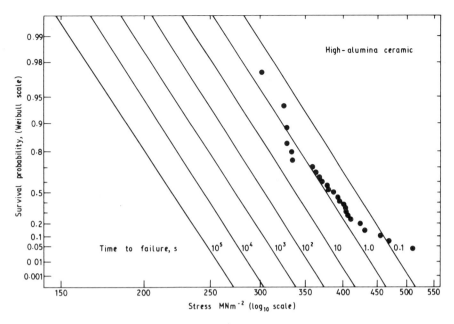

scatter of lifetimes that can be expected. This can be done through a 'Strength–Probability–Time' (S–P–T) diagram of the type shown in Figure 2.5.8. For a set of test results under given steady stressing rate conditions, the equivalent time to failure, t_{eq}, under static stress conditions at the recorded fracture stress is given by the formula:

$$t_{eq} = \frac{t_f}{n+1} \qquad\qquad 2.5.18$$

where t_f is the recorded time to failure. This equation is derived in a similar manner to Eqns. 2.5.16 and 2.5.17. The measured fracture stresses are then corrected to the same time to failure, e.g. 1 sec, using Equation 2.5.16. A Weibull plot is then drawn for the corrected data. This plot will have a slightly lower slope than that obtained by plotting the original results because a test-piece breaking at high stress takes longer to break and the strength figure is corrected upwards, while one breaking at low stress is corrected downwards compared to an average result. For greater periods under load, parallel distributions at lower stresses are drawn using Equation 2.5.16, which makes it possible to estimate maximum use stress for a given probability of failure. Note that Figure 2.5.8 is plotted as survival probability (scale log log 1/S) rather than failure probability (scale log log 1/(1–S)). Corrections to fracture stress levels for different component volumes can be made by the use of stress volume integrals.

For many applications, ceramic components are not used at even 10% of their nominal breaking stress, but there are notable exceptions where conditions are constant enough for lifetime estimates to be needed, or where component design is so critical in terms of applied stress that a design safety margin is required. Some examples are:

high-tension, tensile-loaded insulators

suspended or loaded glass structures

thermally stressed components, due to expansion mismatch in joints etc.

high-speed machinery (thread guides, wire-drawing cones, grinding wheels etc.)

proposed applications for advanced materials in internal combustion engines of various types.

In some cases, an estimate of reliability may not be sufficient if a *guarantee* of survival for a minimum period is required. In such circumstances the only real solution is a short-term overload proof-test which can remove those components in the low strength tail of the distribution. The mathematical basis for this is described in Inset 4, and a schematic proof-test diagram is shown in Figure 2.5.9. A short-term (momentary) overloading of a component (in a manner that is representative of the stressing geometry seen in use) will test whether there is a large defect in the component which under a continuous lesser load might cause failure in a time shorter than desired. Those components that do not break in such a test do not have such large flaws and are then guaranteed to survive in use for a minimum period determined by the load levels employed.

INSET 4

Proof-Testing

If a component survives a short-term proof-test at stress σ_p, then the stress intensity factor generated at the worst flaw, K_{Ip} must be less than the critical value K_{Ic}. Following the notation used in Inset 3:

$$K_{Ip} = Y\sigma_p c_0^{\frac{1}{2}} \leqslant K_{Ic} \qquad\qquad I.4.1$$

where c_0 is the length of the worst flaw at the end of the proof-test. If the test is done quickly enough, c_0 should be similar to its initial length. When the component is used at a lower stress σ_s for longer periods the initial stress intensity factor is:

$$K_{Is} = Y\sigma_s c_0^{\frac{1}{2}} \leqslant \frac{\sigma_s}{\sigma_p} K_{Ic} \qquad\qquad I.4.2$$

In the case that a component only just passes the proof-test we have equality in the above equation. The time to failure of this weakest remaining component is then given by Equation I.3.4:

$$
\begin{aligned}
t_f &= \frac{2}{Y^2 A \sigma_s^2 (n-2)} \left\{ \frac{1}{K_{Is}^{n-2}} - \frac{1}{K_{Ic}^{n-2}} \right\} \\
&= \frac{2}{Y^2 A K_{Ic}^{n-2} \sigma_s^2 (n-2)} \left\{ \left(\frac{\sigma_p}{\sigma_s} \right)^{n-2} - 1 \right\}
\end{aligned}
\qquad\qquad I.4.3
$$

This then represents the minimum time to failure in use of the surviving components. For n large:

$$t_f \propto \frac{1}{\sigma_s^2} \left(\frac{\sigma_p}{\sigma_s} \right)^{n-2} \qquad\qquad I.4.4$$

where σ_p/σ_s can be called the proof-test ratio.

The higher the proof-test ratio or the lower the service stress, the longer the guaranteed life. If the proof-test ratio is kept constant, then the time to failure varies as σ_s^{-2}. If σ_s is fixed, then the proof-test ratio needs to be fixed according to the value of n and the material parameters Y, A, K_{Ic}. This is best demonstrated by Figure 2.5.9 in which are drawn a series of parallel lines calculated for various proof-test ratios. The proof-test ratio required can be read off for a guarantee of a life of, say, 1 year at a particular stress. If failure probability data are added separately to the diagram (e.g. from an S-P-T diagram), then there is additionally an indication firstly of whether proof-testing is likely to be needed at all, and if it is, the level of test failures that might be expected. As a rule of thumb, a 10% loss in proof-testing probably represents a useful elimination of the weakest components without undue financial burden, and the line corresponding to this probability of failure represents an upper stress/time limit on practical usage of the material in the environment for which the diagram was constructed.

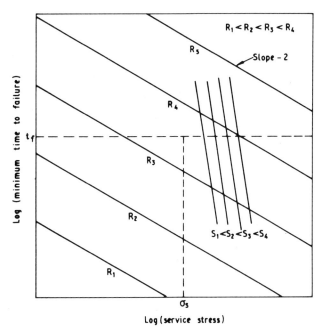

Figure 2.5.9 A proof-test diagram set up on the basis of data derived from slow crack growth and K_{Ic} measurements, with the addition of probability of failure data derived from delayed failure tests or S-P-T diagrams. The diagram demonstrates that for a minimum time to failure of t_f at a service stress of σ_s, a proof-test ratio R between R_3 and R_4 is required. The probability of failure estimated for failure in the absence of proof-testing is in this case less than S_1. If S_1 is sufficiently small, proof-testing may not be essential.

There is some argument against proof-testing because the test itself can promote slow crack growth and thus weaken all the products. As described in Section 3.6, there are techniques for inspecting components for internal defects without stressing them, but there is a risk that the critical defect may not be seen, especially if it is small as it could be in high-strength materials. Proof-testing is the only way of producing some sort of *guarantee* of a minimum life for a batch of components and there is no other way of removing weak members from a batch of nominally identical pieces before putting them into service. However, it must be borne in mind that the parameters inserted into proof-testing equations must be relevant to the conditions of use and take account of all factors such as temperature, chemical attack, vibration etc. Proof-testing is of course no guarantee against failure caused by subsequent damage by external agencies not accounted for in the test. For example, it has been demonstrated that oxidation of reaction-bonded silicon nitride at high temperatures results in a new flaw distribution independent of that in the original material. Proof-testing before oxidation does not guarantee strength after oxidation.

2.5.3.6 Fatigue under cyclic loading

The concepts outlined in the previous section apply also to cyclic loading such as is obtained in vibration. In this case, the tensile parts of each stress cycle contribute to crack growth, and the number of cycles to failure is related to an integral of the varying stress intensity factor with time. Again it is found that lifetime is critically dependent on the cyclic maximum of tensile stress according to parameter n for slow crack growth. This has been demonstrated practically for a porcelain. In fact, since vibrations tend to give somewhat uncontrollable stress cycling, vibration levels should ideally be kept to a minimum for ceramics, particularly those already under significant tensile stress.

2.5.3.7 Strength at elevated temperatures

The short-term strength of many ceramic materials remains constant, or declines only slowly, as the temperature is raised because the physical properties that control strength do not in general change rapidly with increasing temperature, at least up to temperatures at which plastic flow in any of the constituent phases becomes significant. In the longer term, however, it must be remembered that subcritical crack growth is enhanced by increased temperature. The additional effect of water vapour can be marked up to about 150°C. Thus long-term strength may decline more with increasing temperature than short-term strength would lead one to believe. Unfortunately, comparatively little information is available of the high-temperature strength except on some non-oxide materials researched as part of gas turbine development programmes.

Oxide materials are stable in air to high temperatures, but non-oxides tend to oxidize. Silicon carbide, silicon nitride and molybdenum disilicide are the most resistant to oxidation, as a result of the formation of a surface skin of silica glass. The strength of these materials will therefore depend on the extent of oxidation and its influence on strength-determining defects.

At sufficiently high temperatures plastic flow can occur in all types of ceramic material. Very often the temperature capability of the material is determined by the softening of secondary phases, particularly glassy phases that may be present at grain boundaries. In order to realize the potential refractoriness of the principal crystalline phases it is usually necessary to find ways of eliminating these secondary phases completely, so the most refractory materials are those of highest purity. From the point of view of short-term strength, softening of a secondary phase normally results in a progressive fall in strength as the temperature is raised. In materials containing significant amounts of glassy phase, strength as a function of temperature may show a peak at or near the transition temperature of the glass (e.g. Figure 2.5.10). This is often accompanied by an increase in apparent fracture toughness, but is purely an artifact of testing. At the rate of stressing, there is sufficient plastic flow to round off growing cracks, but insufficient flow in the timescale of the test to cause the tearing that a liquid phase would produce at higher temperatures. It is doubtful whether this mechanism would influence long-term strength in the same way.

When plasticity is significant, ceramic materials will creep. Creep deformation in polycrystalline materials is seldom homogeneous, and creep rupture occurs at relatively low strains unless the proportion of viscous glassy material is sufficiently high that it can redistribute itself. The limit on long-term strength at high temperatures may well be that defined by creep rupture. In addition, creep deformation causing cracks to grow will lower the remaining short-term strength in subsequent tests at both high temperature and room temperature.

Figure 2.5.10
Short-term strength as a function of temperature for two glass-containing, high-alumina ceramics. The peaks in strength are due to flaw-rounding in the glassy phase. At higher temperatures the glass softens, and as plastic deformation increases the measured strength falls.

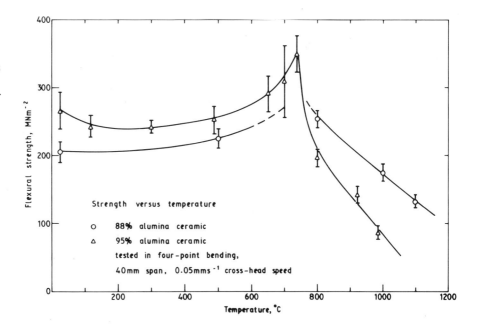

Except in relation to development programmes for high-temperature engines, high-temperature strength and creep are not well studied. In most cases no data are available, apart from statements such as 'upper use temperature'. This is usually undefined and tends to be based on practical evidence of survival, usually under 'no-load' conditions, implying short-term use without disastrous changes of microstructure.

2.5.3.8 Internal friction

Internal fricton is the absorption of elastic energy by the structure of the material, and is normally characterized from the shape of the resonance curve of a vibrating rod. Generally speaking the effect is small in the majority of refractory materials at room temperature, or indeed below 600°C, and this low level results from scattering of elastic waves by the microstructure of the material. Significant internal friction is usually associated with anelastic effects related to ionic movement in the material.

In glass-bonded aluminas, such effects can be seen from 800°C upwards when the bond is above its glass transition temperature. In materials which contain no glass, no effect may be noted until temperatures are reached when plasticity of the individual grains becomes significant.

Another well-known effect producing internal friction in glasses is the so-called 'mixed alkali' effect in which sodium and potassium ions in the glass structure exchange positions under stress, and in doing so absorb energy. The effect is most noticeable in glasses in which both alkali species are present in significant quantities. It can also be seen in some clay-based materials and in debased high-alumina ceramics where no special attention has been paid to reducing dielectric loss (i.e. cutting down on the alkali content).

No general data are available, and since the effect is strongly related to composition, each product should be viewed on its own merits.

2.5.4 Comparative strength data

2.5.4.1 Room-temperature data

It will be apparent from the discussion so far in this Section that a large number of conditions need to be appended to any quoted strength figure. These conditions should include details of the material type, the test method employed, and the specimen geometry and preparation details. Sadly this is seldom done, so it is impossible to compare data from different sources except insofar as it may be possible to give a large band which would cover expected mean bend strength values typically obtained on small test bars. In the Data Sheets in Part 2, these levels are quoted where possible together with any available data on slow crack growth and static fatigue. However, these strength data should not be used to compare different types of material

Table 2.5.2 Grouping of material types by short-term strength

---

Very high strength, $>400\,\mathrm{MNm^2}$

Hot-pressed silicon nitride, silicon carbide, boron carbide and alumina.
Zirconia-toughened alumina, optimally-aged partially-stabilized zirconia.
All-tetragonal zirconia (t.z.p.).
Sintered sialons and sintered silicon nitrides.
Cemented carbides.

High strength, 200–$400\,\mathrm{MNm^{-2}}$

Most sintered aluminas of fine grain size.
High-density reaction-bonded silicon nitride.
Fine-grained reaction-bonded silicon carbide.
Sintered silicon carbide.
Thermally-strengthened soda-lime glass.

Medium strength, 100–$200\,\mathrm{MNm^{-2}}$

Aluminous porcelains of high alumina content, mullite ceramics, low-loss steatite and forsterite.
Medium- to coarse-grained high-alumina ceramics and reaction-bonded silicon carbides.
Low-density reaction-bonded silicon nitride.
Beryllia, stabilized zirconia, titania.
Opaque glass-ceramics.
Single-crystal sapphire.

Low strength, 50–$100\,\mathrm{MNm^{-2}}$

Quartz and cristobalite porcelains, aluminous porcelains, normal steatite, vitreous cordierite.
Coarse-grained porous silicon carbides.
Magnesia ceramics, magnesium titanate.
Glasses in the polished or flame-finished state.
Transparent glass-ceramics, machinable glass-ceramics.
Fired pyrophyllite.
Single-crystal quartz.

Very low strength, $<50\,\mathrm{MNm^{-2}}$

Porous electrical refractories, porous steatite and forsterite, porous cordierite.
Glasses in the ground surface condition.
Unfired pyrophyllite, talc, machinable alumina, sintered fused silica.

Note: This Table groups basic product types into strength categories based on what would normally be obtained for the mean strength in bend tests at ambient temperature and humidity on small (e.g. 5×3 mm cross-section) test bars with a ground surface tested in four-point bending at a rate such that fracture occurs in the time range of about 10–100 seconds. It also reflects minimum acceptable mean strengths quoted in the draft IEC classification for electrotechnical materials. Reports in manufacturers' brochures and in the scientific literature of higher levels of strength may refer to polished or lapped finishes rather than ground finishes, and special test precautions, such as rounded edges on test bars, may have been employed.

because the numbers may bear no relation to the strength of real components made from the materials. Consequently, in this Section no comparative numerical data are given, but instead Table 2.5.2 groups together different types of material which fall into various strength categories based on data typical of bend tests and also on the minimum acceptable mean strengths quoted in the draft IEC classification for electrotechnical ceramics. In this way, the reader will be able to identify materials with levels of strength suitable for his application, or eliminate those which are clearly unacceptable. It must be emphasized that only by obtaining test components in a particular material type will the user be in a position to know whether the strength of any particular product is adequate for his end use.

2.5.4.2 Strength at elevated temperature

Strictly, each case needs to be taken on its own merits, because each material has its own composition and microstructure which determine behaviour at high temperatures. For the purposes of material comparison, Table 2.5.3 lists some materials in approximate order of retention of strength at high temperatures. The figures given are intended to be indicative only, but may vary considerably between different commercial formulations. More detailed descriptions of behaviour are given where possible in the relevant data sheets of Part 2, and in Section 2.6.1, more detailed tables of upper use temperature on a wider range of products are given.

2.5.5 Fracture toughness

As is clear in Sections 2.5.1 and 2.5.2, strength is closely related to the fracture surface energy or to the critical stress intensity factor. These material properties have had considerable scientific effort devoted to them in recent years, which has paralleled the development of fracture mechanics for metals and alloys. By comparison with metals, ceramics have very little toughness as might be measured by an impact test, Izod or Charpy for example, but even so the relative values of fracture toughness amongst ceramics are important for understanding the response to mechanical stress: wear resistance, grinding damage, impact damage, long-term strength and stress-ageing, etc.

For many years attempts have been made to increase the toughness of ceramics. The principal method is to use a metallic binder between ceramic particles, but there is a tendency to lose many of the other useful properties of ceramics, such as electrical insulation or refractoriness. These materials, dubbed 'cermets', have limited applications outside the field of cemented carbides or hardmetals used for machine tool tips and die components. Other attempts to improve fracture toughness are being investigated, and some of these are already commercially viable.

Fibre reinforcement

Strong fibres incorporated into a ceramic increase toughness by holding the open crack faces together, while a running crack has to do extra work to pull the fibres out of the matrix. However, the techniques developed for

Table 2.5.3 Limits on use temperatures under load (see also Figures 2.6.3–2.6.6)

Material type	Temperature, °C, for		
	Long-term use under load	Detectable creep under load	Short-term use, no load
Glass-bonded mica	250	300	350
Soda-lime glass	300	450	470
Borosilicate glass ('Pyrex' type)	300	450	480
Machinable glass-ceramic ('Macor')	600	750	950
Electrical porcelains, steatite, etc.	600	800	1000
Silica glass and sintered fused silica	800	950	1400
'Pyroceram 9606' glass-ceramic	800	900	1100
Aluminous porcelains	800	900	1100
High-alumina ceramics ($>95\%$ Al_2O_3)	900	1000	1100
Refractory porcelains, refractory mullites	1000	1200	1600
High-alumina ceramics ($>99.5\%$ Al_2O_3)	1200	1400	1700
Refractory, high-purity aluminas	1400	1550	1900
Stabilized zirconia	1200[4]	1300	2000
Hot-pressed silicon nitride (with MgO)	1200	1300	1600
Reaction-bonded silicon nitride	1600[1]	1700[1]	1800 (dissociates)
Reaction-bonded silicon carbide	1400[2]	1600[2]	1600
Sintered silicon carbide (fully dense)	>1500[3]	>2000	>2100
Alumina refractories	1500	1650	1850
Thoria	1500	1600	2200
Magnesia refractories	1200(?)	1200(?)	>2000
Hot-pressed boron nitride	1200[3]	1500(?)	>2000
Graphite, in air	400 (oxidizes)		
in inert or reducing gas	>1500	>1500	>2500

[1] In inert conditions. In oxidizing conditions, performance is limited by the tendency to oxidize. Low density materials oxidize internally and begin to creep at around 1100°C. They also crystallize to cristobalite and are weakened by subsequent cooling to room temperature. Higher-density materials, i.e. those with densities greater than about 2.4 Mgm^{-3}, tend to glaze over and are not affected in the same way.

[2] The silicon phase melts at about 1410°C, and tends to vaporize at above 1600°C. For materials that have free silicon removed, temperatures in excess of 2000°C can be achieved in inert conditions. In oxidizing conditions oxidation occurs above 900°C, and the same comments apply as for silicon nitride. Oxidation is not catastrophic at temperatures below about 1600°C. Sintered silicon carbide is not limited by having free silicon, but nevertheless tends to oxidize at temperatures above 900°C to form a surface layer of silica.

[3] In inert conditions. In oxidizing conditions, boron nitride oxidizes to B_2O_3 at temperatures in excess of 800°C. B_2O_3 glazes the surface at low temperatures, but tends to volatilize at temperatures above 1000°C. Use under load may depend on pre-existing B_2O_3 content.

[4] Stabilization is lost slowly on holding at temperatures between 800°C and 1200°C, stabilization by MgO being less effective than by CaO or Y_2O_3.

reinforced plastics are difficult to apply to ceramic manufacturing processes, so most research attention has been applied to producing fibrous or lamellar structures in situ, as in directionally solidified ceramic eutectics.

Second-phase reinforcement

Cracks may be deflected or pinned by the stress fields associated with thermal expansion mismatch between the second-phase particles and the matrix. Of particular note are the increases in fracture energy associated with particulate fillers in glasses. Recent developments in the use of the phase transitions in zirconia for this purpose are likely to be the most successful methods of toughening for ceramics, and several commercial products are already (December 1983) available which incorporate zirconia. The details of toughening mechanisms are given in the relevant Data Sheets of Part 2.

The low fracture toughness of the majority of ceramics has to be accepted in engineering. However, much can be done to alleviate the problem by design rather than by seeking enhanced properties by way of microstructural manipulation.

2.5.5.1 Definitions

FRACTURE ENERGY, OR FRACTURE SURFACE ENERGY is the energy in Jm^{-2} required to create unit new fracture surface by the propagation of a crack. It is somewhat ill-defined because crack velocity affects the value measured. This can be appreciated because of slow crack growth behaviour illustrated earlier in Section 2.5.3.5. As a result, different test techniques or methods of calculating applied to specimens of identical geometry give different answers, sometimes varying by a factor of two. Two of the most frequently used terms are (1) the fracture energy for the initiation of crack movement, which is calculated from the load required to fracture a specimen with a crack of known length in it, and (2) the fracture energy for the continued propagation of a crack once initiated, which is calculated from the work done in this process (i.e. the area under the force–displacement curve in the test).

The fracture energy (γ_i) for the initiation of fast fracture from a crack or notch (i.e. the figure normally implied in the Griffith equation as being the fracture surface energy at the point of failure) may be calculated from the stress at the crack tip, via a calibration equation. If the crack length is uncertain, it may be estimated by measuring the compliance of the specimen prior to fracture and calculating its effective value via another calibration equation. The technical literature provides a number of equations suitable for different geometries. It should be noted that there remains some argument in the scientific literature as to whether a machined notch is or is not equivalent to a planar crack for the purposes of measurement. There is evidence that different materials behave in different ways in this respect. A sharp crack is probably to be preferred since although machining damage exists at the base of a notch it may require extra work to develop a planar crack from the damage to enable propagation.

The fracture surface energy or work of fracture (γ_f) is usually interpreted as the work done to break a notched specimen divided by twice the planar area of fracture face since two faces are created. For this, the notch must be sufficiently deep that the elastic energy stored in the specimen and testing machine up to the point of rapid crack propagation is less than that required to fracture the specimen. Losses due to kinetic and sonic effects can then be ignored, and the crack propagation is controlled. The energy balance is then calculated. In practice the easiest method of doing this is to measure the area under the load-displacement curve recorded for the test (e.g. Figure 2.5.11).

Values of γ_f are usually less than those of γ_i. This stems from the different conditions of crack growth, the former being for conditions of variable crack velocity, and the latter for initiation of fast fracture.

Figure 2.5.11
Specimen geometries for
fracture toughness
measurement:
(a) pre-cracked beam and
(b) notched beam for
    measurement of K_{Ic} or γ_i,
(c) chevron-notched beam for
    measurement of γ_f, and
(d) load-displacement curve
    typically obtained for
    controlled fracture of a
    chevron-notched beam.

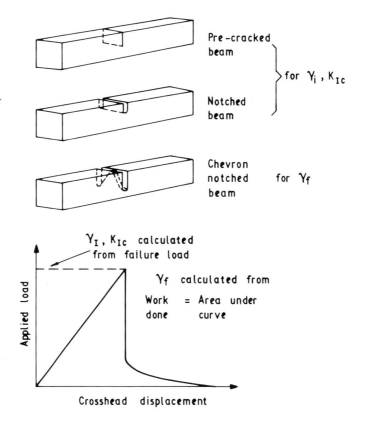

Figure 2.5.12
Schematic diagrams of the
three modes in which a crack
may be propagated:
(a) opening mode I,
(b) sliding mode II, and
(c) tearing mode III.

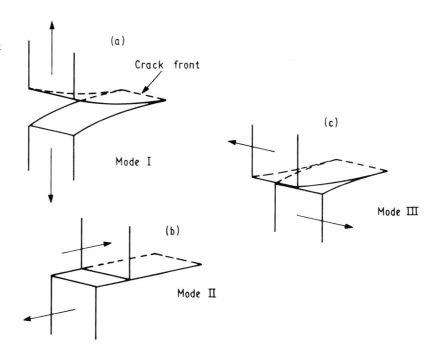

THE STRESS INTENSITY FACTOR (K) is a measure of the stress at the tip of a sharp crack or other discontinuity. It is related to the applied stress by:

$$\sigma(r, \theta) = K.f(r, \theta) \qquad\qquad 2.5.19$$

where $f(r, \theta)$ is a spatial distribution function and K is a constant. For a sharp crack it can be shown that the factor K can be related to the applied stress through a relationship of the form:

$$K = \sigma Y c^{1/2} \qquad\qquad 2.5.20$$

where σ is the overall applied stress perpendicular to the plane of the crack, Y is a constant depending on the geometry of the crack related to the applied stress, and c is the length of the crack (or half-length of an internal ellipsoidal crack). K is entitled the stress intensity factor, and the value of K for rapid crack propagation is called the critical stress intensity factor, K_c. It is considered that this factor, with units of $MNm^{-3/2}$, is a material property, and in recent years it has been used extensively in fracture studies of materials as a figure of merit for fracture toughness. It should be noted that there are three modes in which a crack may be propagated (Figure 2.5.12): mode I, the opening mode due to tensile stress acting perpendicular to the crack plane, mode II, the sliding mode due to shear between the crack faces in the direction of crack propagation, and mode III, the tearing mode due to shear between the crack faces acting in a direction parallel to the crack front. An additional subscript is used to denote the crack mode, e.g. K_{Ic}. For a more complete appraisal of fracture mechanics the reader is referred to texts on the subject.

Under ideal circumstances for an opening mode (I) crack, the fracture energy and the critical stress intensity factor are related by:

$$K_{Ic} = \left\{ \frac{2E\gamma_i}{1 - \nu^2} \right\}^{\frac{1}{2}} \qquad\qquad 2.5.21$$

where E is Young's modulus and γ_i is the fracture energy for high-speed propagation.

K_{Ic}, and K_I for non-catastrophic propagation, are determined from beam or plate experiments similar to those described for fracture energy determinations, but using relevant calibration equations. Each method requires a calibration based on specimen geometry to relate applied loads to actual K_I values. The reader is again referred to various texts on the subject for further practical detail.

It should be noted that:

1. K_{Ic} values determined depend to some extent on the method used. This appears to be so because the various specimen geometries have different types of non-ideal stress field at the crack tip, some of which change with length of crack relative to specimen size. The relative scale of microstructure compared to the stress field is also important. At present there are no standardized procedures, merely preferred techniques and ranges of crack length in which the specimen calibration is considered to be valid. So-called 'R-curves' of crack propagation resistance against length are to be found in the literature, and these demonstrate the problem of uniquely defining fracture toughness for ceramics.

2. The values of K_{Ic} or K_I determined on beam or plate specimens refer to the propagation of macroscopic cracks and may not accurately reflect the

values associated with the propagation of microscopic cracks or processing defects which might be the source of failure in components under stress. Some authors consider that in the latter case flaws grow sub-critically before failure at K_{Ic} and that the critical defect to initiate failure could be rather smaller than Equation 2.5.20 would lead one to believe. There are also questions as to the validity of the fracture mechanics analysis in situations where crack branching occurs as an energy absorbing mechanism in internally micro-cracked materials, or where phase transformation toughening occurs.

Another method of determining fracture toughness is the so-called indentation cracking method. If a hardness impression is made using a Vickers indenter (see Section 2.5.7.), cracks are usually produced from the corners of the impression. The lengths of the cracks are inversely related to the fracture toughness, i.e. the shorter the cracks, the greater the value of K_{Ic}. This technique has some uncertainties associated with it, particularly the difficulty of determining the true crack length by optical means because of difficulties in distinguishing a crack from other microstructural features such as grain boundaries. In addition, the crack length obtained depends on the microstructure around the indentation and thus if a number of impressions is made, there is considerable scatter in results. It is necessary to average over at least 10 impressions. In addition, the equation normally used has an element of uncertainty in it, and the final result should not be considered accurate to better than 30%.

Hardness impressions (particularly Knoop impressions) are also a means of generating controlled pre-cracks in beam specimens. The immediate surface should be ground away to remove the plastic zone of indentation which may pre-stress the crack. The specimens can then be broken and the strength correlated with the observed flaw size produced by indentation. The fracture toughness can then be determined by use of a suitable equation, assuming an elliptical shape of flaw. This method may be relevant to the fracture toughness associated with small machining flaws which determine the strength of small components. Other methods of precracking include diamond wedge indentation, in which case a straight crack front is produced.

2.5.5.2 Relevance of fracture toughness to material performance

Stress intensity factors and the rate of propagation of cracks at values less than critical have already been used (Section 2.5.3.5) to demonstrate the process of strength ageing under load or 'static fatigue' as it is commonly known. Clearly it is useful to understand fracture behaviour as it allows some form of prediction of lifetime to be made, and this can be extended to proof-testing in order to guarantee a minimum life for components in service (subject to various provisos).

Additionally, fracture toughness is a useful indicator of other aspects of behaviour:
1. Machining ceramics with abrasive wheels involves a combination of plastic ploughing and chipping. The tougher and harder the material, the more difficult it is to machine. Also, the tougher the material, the less likely is the machining damage introduced to result in low strength. Edge chipping resulting from machining is probably also related to toughness since, in

general terms, tougher materials show greater ability to retain a sharp edge.

2. In indentation or hardness tests, cracking usually occurs under the indenter, and this is less for tough materials. It is possible to estimate K_{Ic} from the sizes of cracks associated with indentations.

3. Similarly, in wear resistance, higher toughness can minimize the extent of damage introduced by each abrasive particle, whether by impact or by abrasion.

4. In thermal shock, the damage sustained in a shock sufficiently severe to cause cracking is inversely related to fracture toughness, higher toughness being more effective in limiting crack growth and giving higher residual strength.

Toughness seems to be lowest for materials such as glasses or single-crystal materials, in which a pre-existing crack or defect is presented with very little resistance to propagation under stress. The same seems to be true for materials of very fine grain size such as some glass-ceramics. Toughness is greatest in fibre-reinforced materials as a consequence of fibre pull-out. Conventional sintered ceramics with substantial amounts of glassy phase are generally, but not exclusively, less tough than fine-grained, single-phase materials. Those with a high Young's modulus tend to be tougher than those with a lower modulus.

2.5.5.3 Fracture toughness and subcritical crack growth

The processes in which toughness is important are those where the stress is applied rapidly and behaviour is governed primarily by K_{Ic}. Under prolonged loading, behaviour can be very different. It depends on the microstructural process occurring and the environment within the crack:

1. In an unreactive environment (e.g. vacuum or inert gas or liquid) subcritical crack growth is essentially thermally activated, and is generally significant only at K_I levels very close to K_{Ic}.

2. The crack velocity is greatly enhanced by the presence of any chemical species capable of reacting with the surface of the material, and thereby influencing the cracking process by penetrating to the tip of the crack. It is most evident in oxide systems in the presence of water or water vapour, and is influenced by temperature and the pH of the water or solution. This occurs even when bulk corrosion is not detectable. Non-oxides suffer less in this respect, but it should be noted that many non-oxide materials contain significant amounts of oxide phases which may control behaviour. At high temperatures in oxidizing environments, non-oxides will start to suffer in the same way due to the formation of oxide layers within the microstructure and at the crack tip.

3. Creep can occur at high temperatures where one or more of the constituent phases begins to soften. This can lead to development of cracks in much the same way as occurs in metal alloys. The individual ceramic grains tend to be much less plastic than the grain boundary material with the result that deformation tends to be limited to grain boundary sliding and associated cavitation (analogous to a sand and syrup mixture).

It is difficult to generalize on this subject because different materials behave in different ways and have different responses to various environments. However, it is probably true to say that at ambient temperatures the environment is the most important factor after material composition. As demonstrated earlier, the environmentally controlled part of the K_I vs. v curve can often be represented by a relationship of the type:

$$v = AK_I^n \qquad\qquad 2.5.22$$

where A is a constant and n is a parameter often referred to as the crack velocity exponent. The sensitivity of the crack growth process to K_I is inversely related to the value of n. For materials with little tendency for slow crack growth, n may be greater than 200. Values between 50 and 200 imply that the slow crack growth process is significant, and values less than 50 suggest a strong fatiguing effect which requires a substantial design safety factor. It should be noted that Equation 2.5.22 is only one representation of data obtained from fracture toughness type specimens. Others are possible, depending on the nature of the process and the accuracy of the data related to the equation-fitting procedure. There are reports of a lower limit of K_I below which no crack growth occurs, usually termed the fatigue limit K_{Io}. However, since this usually applies to exceedingly low rates of propagation, or very long fatigue lives, there is substantial practical difficulty in measuring in this regime. For calculation it is considered to be safer to assume that no lower fatigue limit exits.

There are relatively few systematic sets of data on slow crack growth of different materials. There are even fewer comparisons between data measured directly on fracture toughness specimens and data determined from static

Table 2.5.4 Grouping of materials by fracture toughness

K_{Ic}/γ_i ranges $MNm^{-3/2}/Jm^{-2}$	Material types
<1.0/<2	Most single-crystal materials. Glasses of all types. Some glass-ceramics, particularly those of a very fine grain size or of high glass content.
1.0–2.5/2–15	Most glass-ceramics. Most porcelains and other clay-based materials. Some alumina ceramics, particularly those of fine grain size designed for acid resistance. Some oxide ceramics, such as MgO.
2.5–5.0/15–50	Most alumina ceramics. Most dense non-oxide ceramics, B_4C, SiC, Si_3N_4. Reaction-bonded silicon nitride. Many porous ceramics (these may be weak but may show high levels of toughness as determined by a fracture toughness test).
5.0–15/50–500	Transformation-toughened ceramics based on alumina or zirconia. Low binder content hardmetals.
>15/>500	High binder content hardmetals. Some fibre-reinforced ceramics. Carbon fibre-reinforced carbon.

Note: This table is intended to give a broad picture of relative values. Allowance should be made for departures from this grouping as a consequence of variations in microstructure in individual products.

Table 2.5.5 Susceptibility to sub-critical crack growth at ambient temperatures*

Range of 'n'	Material types
<30	Most glasses in most water or water-containing environments. Some porcelains and oxides in alkaline solution.
30–60	Glasses in inert conditions. Some porcelains and oxide ceramics in neutral or acid environments.
60–150	Most oxides in dry air or inert conditions. Some porcelains.
>150	Most non-oxides in inert conditions, some in water-containing conditions. Most hardmetals.

*'n' tends to stay constant with increasing temperature, but the actual velocity for a given K_I increases. At temperatures substantially above 100°C, water vapour seems to have little extra influence over and above the effect of temperature. The rankings above assume that no gross chemical attack takes place. If this is not the case (see Section 2.9), slow crack growth rates may have a lower, non-zero limit defined by gross dissolution rather than pH-assisted propagation.

fatigue tests or slow fracture tests. It is therefore not possible to be certain that the two sources of data give the same result, and therefore that the mechanisms of growth of a large deliberately induced crack are the same as those of small cracks originating from defects in components. One method of estimating 'n' is to test batches of test bars or components at a number of loading rates differing by orders of magnitude (Inset 3, Equation I.3.5). This has relevance to the failure of components from real flaws, and also tests over the entire range of crack velocity as the load (and hence K_I) increases during the loading.

2.5.5.4 Fracture toughness and slow crack growth data

As outlined earlier, fracture toughness depends to some extent on the test method used in relation to the type of material. It is therefore not possible to give more than a broad comparison of toughness data on different materials. Similarly, sub-critical crack growth is a sensitive function of material and environment composition, and also of temperature.

In Table 2.5.4 materials are grouped into four categories according to levels of fracture toughness, and in Table 2.5.5 the grouping is made according to susceptibility to sub-critical crack growth in various environments. In this way the reader can see which materials are likely to perform best in conditions where failure is possible. For more specific and detailed data the reader is referred to the individual data sheets in Part 2.

2.5.6 Impact resistance

The impact resistance of ceramic materials is not high since there is no macroscopic mechanism for absorbing mechanical energy other than by the creation of cracks. There is some microscopic plasticity which may affect fracture processes, but nevertheless the amount of plastic work that can be done is very small compared to that obtained in most metals and alloys. Thus it is probably true to say that most ceramics should be handled with more care than is needed with metals or plastics. Obviously some materials can be handled more roughly than others. For example, it requires rather more energy to fracture an alumina ceramic than a glass in the annealed state. Glass in a thermally strengthened state ('tempered' or 'toughened') will resist impact rather better than annealed glass – hence its use in car windscreens. The intrinsic impact resistance of brittle materials is therefore related not only to fracture toughness but also to strength. The energy imparted in an impact on a strong ceramic material will either break it or cause the impacting object to rebound without damage. If the ceramic breaks, much of the impacting energy is usually transferred to the fragments as kinetic energy. Strength related to the stress field produced by the impact determines whether failure is initiated. Toughness as such seems to play a secondary role, controlling the degree to which shattering occurs. Thus in high-speed impact, the tougher materials seem to break into a smaller number of fragments than the less tough ones.

There are no standard impact tests for engineering ceramics as there are for metals and alloys. Such tests are clearly inappropriate. The user is best guided by the general rule that the strongest ceramics resist large-scale impact the best. The recent investigations of the use of ceramic materials other than hardmetals for impact parts in internal combustion engines and for die materials suggest that the high levels of strength and toughness now achievable with transformation-toughened ceramics are widening the range of applications of ceramics in engineering.

Design of components is an important factor in minimizing the risk of failure in impact. Sharp corners prone to chipping should be eliminated. Areas subject to impact should be of as large a radius of curvature as possible. Holes and other stress-concentrating features should be placed to be as far from the site of impact as possible. Components should be supported as rigidly as possible to avoid bending in impact, and should preferably have a low width to thickness ratio.

The result of impact by small particles is different in some respects from that by large masses. The energy involved in individual impacts is insufficient to propagate cracks to cause gross fragmentation. Although some weakening may result from impact damage, the effect is more akin to wear than to impact. The removal of material from the surface is controlled by hardness (resisting indentation and surface fracturing) and toughness (limiting the propagation of cracks and the formation of loose fragments). It also depends on particle velocity, size, shape, hardness, fracture toughness and angle of incidence. See Section 2.5.8 on wear for further discussion and wear data.

2.5.7 Hardness

Many of the advantages of ceramics for use at near ambient temperatures stem from their relative 'hardness' compared to metals. 'Hardness' is a difficult property to define, but is basically a measure of the yield stress of the material. It is normally measured by techniques that scratch or dent the surface in some way. The scratch method is the longest established, Mohs' scale of relative hardness for minerals being well known as a somewhat empirical means of ranking. Nowadays it is more common to use an engineering indentation test, of which there are a number of varieties differing in load applied and geometry of the indenter. They all give a measure of the penetration of the indenter into the material.

Scales of hardness numbers have long been established for metals and alloys, primarily for quality control. Consequently they have been well researched and the scales for particular types of alloy are well defined. For harder materials they are less well defined in the sense that the higher the yield stress, the more prone is the material to crack under the indenter rather than yield. This can affect the apparent hardness in a way that depends on the test parameters. Thus materials that respond in different ways to indentation should not be compared solely on the basis of numerical values of hardness but additionally on other parameters relevant to the application envisaged. For example, even though hardness may be a guide to wear resistance, some wear-resistant ceramics are not especially hard. There is no substitute for a wear test to determine performance.

For quality control, hardness test results on a given material can show up variations in closed porosity levels and in grain size. The collapse of porosity under an indenter can decrease the apparent hardness by allowing greater penetration. Fine-grained materials tend to be harder than coarse-grained ones of the same composition by virtue of the fact that they are less prone to local shattering of grains.

2.5.7.1 Hardness tests

Hardness tests commonly employed for ceramics, as evidenced by data in manufacturers' brochures and the scientific literature, divide into three main types:
1. Diamond square-based pyramid indenter (Vickers test)
2. Diamond ball-ended cone indenter (Rockwell Superficial test)
3. Diamond rhombohedral-based pyramid (Knoop test)
The use of diamond indenters for ceramics is essential because of the risk of distortion with other materials. Even with diamond there is a risk of chipping, and the indenter should be checked regularly. For each of the above types of test there are standard procedures which are based on research into test practice with metals and other more ductile materials. There is also a standard format and style for recording the result. In each case the hardness is calculated from the size of the indentation, and is a figure on a scale defined by the load applied and the indenter geometry. To avoid confusion, current recommended practice is that no units should be given, even though physical quantities are used to calculate the hardness numbers, which have the dimensions of stress. Since most hardness test machines are calibrated using weights of round numbers of kilograms or grams, it is inconvenient to quote the applied load in Newtons, as required for strict adherence to SI units. Consequently, the forces are usually referred to as 'kilograms'. Also, with the exception of the Rockwell test, the dimensions of the impression are in millimetres. Data given in this Handbook conform to the practice of quoting hardness numbers on scales without units rather than using units of stress or pressure, and the term 'load of X kg' should be interpreted as being the force derived from a mass of X kg. Explanations of the test methods are given below.

NOTE: Hardness measured on one scale is usually different from hardness measured on another, i.e. hardness is not a physical parameter but a material response to certain conditions of test. Conversion from one scale to another is not recommended.

1. Vickers test

The diamond pyramid test involves the measurement of the diagonals of the residual pyramidal impression after removing a given applied load. Tests using loads in the range 30 kg down to 1 kg are termed 'macrohardness' tests, and are made on standard engineering test machines, while those at loads in the range from 1000 g down to 10 g are made on adapted microscopes or specialized derivatives of microscopes and are termed 'microhardness tests'.

The result of a test is expressed as a Vickers hardness number under a stated load in 'kg', but without units. It is the force per unit actual area of the impression:

$$HV = \frac{1.8544P}{d^2} \qquad\qquad 2.5.23$$

where P is the load in 'kg' and d is the mean of the two diagonals in mm. For example, a macrohardness test on an alumina ceramic might yield a hardness number of:

1220 HV10

under a load of 10 kg. A microhardness test on the same ceramic might yield the result:

1550 HV0.1

under a 100 g load. Note that the value is different, even though the test geometry is the same, emphasizing the point that scales are not equivalent.

Macrohardness testing of ceramic materials normally results in considerable cracking which may disguise the corners of the impression. The extent of the cracking is related to grain size and fracture toughness, and acceptable measurements are feasible below 5 kg load in most instances. It is seldom possible to avoid some cracking; less tough materials exhibit obvious cracking even in microhardness tests at 50 g load.

Recommended practice is that a quoted number for a material should be the average from 5–10 randomly positioned macrohardness tests, and preferably more than 20 randomly positioned microhardness tests. The reason for doing this is the scatter of results normally obtained on ceramics as a consequence of (i) their multiphase nature, (ii) their generally non-cubic crystal symmetry, and (iii) the porosity which may be unseen below the surface of the test piece. All factors can exert some influence over the local response to the indenter. Thus the position of the indenter relative to microstructural features such as grain boundaries will have a strong effect on the indentation size. Tests performed at NPL indicate the need for care in selecting indentation position, but this is not always possible on fine-grained, well-polished specimens where the details of the microstructure are not visible. Furthermore, especially with microhardness impressions, the small size of impressions can lead to considerable measurement errors. It is therefore not uncommon to obtain coefficients of variation within a group of measurements of 10% in macrohardness measurements and 20% in microhardness measurements. Mean values are more reliable if the number of determinations is large.

2. Rockwell Superficial test

The high hardness of ceramic materials usually ensures that only the spherical end of the indenter penetrates the specimen leaving a crater. The test was originally designed for use on thin metallic components and coatings, but test data on bulk ceramics are often quoted. The test involves applying a minor load of 3 kg to the indenter, zeroing a displacement scale, applying and removing an additional major load of 42, 27, or 12 kg, and reading the displacement when the displacement needle stops moving. This is a measure of the penetration produced by the major load, less any elastic or recoverable strains. The hardness scale is empirical in nature, and machines are usually directly calibrated in hardness numbers. Hardness is related to the depth of penetration by the relation:

$$HRN = 100 - e$$

where e is the depth of penetration in μm. The hardness number is quoted without units and has the total test load (kg implied) appended, e.g. for an alumina ceramic one might obtain a value:

78.2 HR45N

for a Rockwell Superficial (N-scale) test under a total load of 45 kg.

NOTE: *Different hardness numbers are produced on the different load scales, and the scales bear no direct relation to each other.*

As with the Vickers test, cracking is inevitably produced, and it has been found that coarse-grained materials may yield lower hardness numbers than fine-grained ones of the same composition and density due to greater fragmentation under the indenter. Unless the specimen actually shatters, a result will always be obtained in the test. It is therefore possible to use the relatively high loads of the N-scales which would not give measurable impressions in the Vickers case.

The Rockwell scales are relatively compressed at high hardness values (as e becomes small) and the apparent numerical scatter obtained is much smaller than in the Vickers case. The optical reading errors are also absent. Nevertheless it is advisable to make at least 5 determinations and to quote the mean value and scatter of these results.

3. Knoop test

This is essentially a microhardness test originally designed for testing glasses to avoid some of the cracking caused by Vickers indentations. It has been used to study anisotropy effects in polymeric materials, and also to measure hardness in the absence of strain recovery. It has been used extensively for the study of hard ceramics because the long axis of the indentation is typically 2.5 times that of a Vickers impression at the same load, and thus should be more readily measurable. The major axis of the Knoop diamond impression is about 7 times the length of the minor axis. The hardness number is calculated on a similar basis to the Vickers number but uses the projected

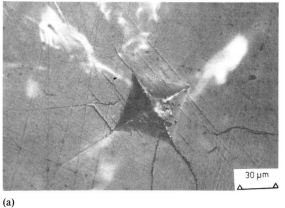

(a)

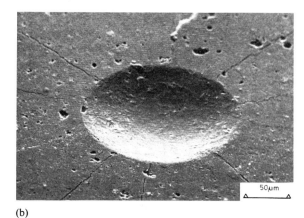

(b)

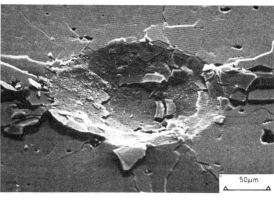

(c)

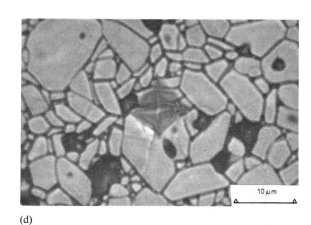

(d)

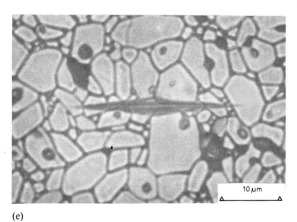

(e)

Figure 2.5.13
The appearance of hardness impressions in ceramics:
(a) a Vickers impression at 2.5 kg load in single-crystal sapphire,
(b) a Rockwell Superficial indentation in a 97.5% alumina ceramic of fine grain size at 30 kg load,
(c) as (b) but with a coarse-grained version of the same material showing the shattering in and around the impression, and
(d) Vickers and
(e) Knoop microhardness impressions at 100 g load in a 99.5% fine-grained alumina ceramic.

area of the impression instead of the actual surface area. It is given by:

$$HK = \frac{14.229P}{d^2}$$

where d is the length of the long diagonal. Again it is quoted without units but is calculated on the basis of the load in kg and the impression length in mm, with the test parameters appended, e.g.:

1200 HK0.1

for a test using a 100 g load.

Specimen preparation for hardness tests is an extremely important factor. In the Vickers and Knoop tests, the test sample needs to have a good metallographic polish, and can be mounted in resin so long as the surface is perpendicular to the loading axis. In the Rockwell test, the test machine records an incremental displacement after application of the minor load. Since the indenter penetrates the surface to some extent under the minor load, a good polish is not important and a finely ground finish, e.g. 300 grit, is acceptable. However, the specimen should be flat and parallel-faced so that it beds down well on to the machine without bending. It should not be mounted in resin which may deform under the major load.

Measuring the size of small indentations by optical methods is subject to some error of judgement in the individual, and to errors of calibration, more especially in microhardness tests. It is important to ensure that both load and optical system are carefully checked and calibrated, the latter with a grating of some sort.

The question may arise as to the best method to employ for ceramics. The answer probably depends on the reason for undertaking the test in the first place. If a measure is required of the resistance to penetration by heavy point loads, a macrohardness test is desirable. The Rockwell Superficial test is probably the easiest to undertake and gives a repeatable answer free from operator-introduced reading error which can bias Vickers measurements. However, the high loads can cause shattering, especially in coarse-grained materials, and a low-load Vickers test, e.g. at 1 kg load, may be preferred in such cases. It is worth checking, however, that the Vickers machine is properly calibrated at that load because, in the author's experience, calibrations made at the normal load of 30 kg may not be reliable at only 1 kg load.

Microhardness measurements are more relevant to the behaviour of materials in light wear or abrasive conditions, and are certainly an indicator of potential performance (see next Section). Under a given load, Knoop impressions are larger and thus, one might think, easier to measure with less error. However, the results of a recent NPL exercise demonstrated that because the impression is shallower, it is more difficult to position the measuring crosswires on the exact ends of the diagonal than is the case with the Vickers impression. The overall measurement errors proved to be almost the same. On the other hand the larger size of the Knoop impression may be advantageous in testing ceramics because it spans more microstructure than the Vickers impression, as is demonstrated by the results shown in Figure 2.5.13, and thus the influence of microstructure in causing scatter should be less. However, if the criterion to be used in assessing a product is the minimum hardness achieved at any point in the microstructure, the Vickers indenter is the more searching in this respect.

2.5.7.2 Indentation size effects

For a given material, the hardness number obtained generally increases with decreasing load. The reasons for this are associated with the varying response of the material under the high local pressure of the indenter, involving plastic flow, densification (of bulk glasses and of porosity in ceramics), and fracture.

In comparing materials, note must be made of the load applied and the grain size in relation to the indentation size to ensure that comparison is made on the same basis. Microhardness tests at low loads give much higher figures than macrohardness tests, as well as much wider scatter as described above, as is amply demonstrated by Figure 2.5.14.

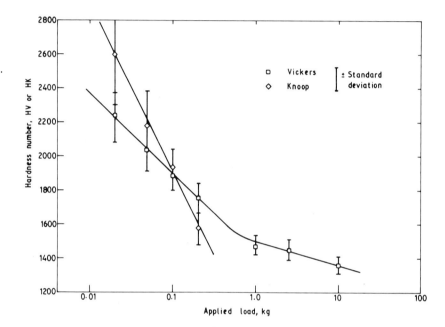

Figure 2.5.14
Hardness as a function of indenter load in Vickers and Knoop tests on a 99.5% fine-grained alumina ceramic. (NPL results)

2.5.7.3 Hardness variation with temperature

In all materials the yield stress drops with increasing temperature to quite a marked degree. Consequently, hardness numbers fall as penetration of the material becomes easier, even though other material parameters such as strength or Young's modulus do not decline so rapidly. The retention of hardness to high temperatures is important for bearing applications and for machine tool tips, but there are few data outside the hardmetal area. At 1000°C, most 'hard' ceramics are no harder than glass is at room temperature, and those containing substantial amounts of glassy phase are even softer. The Bibliography contains two references to hot-hardness data on a range of refractory materials, mostly in coarse-grained, single-phase form.

2.5.7.4 Hardness data

The data tables are intended to present typical relative hardnesses of ceramic materials of various types measured on the same basis. The data have been culled from a wide range of sources including many NPL measurements. In some cases in the literature, hardness is quoted with units of GPa, GNm^{-2} or $kpmm^{-2}$. Where the basis for the measurement is clear, these values have been converted to the equivalent unit-less scales in accordance with preferred practice.

Literature sources frequently do not quote the scatter of results. Typically it can be expected than on polycrystalline ceramics, the range of mean values, the coefficients of variation, and the measurement errors will be as demonstrated in Table 2.5.6.

Table 2.5.6 Scatter and measurement errors in hardness tests

Test	Typical range of hardness numbers	Typical coefficient of variation in hardness number, %	Typical error in each determination, %
HV30–HV1.0	600–2400	5–10	1–2
HV0.5–HV0.01	800–5000	10–20	2–5
HR45N	65–90	2 scale points	0.3 scale point
HR15N	80–97	1 scale point	0.3 scale point
HK0.5–HK0.01	600–5000	10–15	2–5

Table 2.5.7 Hardness numbers for various ceramic materials

Material (IEC class)	Hardness numbers				
	HV2.5	HV0.1	HK0.1	HK0.05	HR45N
Porcelains and clay-based materials:					
Porcelains, siliceous (C-110)	—	—	—	790	—
Porcelains, pressed (C-111)	—	—	—	—	—
Porcelains, cristobalite (C-112)	—	—	—	—	—
Porcelains, aluminous (C-120)	—	800	—	—	—
Porcelains, aluminous (C-130)	—	—	—	—	68
Steatite, low-voltage (C-210)	—	650 (HV0.5)	—	—	60
Steatite, normal (C-220)	—	—	—	—	65
Steatite, low-loss (C-221)	—	—	—	—	—
Forsterite, dense (C-250)	—	800–900 (HV0.5)	—	—	—
Vitreous cordierite (C-410)	—	—	—	—	60
Celsian, dense (C-420)	—	—	—	—	—
Zircon, dense	—	850 (HV0.5)	—	—	—
Mullite (C-610)	—	—	—	—	—
Mullite (C-620)	—	—	—	—	—
Oxide ceramics:					
Alumina, >99% Al_2O_3 (C-799)	1450	1900	1930	2030	83
Alumina, 95% Al_2O_3 (C-795)	1170	1600	1590	1780	78
Alumina, 90% Al_2O_3 (C-786)	1050	1400	1400	1620	77
Alumina, 85% Al_2O_3 (C-780)	970	1250	1250	1500	73
Beryllia, 99% BeO (C-810)	—	1100–1300	—	—	62
Magnesia, dense	500	—	~ 600	—	—
Spinel, dense	1200	1500	1700	—	—
Thoria, dense	—	—	—	—	—
Tin oxide, dense	—	—	—	—	—
Titania, dense	—	—	—	—	70
Zircon	—	—	—	—	—
Zirconia, stabilized (C-830)	—	—	1200	1500	—
Zirconia, partially stabilized	—	—	—	—	—

Table 2.5.7 (*contd*)

Material (IEC class)	Hardness numbers				
	HV2.5	HV0.1	HK0.1	HK0.05	HR45N
Non-oxides:					
Boron nitride, hot-pressed	very soft, anisotropic				
pyrolytic	soft				
Silicon nitride,					
reaction-bonded 2.27 Mgm^{-3}	—	750	—	—	—
hot-pressed	—	1600–1800	2500–2700	—	—
Sialons, sintered Si$_3$N$_4$	—	—	—	1840	84
Boron carbide	2800	3200	2800	—	89
Silicon carbide,					
silicon-infiltrated	—	2000	2500	2900	—
hot-pressed	—	2400–2800	—	—	—
sintered dense	—	~2500	—	—	90
Carbon and graphite					
diamond	—	~8000	—	—	—
graphites	soft to very soft				
vitreous carbon	—	—	—	—	—
pyrolytic graphite	soft, anisotropic				
Tungsten carbide, 6% Co	—	1300—1600	—	—	—
Glasses:					
Soda-lime 'Float'	n/a	450	460	—	n/a
Borosilicate, 'Pyrex' type	n/a	—	420	—	n/a
Vitreous silica	n/a	—	490	—	n/a
Glass-ceramics:					
'Pyroceram' 9606 (Corning)	n/a	—	660	—	n/a
'Pyroceram' 9608 (Corning)	n/a	—	590	650	n/a
'Zerodur' (Schott)	n/a	950(HV0.5)	—	—	n/a
Machinable ceramics:					
'Macor' machinable glass-ceramic	—	—	—	420 (HK 0.02)	—
Single-crystal materials:					
Alpha-quartz	—	~900	700	—	—
Sapphire	—	1800–2400	—	—	—

Note: Data quoted above are intended as typical figures. Materials of very low porosity tend to be harder. Low-density products show poor macrohardness but microhardness approaching that of principal phases. For this reason they are excluded from the Table. Single-crystal products show variable hardness depending on orientation of test face. Anisotropic polycrystalline materials tend to have anisotropic hardness. See Part 2 for more detailed data and sources.

2.5.8 Wear resistance

2.5.8.1 General points

Ceramic materials are resistant to wear in the general sense. There are exceptions, but these are the weak, highly porous, friable types, or those which are deliberately designed to be machinable. Most vitrified and highly crystalline, fine-grained ceramics are abrasion resistant, and many of the uses of engineering materials stem from this property.

Wear resistance, like strength and resistance to corrosion, is not a readily quantifiable property because it depends on the exact circumstances under which the material is abraded away. In general terms, the action of an abrasive on a ceramic is a combination of limited local plastic flow and fracture similar to that seen in hardness impressions. Abrasive particles produce cracks as well as wear grooves. Material removal is considered to be the result both of plastic ploughing and of fracturing, particularly of cracks that run laterally and then turn and intersect the surface. The dominant process is likely to be determined by the applied load and the abrasive particle size and hardness. For very fine abrasives and low loads, plastic processes lead to polishing with insufficient local energy to cause significant chipping fracture, whereas with coarse abrasives and higher loads indentation fracture and chipping are the dominant mechanisms. This is however an over-simple picture because the deterioration of the abrasive is an additional factor when abrading hard materials, reducing the effective abrasive size and producing less chipping. These and other factors lead to a complex picture where it is difficult to quote meaningful data since they are not universally applicable. Table 2.5.8 summarizes the types of abrasive wear commonly encountered with ceramics and Table 2.5.9 summarizes the wear and material parameters that influence the rate of wear.

The choice of material will be governed by the conditions of use and the cost of the components (or the failure if cheaper materials are used). Hardness is clearly an important property, the hard materials like hot-pressed silicon carbide, boron carbide, and carbide-based hardmetals being the most resistant to wear. These materials tend to be rather expensive because of the difficulties

Table 2.5.8 Types of wear

1 Fixed abrasive particles (similar to machining by grinding)
2 Rolling abrasive particles
3 Impact by small hard particles
4 Impact by large objects
5 Abrasion by sliding surfaces, self-abrasion, surface fatigue
6 Adhesive wear (adhesion of abrading material followed by removal with some substrate)
7 Chemical wear with or without any of the above

Table 2.5.9 Effect of material properties on wear behaviour

Material properties and wear parameters	Requirements for:	
	low wear rate	high wear rate
Material toughness	high	low
Material hardness	high	low
Porosity	low	high
Abrasive size	low	high
Abrasive shape	rounded	angular
Abrasive hardness	low	high
Applied pressure	low	high
Speed	low	high
Abrasive particle movement	rolling	fixed, impact
Lubricant	present	absent
Coefficient of friction	low	high
Chemical conditions	inert	corrosive, with integranular attack

of fabrication, and thus other, less hard materials such as alumina ceramics are in much more common usage. The principal microstructural features required are fine grain size, low porosity and sufficient chemical inertness in corrosive conditions (see also Section 2.9).

Figure 2.5.15 presents a histogram based on the work of Moore and King who studied the relative wear rates of various ceramic pins on fixed abrasive paper discs. The tests were done dry. Immediately apparent is the dependence on material hardness, but factors such as grain size, porosity, and phase content are also important and give rise to the spread of results indicated for each type of material. The softer, coarse flint abrasive is less effective than the fine silicon carbide on the harder materials, but more so on the softer materials. The ranking order of performance is broadly the same for the two abrasives, but there are minor changes. This illustrates the point about the need to consider all the parameters. It is not possible to use a ranking such as is implied by Figure 2.5.15 for other conditions except insofar as materials of high hardness will usually out-perform those of low hardness. However, there are anomalies where some softer materials wear at a slower rate than harder materials, as seems to occur with sialons.

Figure 2.5.15
Relative wear rates of ceramic materials under fine fixed grit silicon carbide and coarse fixed grit flint abrasives, from Moore, M A, and King, F S (1979), (see Bibliography).

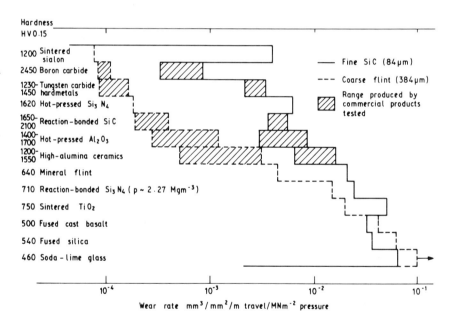

There are very few wear data in the literature. The work of Moore and King is probably the most extensive, and is given here to illustrate the trends. A similar ranking has been found in short-term, slurry abrasion, pin-on-disc tests at NPL using 320 grit silicon carbide. No other comparative data are given in this Section. Instead the following Section discusses individual wear problems and the ceramic materials that have been used to combat them.

2.5.8.2 Specialized wear problems

1. Chute linings

Cheapness rather than optimum performance is usually the chief criterion where a large area is to be covered. For this reason cast fused basalt is the principal material used for large-scale mineral processing plant, coal plant, power stations, etc. Sintered alumina ceramics have also been used in such applications, and have much better wear properties, but tend to be more expensive, even though they can be used in a lesser thickness. Impact resistance and toughness are important parameters. Thin tiles must be well supported to avoid breakage under heavy impact.

2. Milling media and mill linings

Cheapness and low levels of contamination are the important factors in milling fine powders for various uses. In the ceramic and glaze industries the mill linings tend to be of aluminous porcelain or high-alumina (typically 85% Al_2O_3) ceramic, and milling media are of the same or of higher-quality materials. If contamination is of minor concern, flint pebbles may be used. In the paint and pigment industry, steatite media are commonly used, primarily for cheapness. In cases where contamination of the mill charge is to be avoided, milling materials may have to be chosen such that the contamination is either minimized, or is of the same species as the charge. Ceramic milling materials cannot usually be removed by simple chemical processing afterwards since the contaminants are often chemically more resistant than the charge.

3. Fluid seals

High-alumina and silicon carbide materials are now in common use as shaft and pump seal rings in substitution for hard alloys, hardmetals based on tungsten carbide and hard coatings on metals. Valve parts now commonly employ alumina ceramics as non-corroding sealing faces, as in mixers for domestic showers. Ceramics show advantages not solely in wear resistance but also in corrosion resistance. Shaft seals may be static or rotating, generally bearing against a carbon or carbon-based material which is partly lubricating and may be run wet or with intermittent dry periods. Pumping liquids may require seals with good resistance to corrosion, and the type of liquid may dictate the seal material needed (see Section 2.9). Pumping of slurries or liquids containing unfiltered grits presents more of a problem, and tungsten carbide hardmetals or silicon carbide are used. The wear of seals for such pumps results from abrasion by grit particles traversing the seal face. The carbon sealing material may be replaced in such cases by a hard ceramic. Thermal shock resistance is another material parameter to be considered if pumps intermittently run dry.

A point that should be noted is that the wear may be greatly accelerated by corrosion. From the practical viewpoint, there is no substitute for trials or tests on individual products since detailed information is not freely available. While not an exact model of a wear situation, a simple test which does show up some aspects of performance is the rate of loss of material during ball milling in the required corrosive agent relative to that obtained by milling in, say, water.

4. Thread guides, paper guides, wire-drawing cones

Wear-resistant parts for high-speed machinery have been a major growth area for the use of a variety of ceramic materials over the last decade.

Considerable improvements in productivity have resulted in many instances. In these examples, the friction between the ceramic component and the passing product is important, and is frequently determined by the nature of the surface finish both initially and as wear proceeds.

In the case of thread guides, fine-grained aluminas and alumina-chromia materials are the hardest and most abrasion resistant in current use. Titania-based materials offer lower coefficients of friction, but show greater rates of wear with the more abrasive, filled synthetic yarns. The surface finish aimed for by manufacturers is macroscopically smooth but, at the microscopic level, well-formed grains standing slightly proud of the surface are required to minimize the contact area with the yarn. Precise techniques for achieving such finishes are usually commercially confidential, but they clearly involve machining and thermal annealing procedures. The wear on the guide that can be tolerated before the original finish is lost is usually quite small. A worn surface may lead to breakage of the yarn and substantial downtime. Resistance to chemical attack is another important factor since guides often run in contact with corrosive liquids used for processing. Experiments with materials intrinsically harder than alumina, such as some non-oxides, have not yielded improved results. The reasons for this are unclear, but may be associated with difficulties in producing the required surface finish and also local oxidation of the surface by the rubbing action of the thread.

Similar abrasive conditions arise in paper manufacturing and high-speed paper handling owing to the mineral content of many types of paper. Again alumina ceramics have proved invaluable in reducing wear on critical rollers and guides. Under strongly alkaline conditions, sintered silicon carbide is said to show better performance than alumina.

In wire-drawing cone pulley systems, a moderate coefficient of friction is required to maintain the correct degree of tension on the wire. Alumina and zirconia ceramics are beginning to take precedence over coated metal components because they show less wear with slippage of the wire across the surface. Alumina is used for thicker wires where mechanical loading is higher. Zirconia, especially in the toughened condition, is used for finer gauges of wire, or in the final stages of drawing, and has a lower coefficient of friction against metals than alumina.

5. Plain bearings

Ceramics have been used for plain bearing surfaces run with or without lubricant because they can be lapped to precise dimensions and can withstand touch-down during starting and stopping. Depending on the value of the application, materials include boron carbide, silicon carbide, hot-pressed silicon nitride and high-alumina ceramics. Some domestic central heating pumps use an alumina ceramic impeller system running in alumina ceramic plain bearings and lubricated by water. Some small industrial chemical pumps also use corrosion-resistant alumina ceramic plain bearings with magnetically-driven impellers, e.g. Figure 2.5.16. Advanced gyroscopes have been made incorporating air bearings made of boron carbide. Trials have been reported using hot-pressed silicon nitride bearings at high temperatures in corrosive conditions. Partially-stabilized zirconia is claimed to wear only slowly in sliding bearings, such as tappets and cam followers, and similar results are also claimed for sialon materials. In both cases, low coefficients of friction are obtained.

Figure 2.5.16
Magnetically driven plastic pump impeller moulded on to an alumina ceramic plain bearing running on an alumina ceramic shaft.

6. Shot blasting

The abrasive action of high-velocity grit particles requires that blasting nozzles have a high degree of resistance to impact wear. For this reason, a variety of hard ceramics are used, including aluminas, silicon carbides and boron carbide (one of its major uses). Scientific modelling of particle impact damage has shown that hardness, stiffness and toughness are primary criteria in determining resistance to progressive wear.

7. Slideways on machinery

There is potential for the use of ceramic materials on slideways of machinery to resist wear by abrasion from swarf or other machining debris. Because of size limitations on solid fired components, there may be design problems, but the incorporaton of wear-resistant pads is a possibility, and would probably show a performance improvement compared to the use of a hard coating sprayed on to a metal substrate or to 'boronizing' treatment (producing a surface layer of hard iron boride).

8. Other applications

Agricultural machinery suffers severe wear in certain types of soil. It is now possible to purchase spring tine tips in alumina ceramic bonded to mild steel to combat wear and prolong life. Engineering trials are being undertaken using ceramic parts for other types of soil working machinery. Impact by large stones or flints is a problem which may be eliminated with the application of some of the tougher materials now being made commercially.

2.5.8.3 Machining ceramics

The factors controlling wear resistance also influence machining of ceramics since in the main this is accomplished by the use of fixed or rolling diamond abrasives in grinding and in lapping. In general terms, one can expect the relative rates of machining of different materials to be roughly similar to that portrayed in Figure 2.5.15, glass being the most readily cut and hot-pressed boron carbide the most resistant.

Natural or synthetic diamond grit is the most widely used abrasive medium because of its unparalleled hardness and resistance to attrition in the grinding process. Grits based on silicon carbide and alumina are also used for fixed grit grinding, but generally for glasses only. These materials are less efficient at stock removal, blunt more readily and show higher levels of friction than diamond.

The need to achieve close tolerances in machine-ground components using impregnated grinding wheels means that wheel wear has to be minimized while maintaining cost-effective rates of machining, and the grit size and concentration, coolants, and the rate of stock removal are chosen to suit the material being ground. By comparison with shaping metals, machining the harder ceramics is slow and expensive. However, the development of specialized, in some cases automated, grinding machines by many manufacturers has meant that for specific shapes in long runs, grinding blanks to close dimensions can be fairly cheap. For example, centreless grinding of small rods, and face grinding and lapping of shaft seals and electronic substrates are routine operations for many suppliers. Machining, surface finishes, tolerances, etc., are discussed at greater length in Section 3, but it should be noted that as with hardness impressions and abrasive wear, the machining conditions dictate the final condition of the surface and the properties achieved.

In grinding with fixed abrasive wheels, with grit sizes in the range 80 down to 300 mesh (approximately 180–40 μm), the surface finish usually shows a mixture of chipped areas and ploughed grooves. To improve upon this it is necessary to use finer grits in loose abrasive lapping with a succession of diamond grits down to say 1 μm particle size. The result of lapping is a smooth flat surface, but not a polished one because lapping usually produces a degree of grain tear-out which is not removed except by prolonged polishing with micron or sub-micron grits. This latter procedure is normally required to achieve a 'metallographic' finish.

There is still much uncertainty as to the exact mechanism of polishing of ceramics and glasses. The most likely explanation is that the small size of the abrasive particles results in plastic flow of the surface rather than the cracking produced by coarser abrasives. The energy associated with the lightly-loaded grit particles is insufficient to produce a crack, but the local stresses are high enough to cause plastic redistribution of the surface material. As with hardness impressions, only very small loads are needed to cause cracking, so polishing grit sizes required are usually very small, less than 1 μm. For the majority of hard ceramics, diamond polishing media are needed, but for glasses and other relatively soft materials, a range of other abrasives are in common use, including alumina, silicon carbide, chromic oxide, cerium oxide and other proprietary rare earth oxide mixtures. The performance of some of the oxide abrasives, especially those based on ceria, is remarkable, and at present this is considered to result from self-attrition of the abrasive. It is true also to some extent that polishing to high standards of finish and figure is still more of an art than a technology.

2.6

Thermomechanical properties

Higher temperatures degrade most properties of ceramics, usually decreasing strength, stiffness, thermal conductivity, and hardness, and increasing thermal expansion coefficient, slow crack growth rates, fracture toughness, plasticity, and creep. There are exceptions, of course, for individual materials, and some changes with temperature are very small, e.g. fracture toughness may stay constant to high temperatures. Nevertheless the refractory nature of many ceramics makes them an extremely useful class of material. The previous Sections have highlighted individual properties as functions of temperature, and the aim of this Section is to put the individual properties together to describe the concepts of refractoriness and thermal shock resistance.

2.6.1 Refractoriness, hot strength and creep

Bulk plasticity becomes measurable at temperatures of typically 0.6–0.7 of the absolute melting temperature of any major phase or, if there is a glassy phase, at about 50°C above the glass transformation temperature. A sample subjected to load at elevated temperature will suffer permanent distortion, and as a consequence may no longer be fit for use. The rate of distortion is a function of:

    time
    applied load
    accumulated strain
    temperature
    microstructure
    environment

and therefore a description of 'refractoriness' is a complex business, and the ranking of materials will clearly depend on the parameters used to specify it.

2.6.1.1 High-temperature creep processes

Fundamental research into creep in ceramics has shown that a number of different mechanisms can operate at rates that may depend differently on temperature and stress.

In essentially *single-phase* materials, creep at high temperatures and moderate loads is usually by some form of grain boundary sliding mechanism, which is sensitive to levels of impurities segregated there. Creep strain at grain boundary intersections can be accommodated by diffusional migration of atoms, but more often the result is cavitation, a weakening of the material and the onset of creep rupture as cavities propagate into cracks. Two models exist for continuous deformation *without* cavitation: Nabarro-Herring creep is a self-diffusion process throughout the bulk of each grain, and Coble creep is a grain boundary diffusion process. Both occur at a rate directly proportional to stress, but the essential difference is that the first is proportional to (grain size)$^{-2}$, and the second to (grain size)$^{-3}$. These processes tend to occur principally at low stresses and very high temperatures in pure materials, but normally the grain boundaries are the site of creep and the source of failure.

Dislocation movement within grains can occur at high stresses, more especially in the softer ceramics such as MgO, and can be observed in hard single-crystal materials, such as sapphire. Dislocation mechanisms operate in polycrystalline materials without cavitation if five independent slip systems are available, and the creep rate observed is usually dependent on stress to powers of three or more. However, homogeneous deformation by dislocation movement is seldom observed with the complex crystal structures of most ceramics of practical interest. The grain boundaries are more often the weak point.

Materials with *secondary phases* at grain boundaries, either crystalline or glassy in type, as in the vast majority of technical ceramics, glass-ceramics, and some non-oxides, tend to be less creep-resistant than single-phase materials. Deformation tends to be restricted to the secondary phase. If this phase is glassy, creep is often of a viscoelastic type. Again, grain sliding leads to accommodation problems at grain junctions and cavitation can occur. This has been detected in glass-ceramics and in hot-pressed silicon nitride. If a solution/reprecipitation mechanism can occur to accommodate deformation, cavitation is less likely. The creep rate can be dependent on stress to a power between 1 and 8 depending on microstructure and composition.

Temperature has a strong influence on creep rate, and typically a 20–50 K rise in temperature can accelerate creep processes by a factor of 10.

It is therefore clear that creep rates are sensitive functions of materials and conditions. To ensure a sufficient ability to withstand high temperatures under load without excessive distortion it is necessary to choose the correct materials. *In the absence of detailed creep data on many products, care must be taken over the interpretation of terms used to describe refractoriness and hot strength.*

Generally speaking the materials which are resistant to creep have the following characteristics:

1. Refractory primary phases
2. High purity, low glassy phase content
3. High proportion of crystal-crystal bonding rather than grain boundaries with segregated impurity phases
4. Comparatively large grain size, which resists grain boundary sliding in creep.

For very high temperature use, aluminas or stabilized zirconias of coarse grain size, up to 100 μm, and of high purity (e.g. greater than 99.7% Al_2O_3) are generally recommended. Finer-grained materials of similar purity deform at lower temperatures, as do less pure materials. In high-temperature metallizing a medium grain size material (10–20 μm grain size) is commonly used as a compromise to withstand the metallizing process, minimizing distortion but retaining moderate strength at ambient temperature. The potential advantages of self-bonded and sintered silicon carbides for high-temperature uses stem from their refractoriness and their low expansion coefficients coupled with the development of a high proportion of crystal-crystal boundaries which resist creep compared to conventional clay-bonded silicon carbides. Their limitation is usually the rate of oxidation.

2.6.1.2 Effect of plasticity on strength and fracture toughness

Whereas fracture is essentially brittle in nature at low temperatures, the operation of creep processes during the timescale of a high-temperature test may cause cavitation which enables crack growth to proceed readily. The net effect is generally to reduce the strength measured in a short-term constant strain or loading-rate test, even though the fracture toughness may apparently be increased as a small amount of plastic work is done in the vicinity of the crack. However, it should be borne in mind that plasticity never rises to the level that gives useful ductility comparable with that of metals because truly homogeneous deformation is never attained. The term 'hot-shortness' is sometimes used for metals that show a similar lack of ductility at high temperatures.

In materials that contain significant amounts of continuous glassy phase, a peak in strength is sometimes noted at high temperatures. This is reputedly due to the existence of just sufficient plasticity to blunt the tips of flaws or cracks in a fairly narrow temperature range where the glass phase is near its transition temperature. The effect is dependent on loading rate and is essentially a test artifact. Longer-term strength under steady load is not likely to be affected and the temperature at which the peak occurs is likely to be close to an upper limit for long-term use. Some examples are shown in Figure 2.5.10.

2.6.1.3 Long-term use at high temperatures

Many brochures on ceramics quote an ''upper use temperature'' or similar measure of refractoriness. This term can generally be taken to imply the maximum temperature at which the product has useful properties under no-load conditions. Very often this temperature approaches the original fabrication temperature, sometimes exceeding it. Since fabrication generally involves sintering and grain growth, processes involving some degree of plasticity, claims for use at temperatures as high as this must be treated as optimistic unless for a very short period only. For most applications the materials will have to be substantially de-rated. For example, a coarse-grained, high-purity alumina ceramic may have a firing temperature of 1850–1900°C, a quoted maximum use temperature of 1900°C, and a melting point of 2050°C, but will creep under self-load if not fully supported in continuous use at 1600°C. For many high-temperature applications such a factor may not be important because free-standing components may be hung vertically (some rod and tube products are suspension-fired) and large blocks are generally well supported. For others the useful life might be quite short. Life can also be limited by corrosive attack rather than refractoriness under non-reactive conditions.

The refractoriness under load (R-u-L) test has been established for many years as a test for refractory bricks, but there has been no equivalent test for dense ceramics, and there are no standard methods of test for long-term use.

A short-term test which can provide a guide to performance is the sag of a cantilever bar as a function of temperature (BS 4789:1972). The test was in fact devised to determine the tendency of oxide ceramics to distort in high-temperature metallizing, and is essentially a self-load creep test. The result is quoted as the 'deformation temperature' (sometimes 'softening point') which is the highest temperature at which the angle of bend does not exceed 5° in 1 hour. The actual applied maximum stress in bending is very low, ~0.01 MNm^{-2}. ASTM D2442 gives a similar test using the sag of a defined rectangular section beam supported near its ends and heated to 1500°C in hydrogen for 30 minutes. Material specification is based on the sag recorded.

For longer-term use, and for use under significant load there is no substitute for creep tests to indicate the strains likely to result. Applications in which such information is important include:

kiln furniture
parts for high-temperature furnaces and testing equipment
high-temperature engines
high-temperature secondary processing of ceramic components.

In addition to creep, consideration should also be given to microstructural stability (e.g. tendency to grain growth) and to the effects of atmosphere on composition (e.g. oxidation, reduction, vaporization, etc.).

2.6.1.4 Creep test methods and presentation of data

Since the same problems of specimen alignment apply to creep testing as to ordinary tensile strength testing, most creep testing is undertaken in three- or four-point bending. However, whereas in a strength test with negligible plasticity there is a linear distribution of stress through the thickness of a bent beam as a consequence of linearity in the relationship between stress and strain, this may not be the case with creep, where the rate of deformation is linearly distributed through the thickness. Stress, σ, and strain rate, $\dot{\epsilon}$, are usually related through some form of power law:

$$\dot{\epsilon} = F(s,T)\sigma^n \qquad\qquad 2.6.1$$

where F(s,T) is a function of material structure (both original and as a result of accumulated strain) and temperature, and n is the so-called stress exponent of creep. The distribution of stress will be linear through the beam thickness only if n = 1, i.e. creep is viscous in nature. In the general case of n > 1, the distribution of stress is not linear through the thickness, and may also be a function of strain (Figure 2.6.1). The actual stress cannot therefore be calculated. It can only be estimated either for n = 1 (the same as the purely elastic condition) or, if n is known, on the assumption that it is independent of strain. Stresses quoted in bend creep data are therefore usually nominal,

Figure 2.6.1
Stress and strain distributions
in test specimens used in bend
creep testing.

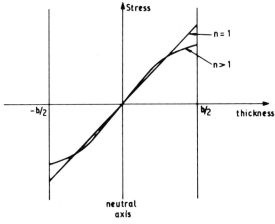

Stress distribution through thickness

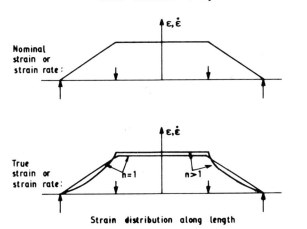

Strain distribution along length

n = 1, outer surface stresses, which will be overestimates of true surface stresses if n > 1. Strains too are usually nominal, based on elastic bending equations, but in general the shape of a bend creep test piece is not the same as that of an elastically bent specimen because the strain distribution in the areas between the inner and outer loading points depends nonlinearly on stress (Figure 2.6.1). If measurement of displacement is recorded as the relative movement of the loading and support points, this leads to an underestimate of true strain in the central span of the specimen.

The overestimation of applied stress and the underestimation of resulting strain can be significant in critical applications or in extrapolation of data for design purposes. Bend data quoted or referenced in this Handbook or in the technical literature should be viewed as tentative and merely indicative of performance rather than treated as accurate.

The number of variables involved in creep test data, and the varying shapes of creep curves cause problems with presentation of data. Usually a set of strain-time curves is given for various conditions of temperature stress and environment, from which temperature, stress and environment sensitivity can be deduced by appropriate additional plots under conditions of fixed strain.

Some creep tests were undertaken at NPL as part of this programme to compare the creep performance of a range of alumina ceramics. The criterion used, the temperature at which a nominal strain of 0.1% in four-point bending was achieved in 1 hour at nominal stresses of 50 and 20 MNm^{-2}, was intended to demonstrate the temperature at which creep could readily be detected, rather than to provide engineering data, i.e. to compare the temperature at which high-load creep was detected compared with nominal maximum use temperatures. Figure 2.6.2 shows some of the results.

Figure 2.6.2
Time to 0.1% nominal bend strain as a function of temperature under a nominal bend stress of 50 MNm^{-2} for a range high-alumina ceramics. Note that creep resistance is not directly related to alumina content. (NPL results)

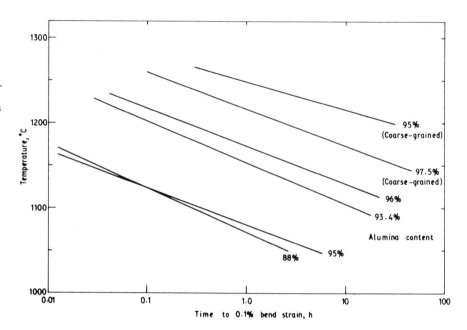

2.6.1.5 Data tables

Melting points (T_M) of pure refractory oxide phases are given in Figure 2.6.3, together with 'short-term maximum no-load use temperatures' (T_S) and long-term use temperatures for dimensional stability (T_L) (where appropriate or known) for each oxide in dense polycrystalline form. Commercial products consisting of more than one phase are dealt with in Figure 2.6.4., where T_S and T_L figures are given. Clearly, such figures are subject to some uncertainty as a result of variations in composition and precise criteria used to define the behaviour of any one product. For example, some forms of 95% alumina are clearly more resistant to creep than others and thus have higher T_L values appropriate, for example, to metallizing.

Figure 2.6.5 shows the melting, dissociation or vaporization temperatures for non-oxide phases, together with T_S figures for use in inert conditions. In addition, the limitations imposed by oxidation are shown as the approximate temperatures at which oxidation rates become significant on dense polycrystalline bodies (T_O). For commercial polyphase non-oxide products, or those produced by methods resulting in alternative microstructures, e.g. porous reaction-bonded silicon nitride, Figure 2.6.6 similarly gives T_L and T_S in inert conditions, and T_O in oxidizing conditions. Generally T_O is less than

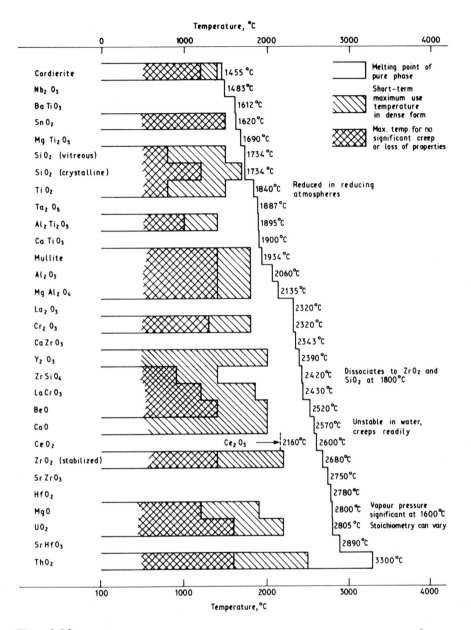

Figure 2.6.3
Melting points, maximum short-term use temperatures,
and temperatures for the onset of significant creep for pure
single-phase oxide materials.

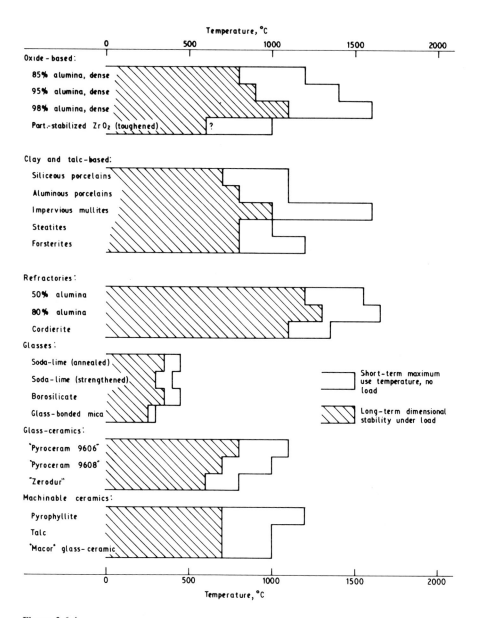

Figure 2.6.4
Maximum short-term use temperatures and temperatures
for the onset of creep in commercial polyphase oxide
materials.

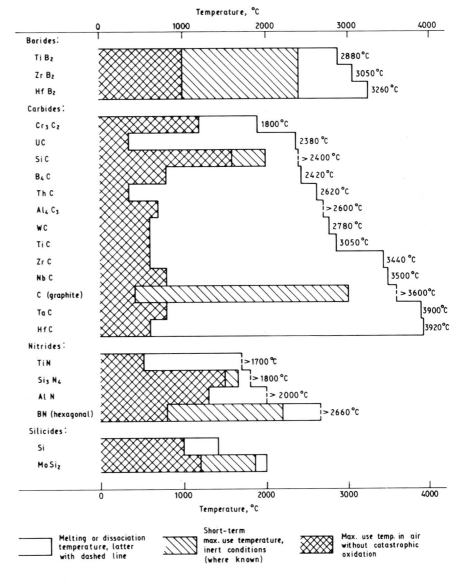

Figure 2.6.5
Melting, vaporization or dissociation temperatures
for single-phase, dense, non-oxide materials compared with
maximum use temperatures in inert conditions and
temperatures for the onset of significant rates of oxidation
in oxidizing conditions.

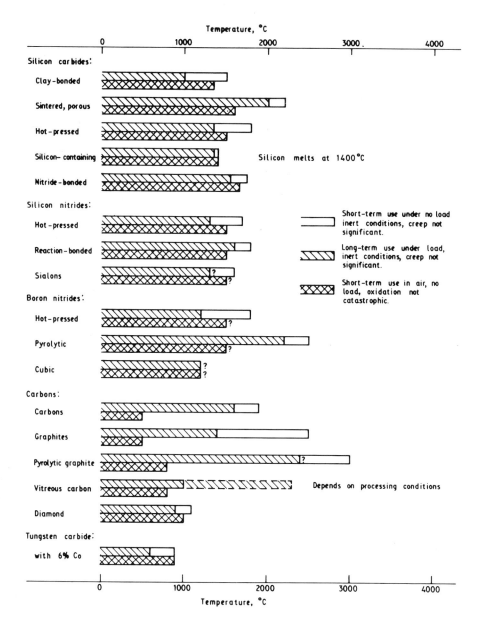

Figure 2.6.6
Maximum short-term no-load temperatures in inert
conditions compared with temperatures for the onset of
creep under load and with temperatures for significant rates
of oxidation in commercial types of non-oxide materials.
Note that oxidation can enhance creep rates in some
materials.

T_S and often less than T_L except in cases where a stable oxide film is produced which does not affect creep properties, as with reaction-bonded silicon carbide.

In using these diagrams, allowance must be made for the nature and composition of the material. Performance can be worse than shown if products have high levels of porosity or fine grain sizes, or contain deleterious minor phases. Strictly, each case should be treated on its own merits, and the figures should be used only as a rough guide. In particular, the influence of corrosive conditions may be dramatic and place severe limitations on use temperatures. Liquid phase may be produced within materials at low temperatures either as a result of composition or by contact with other materials. Reference to compilations of phase diagrams can be useful for specific phase combinations, especially *Phase Diagrams for Ceramists* (see Bibliography). See also Section 2.9 for some relevant information.

At very high temperatures, vapour pressures may become appreciable. The maximum use temperature is then controlled by the partial pressure of the constituent species in the immediate atmosphere. For example, boron nitride is said to be usable to 2000°C in vacuum, to 2700°C under one atmosphere of nitrogen and to even higher temperatures under high nitrogen pressure. In vacuum, continuous pumping away of nitrogen causes significant dissociation of the ceramic which would be prevented by one atmosphere of nitrogen in a closed environment.

2.6.2 Thermal stress and thermal shock

The rate at which heat is transferred to or from the surfaces of a component, together with the thermal conductivity or diffusivity, determines the local temperature gradient at the surface. At temperatures where there is no significant plasticity to allow a degree of stress relaxation, temperature gradients produce thermo-elastic strains of magnitude governed principally by the thermal expansion characteristics. If these strains are tensile or shear and exceed the local fracture strains, failure can result. Furthermore if two materials of different expansion coefficients are rigidly fixed together at one temperature, and then used at another temperature, static thermal strains result, with similar potential consequences.

In this Section, static and time-variant thermal strains are considered in general terms, and the importance of thermal properties is emphasized.

2.6.2.1 Static thermal strains

The Fourier heat flow equation yields a solution to any problem involving heat flow:

$$\frac{\lambda}{\varrho C}\nabla^2 T + \frac{Q}{\varrho C} = \frac{\partial T}{\partial t} \qquad\qquad 2.6.2$$

where $Q(x,y,z)$ is the heat supplied at (x,y,z), λ is the thermal conductivity, ϱ is the density and C the specific heat. For most ceramic problems, Q is determined by rates of heat transfer at surfaces, and under steady-state conditions, $\dfrac{\partial T}{\partial t} = 0$.

The temperature distribution resulting from the heat flow pattern and the geometry in question sets up thermal strains which show a complex dependence on the thermal and elastic properties of the material. If the properties are isotropic, solutions can be obtained analytically in some simple circumstances (see Bibliography for references to simple worked examples of solutions). In the more general case of complex geometry, material anisotropy, and properties that vary with both temperature and position, approximate solutions can be achieved only by numerical methods such as finite element analysis. Thermal stress analysis is exceedingly complex. *The accuracy of the solutions is critically dependent on the accuracy of the property data used, particularly the temperature dependence of properties and properties that are difficult to measure accurately, such as Poisson's ratio.* Thermal stress analysis therefore cannot be used reliably as a tool to estimate failure probability, but rather is a method of studying the tendency of particular geometries or materials to produce high thermal stress levels. Applications to which this type of analysis is appropriate include seals and joints between ceramics.

As a general guide, the material properties that are advantageous in minimizing the risk of thermal failure in static situations are:

low α or appropriately matched α in joints

high fracture strain (i.e. σ_f/E)

high K_{Ic}

high λ.

The joining of ceramics is dealt with in detail in Section 3, but it is useful to note that direct measurement of stress is well established for glasses. There are two types of technique. For glazes, the curvature of a thin flat tile glazed on one side can be measured as a function of temperature (Steger's bar). The stress in the glaze at the use temperature can be estimated fairly accurately if the relevant elastic properties are known. In practice it is not necessary to obtain accurate measurements since provided the glaze is in adequate but not excessive compression (i.e. of convex curvature between known limits), crazing or spalling should not result. For other types of seal, the sandwich method can be used. A ceramic/glass/ceramic or even a glass/metal/glass sandwich is made, and the glass stress is measured from its optical birefringence when viewed parallel to the plane of the seal. This technique can be used with advantage to check the effects of rates of cooling on setting temperatures, and also of glass densification when held at temperatures below the glass transition temperature for long periods.

2.6.2.2 Thermal transients and thermal shock

As with steady-state thermal stresses, resistance to thermal transients depends on material parameters and geometry, and virtually every case needs to be treated on its own merits. Subjecting the surface of a body to rapid changes of temperature produces a transient stress distribution, the magnitude of which depends on the heat transfer coefficient at the surface relative to the rate at which heat can be conducted to or from the surface through the component. It is therefore difficult to predict the ability of a ceramic body to withstand severe conditions, and in view of the fact that geometrical factors influence heat transfer rates, it is usually most convenient to make practical trials. In fact it is probably true to say that *thermal shock testing with shapes other than that of the final component can be totally misleading. Quotation of a thermal shock temperature difference required to fracture a simple rod shape under certain heat transfer conditions will almost always overestimate the performance of a complex shape.* However, different materials can be compared readily in simple rod form to give a feel for relative performance and the rest of this Section discusses this in more detail with respect to material properties.

The simplest view is to consider the case of a body subjected to an infinite heat transfer rate so that the surface layer changes instantly from temperature T_0 to T_1. The stress generated at the surface is biaxial tension (on downward shock) or biaxial compression (on upward shock), while the stress remote from the surface remains low. The maximum thermal stress, σ_{max}, can be equated to the surface fracture stress, σ_s, under the prevailing stress state when the temperature change is just sufficient to cause fracture, i.e.:

$$\sigma_{max}^\infty = \sigma_s = \frac{E\alpha(T_0-T_1)}{(1-\nu)} \qquad 2.6.3$$

where E is Young's modulus, α is the expansion coefficient (assumed constant over the temperature range involved), and where ∞ represents an infinite heat transfer rate. The resistance to thermal shock can then be defined as the temperature change required to effect fracture:

$$R = (T_0-T_1)_{max} = \frac{\sigma_s(1-\nu)}{E\alpha} \qquad 2.6.4$$

The short-term fracture stress that should be inserted into this expression is that corresponding to the biaxial stress state at the surface, with allowance for an appropriate distribution of strengths and for the surface environment. Since the ratio of short-term fracture stress to Young's modulus is generally in the region 0.0005–0.0010 for well-made ceramics free from gross defects, it can be seen that ranking for thermal shock resistance is determined basically by the thermal expansion coefficient α.

In practice, an analysis for finite rates of heat transfer becomes extremely complex. For constant heat transfer rate, h, across a surface, an approximate analysis shows that:

$$\sigma_{max}^h = \frac{E\alpha(T_0-T_1)}{(1-\nu)} = F(\beta) \qquad 2.6.5$$

where $F(\beta)$ is a function of the Biot modulus, β, a non-dimensional quantity:

$$\beta = \frac{rh}{\lambda} \qquad 2.6.6$$

which essentially relates the heat transfer coefficient, h, to the material thermal conductivity, λ, and a characteristic dimension of the shape in question, r, which may be the radius of a rod or half the thickness of a plate, for example. The function F is roughly proportional to β for β less than about 1, so:

$$\sigma_{max}^h = \frac{E\alpha(T_0-T_1)}{(1-\nu)} \cdot \beta \qquad 2.6.7$$

If a second thermal shock resistance parameter is defined:

$$R' = \frac{\sigma_s(1-\nu)\lambda}{E\alpha} = R\lambda \qquad\qquad 2.6.8$$

then:

$$(T_0-T_1)_{max} = \frac{R'}{h} \times \text{(shape factor)} \qquad\qquad 2.6.9$$

For a given shape and heat transfer coefficient, R' is again a comparative measure of performance, which takes into account the thermal conductivity. Some examples of heat transfer coefficient are given in Table 2.6.1, where it can be seen that water quenching is the most severe condition.

Table 2.6.1 Typical values for heat transfer coefficients

Condition	h, $Wm^{-2}K^{-1}$
Air flow past cylinder at:	
0.12 $kgm^{-2}s^{-1}$	10
12.0 $kgm^{-2}s^{-1}$	100
120 $kgm^{-2}s^{-1}$	500
300 $kgm^{-2}s^{-1}$	1100
Radiation to 0°C from 500°C	40
from 1000°C	150
(assuming a black body surface)	
Water quench to 20°C	6000–60000

Table 2.6.2 Thermal shock parameters and ranking of materials

Property	Symbol	Unit	Materials:		Soda-lime glass		Cordierite (dense sintered)
			Silica glass	'Pyrex' glass	annealed	thermally strengthened	
Density	ϱ	Mgm^{-3}	2.2	2.4	2.5	2.5	2.5
Specific heat at 200°C	C_p	$Jg^{-1}K^{-1}$	0.91	0.94	0.98	0.98	0.94
Strength	σ_s	MNm^{-2}	70	70	70	250	100
Young's modulus	E	GNm^{-2}	70	70	72	72	120
Expansion coefficient	$\bar{\alpha}$	$10^{-6}K^{-1}$	0.62	3.2	7.8	7.8	1.0
Thermal conductivity at 200°C	λ	$Wm^{-1}K^{-1}$	1.8	1.5	1.8	1.8	2.5
Thermal diffusivity at 200°C	D	$10^{-6}m^2s^{-1}$	0.90	0.66	0.73	0.73	1.06
Fracture energy	γ_f	Jm^{-2}	~1	~1	~1	~1	~5
Poisson's ratio	ν	—			(0.25 assumed for all materials)		
Thermal shock parameters:							
R (h = ∞)		K	1200	230	90	330	625
R' (h = const.)		Wm^{-1}	2160	345	160	590	1560
R" (ϕ = const.)		$10^{-6}m^2Ks^{-1}$	1080	150	65	245	240
R"" (damage)		$10^{-6}m$	~20	~20	~20	0	~80

Note: The values chosen for material properties in this Table are for demonstration purposes only, and do not necessarily pertain to any particular product. Consequently the rankings given here are only a demonstration of the difference in performance of broad product groups when such data are inserted into the thermal shock resistance parameters. The parameters are fairly sensitive to material properties, particularly γ_f in R''''.

By similar argument, a third simple condition, constant rate of change of surface temperature, results in a biaxial surface stress:

$$\sigma\phi = \frac{E\alpha}{(1-\nu)}\ \frac{\phi}{6D}\ x\ \text{(shape factor)} \qquad\qquad 2.6.10$$

where ϕ is the heating rate and D is the thermal diffusivity. The maximum tolerable heating rate is when $\sigma\phi = \sigma_s$, the biaxial failure stress:

$$\phi_{max} = \frac{\sigma_s(1-\nu)D}{E\alpha}\ x\ \text{(shape factor)}$$

$$= R''\ x\ \text{(shape factor)} \qquad\qquad 2.6.11$$

where R'' is a third parameter, similar to R' but including additionally density and specific heat.

It should now be easily appreciated that a thermal shock resistance parameter for downward shock may be indicative of relative performance only under certain specified conditions. Material properties enter each parameter in different ways, resulting in different ranking orders of performance. A material of low coefficient of expansion may rank higher with respect to R than one of medium coefficient of expansion, but lower with respect to R' and R'' as a consequence of poor thermal conductivity. Table 2.6.2 gives some examples of rankings for various types of material to illustrate this point. Under yet different conditions, other rankings may result. While it is

Silicon nitride (RBSN)	Boron carbide (hot-pressed)	Siliceous porcelain (electrical type)	Alumina 99.5% (fine-grained)	Silicon carbide (RBSC)	Zirconia (partially-stabilized)	Magnesia (dense)	Firebrick (insulating type)
2.2–2.6	2.5	2.6	3.9	3.1	5.6	3.55	1.2
0.86	1.46	0.95	0.99	0.88	0.53	1.05	0.95
120–200	300	80	380	300	200	170	3
150–250	440	100	400	400	200	276	10
2.6	4.5	6	7.7	4.5	11.0	11.6	4.5
6.0–12.5	20	1.9	25	100	1.3	25	0.4
3.2–5.6	5.5	0.8	6.5	37	0.43	6.7	0.35
10	25	5	25	25	50	1	10
410	110	100	90	125	70	_40_	50
2400–5100	2200	190	2250	_12500_	90	1000	_20_
1300–2300	600	77	580	_4580_	30	270	_17_
140–80	160	100	90	150	_300_	15	150

Underlined values for each thermal shock parameter indicate the extremes of performance.

possible in general terms to say that a low coefficient of expansion coupled with high thermal conductivity gives the best potential performance, prediction of suitability for a given application is difficult. Other factors such as shape, cost and availability may control choice in the end, and there is certainly no simple substitute for a practical test to determine fitness for purpose. From the specification viewpoint, tests on simple test pieces are probably irrelevant. It is better to pour boiling water into a tea-cup, than to specify a thermal shock parameter on a glazed clay rod.

For upward shock, failure is normally controlled by shear or tensile stresses remote from the immediate surface. In very rapid upward shock, e.g. into molten metals from ambient, surface spalling can occur. At slower rates, the surface is still in compression but the associated shear stresses are reduced, and failure tends to be initiated in the cold zones where tensile stresses reach a maximum. For example, a disc rapidly heated around its circumference fails from the central zone with a diametral crack. Generally speaking ceramics withstand more severe conditions on heating than they do on cooling.

At higher temperatures where radiation heat transfer is involved, many ceramics become translucent to radiation, and the effective surface for radiative heat transfer tends to lie inside the physical surface. Temperature transients are not so localized and thermal shock performance tends to be a little better.

2.6.2.3 Thermal shock cracking in ceramics

Linked to thermal shock is the important aspect of what happens after the fracturing process is initiated. In glasses complete shattering generally occurs, but this is not the case with many polycrystalline materials which may show just surface crazing and have some residual strength. Hasselman's thermal shock damage concepts go a long way in explaining the role of material parameters in determining resistance to catastrophic failure.

The elastic energy stored in the material during the thermal shock process up to the point of failure is released in the fracture process and can be equated to the work done in propagating say N cracks per unit volume, each to a final area A where:

$$A = \frac{\sigma_s^2(1-\nu)}{2NE\gamma_f} \text{ x (shape factor)} \qquad 2.6.12$$

where σ_s is the strength at fracture, E is Young's modulus and γ_f is the work of fracture.

To minimize the crack area, and hence the strength-reducing damage that occurs, high values of N, E and γ_f, but low σ_s are advantageous. Thus a thermal shock damage resistance parameter R'''' can be defined where:

$$R'''' = \frac{E\gamma_f}{\sigma_s^2 (1-\nu)} \qquad 2.6.13$$

Some typical figures for this parameter are also given in Table 2.6.2.

This approach explains why glass normally fails catastrophically, since N and γ_f are low, and why weak friable materials, or those with high densities of defects, retain a good proportion of their original strength, such as some partially-stabilized zirconias, and insulating firebrick, as demonstrated in Table 2.6.2.

Again following Hasselman's approach, it can be shown that assuming infinite heat transfer rates and relating strength to an initial crack length l_i and to a fracture energy γ_f, the maximum thermal shock temperature difference is given by:

$$\Delta T_{max} = \left[\frac{\gamma_f (1-2\nu^2)\ \pi}{2E^2(1-\nu^2)^2 l_i} \right]^{\frac{1}{2}} \qquad\qquad 2.6.14$$

for short cracks. After fracture the cracks have grown to a length l_f where:

$$l_f = \left[\frac{3(1-2\nu)}{8(1-\nu^2)N_i l_i} \right]^{\frac{1}{2}} \qquad\qquad 2.6.15$$

which depends only on ν and N as material properties. The residual strength is governed by l_f, and using the Griffith equation, Equation 2.5.1:

$$\sigma_f = \left[\frac{E\gamma_f}{4(1-\nu^2)} \right]^{\frac{1}{2}} \cdot \frac{1}{l_f^{1/2}} \qquad\qquad 2.6.16$$

which is related to the initial strength σ_s through

$$\sigma_f = \left[\frac{\pi^3 E^3 \gamma_f^3 N}{24(1-\nu^2)^2(1-2\nu)} \right]^{\frac{1}{4}} \cdot \frac{1}{\sigma_s^{1/2}} \qquad\qquad 2.6.17$$

More strength is retained for tough, high-modulus, low-strength materials with a high density of flaws that can initiate cracks. Figure 2.6.7 shows schematically strength as a function of quenching temperature difference which illustrates these points.

One would therefore expect materials such as porous refractories, firebrick, and internally microcracked structures such as partially-stabilized zirconias to be more resistant to thermal shock damage than fully dense materials such as the majority of engineering ceramics. *If reliability under thermal shock is essential, a refractory may out-perform a technical ceramic, but this usually implies low initial strength or the presence of open porosity.*

Figure 2.6.7
Strength after thermal shock as a function of quenching temperature difference, illustrating the sharp drop in strength shown by strong materials when subjected to greater than critical shock, compared with the slow decline in strength of weaker low modulus materials.

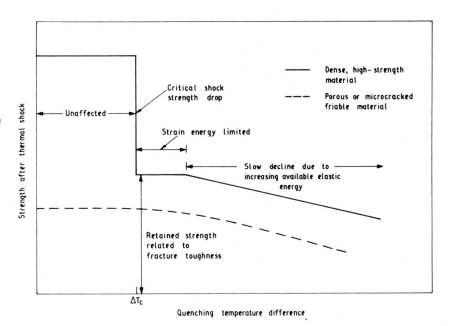

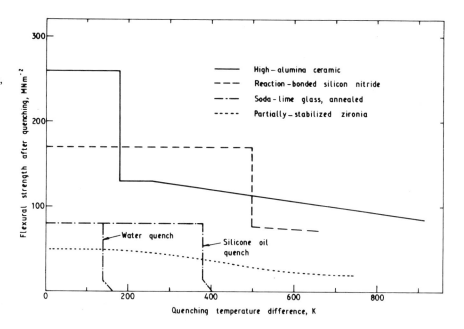

Figure 2.6.8
Strength as a function of quenching temperature difference for various materials in small diameter rod form quenched into water, demonstrating the varying levels of retained strength after shock.

This approach to explaining thermal shock behaviour has been shown to be consistent with experimental results. For example, if the strength of bar samples is measured after thermal shock of varying severity, a plot of the type shown in Figure 2.6.8 is found in which the level of retained strength depends on material properties. The low-strength plateau for super-critical temperature differentials results from the fact that the energy stored elastically at the point of failure is determined by strength and not by the temperature differential. The energy available determines the area of fracturing, which in turn determines the residual strength. The rate of heat transfer can affect the value achieved for the critical temperature differential, and to some extent that of retained strength. The lower the rate of heat transfer, the higher is the critical temperature differential required to achieve the fracture stress. Since the thickness of the tensile skin on the sample is also greater for slower heat transfer, the volume under stress is larger and the effective strength of the material is lower (see Section 2.5.2). Changing the fracture stress changes the strength after thermal shock. If failure is predominantly surface defect controlled, then the density of flaws, N, is constant but there is more elastic energy to be dissipated at slower heat transfer rates which results in larger cracks.

Again the conclusion must be drawn that while strength testing of thermally shocked samples gives a clear indication of the extent of damage resulting, tests on test bars do not model performance of actual components. There is no substitute for testing the component in realistic conditions. Features of design to minimize the risk of thermal shock failure are described in Section 3.4.2.

2.7

Electrical properties

Of major relevance to this Handbook are properties which affect performance as electrical insulators or conductors. Materials used for their magnetic and piezoelectric properties are outside the scope of this Handbook, as are also high-permittivity materials such as those used for capacitors, because in general these classes of material are not the same as those employed for mechanical purposes.

For a detailed understanding of electrical conduction processes, the reader is referred to text books on the subject (see Bibliography). A brief summary of relevant properties only is given here.

Essentially, electricity can be conducted through a ceramic by two methods:
1. by electrons
2. by ions

The majority of ceramics are ionic conductors at high temperatures, but with only very limited ionic conduction at ambient temperatures. Electronic conduction is usually low, except in some specific cases, because the electron energy level band gap is very wide. Most ceramics are therefore insulators at ambient temperature, but progressively lose their insulating characteristics as the temperature rises. In some materials, ionic conduction is high at relatively low temperatures, and this can be used to good effect in various types of device. Mobile ions may be positively charged, such as sodium in beta-alumina used in the sodium/sulphur battery, or negatively charged, such as oxygen in zirconia used as an oxygen sensor.

Some types of ceramic are electronic semiconductors, in which the conduction band of electrons is partially occupied. The resistivity can often be controlled to values appropriate for resistive heating elements. Metallic conduction exists in a few types of materials that might be covered by the term 'ceramic', but these are not used for mechanical purposes.

In this Section, the properties of ceramic insulators and ceramic conductors, and the test methods for determining them, are discussed with reference to applications.

2.7.1 Insulators

Most structural ceramics are insulators, and this fact has been used to advantage for decades in the isolation of electrical power lines, from the smallest thermocouple to large, stacked, high-voltage insulators for power transmission. From the user's point of view, the major properties of significance are:

1. dielectric constant or relative permittivity
2. dielectric breakdown voltage
3. a.c. loss
4. electrical conductivity or resistivity

all as functions of temperature and frequency.

Because of the scale of the electrical and electronics markets for ceramic materials, there are many standards and classification schemes for insulating and dielectric materials. In fact, specifications for electrical properties are much tighter than for mechanical ones, and there are a large number of subdivisions of materials within the various schemes based on minimum performance for various types of application. Consequently, the formulation of many ceramics is in accordance with the properties required by these specifications. Purely mechanical applications for the materials are secondary considerations and may have developed rather later. Some materials are not really suited to purely mechanical use, being surpassed by other types of product in strength, hardness and corrosion resistance, for example. Nevertheless, the classification of products being proposed for the IEC scheme (IEC 672), essentially based on the DIN scheme (DIN 40685), provides the most useful breakdown of product types, and this is followed for the purposes of this Handbook. Although in some of the Tables the impression is given that there is equivalence between various national Standards, it must be emphasized that this is not generally the case. The comparison is made only as a guide, and the classifications of materials are usually different in some respect. For full details, the individual Standards cited must be examined.

The various electrical properties are described first, together with relevant detail, and this is followed by a Table showing the materials that are typically used for various insulating applications, based on performance requirements and costs. This Section cannot be considered to be complete in any sense. It is not intended for specialists in the field but to convey the generalities of the subject and to act as an explanation of the factors that affect properties, and how properties affect performance and choice of material.

2.7.1.1 Dielectric constant or relative permittivity

The relative permittivity of a material is essentially the enhancement charge storage capacity in an electric field as a result of electrical polarization of its crystal structure, resulting in partial neutralization of the applied field.

In a.c. conditions, dielectric loss processes result in some out-of-phase component in the polarization, and to account for this, permittivity should be considered as being composed of real and imaginary parts:

$$\kappa = \kappa' + \kappa'' \qquad\qquad 2.7.1$$

where the phase lag resulting is given by:

$$\tan \delta = \kappa'' / \kappa' \qquad\qquad 2.7.2$$

where δ is the phase angle. When reference is made to relative permittivity it is the real part, κ', that is conventionally quoted. The imaginary part is normally expressed as $\tan \delta$, or as $\kappa' \tan \delta$ (see Section 2.7.1.2).

Permittivity and loss are usually measured together by using a disc or tube of the test material with suitably applied opposing electrodes as a capacitor in a tuned circuit. For high frequencies, various other methods are available. For example, for microwave frequencies, 10^9 Hz and above, resonant cavity and wave-guide methods are commonly used.

In most materials, permittivity is not especially frequency-dependent at ambient temperature, except at low frequencies where ionic drift and relatively high values of tan δ tend to enhance κ' levels. At frequencies of 10^9 Hz or more, some increase is seen due to ionic vibration effects. As the temperature is raised, ionic drift and other loss-causing processes tend to increase in significance, causing increases in κ' and quite large increases in tan δ. Thus in general the effects of both frequency and temperature need to be considered. However, data across the full ranges of both parameters are not plentiful for several reasons. Firstly, each method of measurement has a limited range of use in both temperature and frequency terms, so full characterization requires an extensive series of tests. Secondly, measurements have been semi-standardized in various standard specifications, and have been limited to test conditions that are considered sufficient to determine whether a particular product broadly meets the requirements of its type. Consequently, data quoted for commercial materials are usually restricted to these specific conditions of test.

As an indication of typical values of κ' for a range of materials, Table 2.7.1 gives the effect of frequency at room temperature, and the effect of temperature at fixed frequency expressed in terms of a temperature coefficient of permittivity, usually in parts per million per kelvin. This latter is of significance in components that see temperature rises which change the electrical performance of the device, requiring electronic correction. BS 4789:1972 recommends that for microwave applications measurements of permittivity are made at ambient temperature and at 200°C at a frequency of 9.4 GHz, and that the mean temperature coefficient is calculated over this range.

The material factors that affect permittivity most significantly are the relative proportions of the individual crystalline and glassy phases, and the level of porosity. The distribution of the phases affects the mixture rule expression that might be used to calculate permittivity from data for individual phases, but as an example for a dispersed spherical phase of solid material or porosity of relative permittivity κ'_d and volume fraction v_d in a matrix of permittivity κ'_m and volume fraction v_m, the Maxwell equation gives the mean as:

$$\bar{\kappa}' = \frac{v_m\kappa'_m\left\{\dfrac{2}{3}+\dfrac{\kappa'_d}{3\kappa'_m}\right\} + v_d\kappa'_d}{v_m\left\{\dfrac{2}{3}+\dfrac{\kappa'_d}{3\kappa'_m}\right\} + v_d} \qquad\qquad 2.7.3$$

For cases where κ'_d is small compared with κ'_m, and for v_d small compared with v_m:

$$\bar{\kappa}' \approx \kappa'_m\,(1-\mu_\kappa v_d) \qquad\qquad 2.7.4$$

where μ_κ is a constant embodying the ratio of κ'_d to κ'_m. This would be appropriate to low levels of porosity normally encountered in sintered materials, in which case $\mu_\kappa \approx 1\text{--}1.5$. The effect of small amounts of porosity

Table 2.7.1 Permittivity of insulating ceramics

IEC class	Material type	IEC κ' min. or range 50 Hz	Typical values of κ', 25°C				Temperature coefficient, $10^{-6}K^{-1}$ at 1 MHz
			50 Hz	1 kHz	1 MHz	1 GHz	
Ceramics:							
C–110	Porcelains, siliceous	6–7	6–7	6–7	6–7	—	500–600
C–111	Porcelains, pressed	—	6–7	6–7	6–7	—	—
C–112	Porcelains, cristobalite	5–6	—	—	—	—	500–600
C–120	Porcelains, aluminous	6–7	—	—	—	—	500–600
C–130	Porcelains, aluminous	6–7.5	—	—	—	—	500–600
C–210	Steatites, low voltage	6	—	—	—	—	70–160
C–220	Steatites, normal	6	6–6.2	6–6.2	5.8–6	—	70–160
C–221	Steatites, low loss	6	—	—	6.1	5.9	70–160
C–230	Steatites, porous	none	depends on density				
C–240	Forsterites, porous	none	depends on density				
C–250	Forsterites, dense	7	—	—	6–7	—	—
C–310	Titania	40–100	—	—	~100	—	−280 to −900
C–410	Cordierite, dense	5	—	5.7	—	—	500–600
C–420	Celsian, dense	7	—	—	~9	—	30–100
—	Zircon, dense	—	~10	—	~9	—	—
C–500	Electrical refractories	none	depends on density and alumina content				
C–610	Mullite	8	—	—	—	—	—
C–620	Mullite	8	—	—	—	—	—
C–780	Alumina, 80–86%	9	—	—	8–9	—	~100
C–786	Alumina, 86–95%	9	—	—	8–9	—	~100
C–795	Alumina, 95–99%	9	—	—	8–9.5	8–9.5	~100
C–799	Alumina, >99%	9	—	—	9–10	9–10	~100
C–810	Beryllia	7	—	—	6.5–7.5	—	~100
C–820	Magnesia, porous	10	depends on density				
C–830	Zirconia, stabilized	22	—	—	—	—	—
Glasses:							
G–100	Alkali-lime-silica	6.5–7.6	—	7.6	6.9	6.5	>3000
G–200	Borosilicate	4.0–5.5	—	—	—	—	>3000
—	Fused quartz	—	4.2	4.1	4.0	—	—
Other ceramics:							
—	Silicon nitride (dense)	—	—	—	~10	—	—
—	Pyrophyllite	—	—	—	~5.3	—	—
—	Sapphire, // c-axis	—	—	—	11.53	—	—
—	// a-axis	—	—	—	9.35	—	—

and second phases in alumina ceramics has been estimated in the various relevant data sheets in Part 2 by this method, assuming that $\mu_\kappa = 1$.

Anisotropy of dielectric properties may need to be taken into account if the permittivity of a single crystal of any of the major phases is anisotropic. For example, there is a 20% difference in permittivity between the a- and the c-axis directions in sapphire. A fine-grained alumina ceramic in which the individual crystals have a non-random orientation, as in an extruded or tape-cast product, will also be anisotropic. This accounts in part for the spread of values of κ' seen in manufacturers' brochures, and for κ' values apparently exceeding that of the mean value of sapphire.

Permittivity can also be controlled in many types of ceramic by adding amounts of a high-permittivity phase to a low-permittivity matrix. An example is the use of TiO_2 or a titanate in alumina to increase κ' or reduce its variation with temperature, e.g. for missile nose cones which are required to keep consistent properties over a wide temperature range in use.

2.7.1.2 Loss tangent and dielectric power loss

Applying an alternating voltage to a dielectric results in generation of heat and loss of electrical power by a number of different mechanisms which contribute in various frequency ranges. At microwave frequencies (10 GHz and above), ionic vibration may be the most significant factor, but at lower frequencies, say below 1 MHz, the migration of ions under the imposed fields is the principal mechanism, either as d.c. conductivity or as ion jump and dipole relaxation losses. In general, dielectric loss appears to be at a minimum between 1 and 100 MHz.

The normal way of describing dielectric loss is by the phase angle introduced by the time taken for polarization to occur on application of a field. For no losses, the charging current is 90° in advance of the voltage, but this is reduced to 90°−δ when losses occur.

The corresponding energy loss per cycle is then:

$$W = \pi \epsilon_o \kappa' V_o^2 \tan \delta \qquad\qquad 2.7.5$$

where ϵ_o is the permittivity of free space (8.854×10^{-12} F m^{-1}), V_o is the maximum of the sinusoidal voltage, and $\tan \delta$ is the tangent of the loss angle as defined in Equation 2.7.2. The power loss per unit volume is then:

$$P = \pi f \epsilon_o \kappa' V_o^2 \tan \delta \qquad\qquad 2.7.6$$

where f is the frequency. The energy losses are therefore proportional to frequency but, as has been noted above, $\tan \delta$ is also frequency-dependent, often in the opposite sense up to around 100 MHz. This gives partial compensation for the frequency effect.

The loss tangent of materials at lower frequencies depends on the ease of migration of ions under the influence of the a.c. field. It can be readily appreciated that the strong atomic bonding in many pure oxides and non-oxides permits very little migration, and losses are correspondingly low. However, in glasses, especially those with alkali metals, Na and K, movement is relatively easy, and these have lower resistivities and losses are higher. Since the vast majority of ceramics are not of high purity, they contain glassy phases, which even in small amounts at grain boundaries can have a significant effect on loss. If low electrical loss is required, the resistivity must be as high as possible, and the proportion of lossy glass phase must be minimized. Alkali contents must be reduced, which in many cases means using high-purity raw materials. At low frequencies, even though $\tan \delta$ may be quite high, the actual power loss levels obtained from feldspar-containing porcelains and some silicate glasses are sufficiently small that $\tan \delta$ itself is of no real significance. It is therefore economically viable to use such cheaper materials for power-frequency insulators, at least up to 200°C. Above this temperature level, resistivities of these materials have fallen so far that power losses become unacceptable, and low-alkali materials have to be used.

The nomenclature of power loss tends to be confusing because of the variety of terms used to describe it. The principal ones are:

$\tan \delta$ *loss tangent* or dielectric *dissipation factor.*

$\kappa' \tan \delta$ *dielectric loss index* or *loss factor.* Materials are frequently classified on the basis of maximum dielectric loss index at a given frequency, e.g. in US military specification schemes.

$\sin \delta$ *dielectric power factor* is the ratio of power dissipation to effective power input (volts × amps). For small power losses, $\delta < 0.1$, sin δ is not significantly different from tan δ.

Clearly the interrelation of these properties is simple, and therefore only κ' and tan δ are shown in the Tables, from which the other parameters can be calculated. Table 2.7.2 shows tan δ as a function of frequency at 25°C for a range of insulating materials, and also typical changes in tan δ with increasing temperature at 1 MHz. It should be borne in mind that, especially with the lower-loss materials, loss levels measured are extremely sensitive to trace impurity levels and to the cleanliness of preparation of the test-piece. Furthermore, since there are few sets of data showing continuous figures for tan δ over a wide frequency range, again because of the limited range of frequencies used in the specification of materials in Standards, it cannot be assumed that loss shows a smooth trend with changing frequency or temperature. Each product will show different behaviour, possibly with peaks or troughs at particular frequencies. Conformity of a particular batch to a particular specification may have to be checked if loss levels are critical.

Table 2.7.2 Loss tangent, typical figures

IEC class	Material type	IEC maximum tan δ, 10^{-4}, at 25°C and			Typical tan δ, 10^{-4}, at 25°C and		Temperature variation of tan δ at 1 MHz and		
		50 Hz	1 kHz	1 MHz	1 MHz	10 GHz	100°C	300°C	500°C
Ceramics:									
C–110	Porcelains, siliceous	250	—	120	80	n/a	300	n/a	n/a
C–111	Porcelains, pressed		none		*		—	n/a	n/a
C–112	Porcelains, cristobalite	250	—	120	—	n/a	—	n/a	n/a
C–120	Porcelains, aluminous	250	—	120	10	20	5	10	30
C–130	Porcelains, aluminous	300	—	150	—	—	—	—	—
C–210	Steatite, low-voltage	250	—	70	—	—	—	—	—
C–220	Steatite, normal	50	—	30	20	30	20	70	1000
C–221	Steatite, low-loss	15	—	12	8	20	10	200	1000
C–230	Steatite, porous		none		—	—	—	—	—
C–240	Forsterite, porous		none		—	—	—	—	—
C–250	Forsterite, dense	15	—	5	5	20	—	—	—
C–310	Titania, dense	—	65	20	—	—	—	—	—
C–410	Cordierite, dense	250	—	70	—	—	—	—	—
C–420	Celsian, dense	100	120	5	—	—	—	—	—
—	Zircon, dense		none		4–14	n/a	70	700	n/a
C–500	Electrical refractories		none		n/a	n/a	—	—	—
C–610	Mullite		none		n/a	n/a	—	—	—
C–620	Mullite		none		n/a	n/a	—	—	—
C–780	Alumina, 80–86%	10	15	15	—		—	—	—
C–786	Alumina, 86–95%	5	10	10	5		—	—	—
C–795	Alumina, 95–99%	5	10	10	3	10	5	50	300
C–799	Alumina, >99%	2	5	10	1	5	—	30	130
C–810	Beryllia	10	10	10	2	3	2	3	10
C–820	Magnesia		none		n/a	n/a	—	—	—
C–830	Zirconia, stabilized	—	—	20	—	—	—	—	n/a
Glasses:									
G–110	Alkali-lime-silica	300	200	100	100	100	100	3000	n/a
G–120	Alkali-lime, toughened	600	600	600	—	—	—	—	n/a
G–200	Borosilicate	200	100	100	—	—	—	—	—
—	Silica		none		3	2	5	10	100
Other ceramics:									
—	Sapphire		none		<1	<2	—	—	—

*For many pressed porcelains, similar formulations to those employed for plastic processed material are used, so loss levels may be similar under dry conditions.

2.7.1.3 Resistivity

The ability of electrons or ions to pass through an insulating solid is usually a strong function of temperature determined by the nature of the crystal or glassy structure and in particular by its composition. The flow of current between two metal electrodes takes place either by surface or by bulk conduction, both requiring consideration because the surface state and path length may be such that the conduction path is easier along the surface than through the bulk.

The volume specific resistance, or volume resistivity, ϱ_R (unit Ωm), of a material is the resistance in ohms of a unit cube of the material, such that the resistance of a body of length l and uniform cross-section A is:

$$R = \frac{\varrho_R l}{A} \qquad\qquad 2.7.7$$

Volume resistivity is normally measured by a simple current flow technique in a geometry such that preferential surface conduction is avoided or minimized. The recommended practice in BS 1598:1964 is to use a disc sample with electrodes on either side. On one side, the circular electrode covers most of the disc area; on the other side is a smaller central electrode surrounded by an annular electrode. Volume resistivity is measured through the thickness while surface resistivity can be measured across the annular gap on one face. It should be remembered that humidity plays an important role in determining surface resistivity, and Standard test methods usually spell out the conditioning of the test-piece prior to the test in order to standardize conditions.

The main factor which determines the electrical conductivity of an insulator is the conductivity of its individual components, particularly those which provide a continuous path through the material. In traditional clay-based ceramics, the main contributory factor is the alkali metal content of the glassy matrix. Conduction in glasses is associated with ionic motion and this causes polarization at the electrodes if the ions cannot pass into or out of the material. As a result, when tested with d.c., the resistivity is initially low but builds up to a steady higher value determined by electrode conditions. For this reason, most Standard test methods specify that the current flowing should be measured one minute after application of the test voltage. An alternative method is to measure with a.c. (e.g. at power frequency as in DIN 40685) which avoids the problem of polarization, but sensible results are difficult to obtain at high resistivity levels. The a.c. resistivity may be as much as two orders of magnitude lower that the one-minute d.c. resistivity, a point that has to be remembered when interpreting manufacturers' data which often do not specify the method of measurement. Data for d.c. are clearly of greater commercial advantage compared with data for a.c. In Table 2.7.3, the minimum volume resistivities quoted in various Standards are compared for various types of materials. There is not exact equivalence between material classifications in the different Standards, but the Table is given as a guide.

In the absence of alkali metals, particularly sodium, conductivity in glasses is much reduced, but still depends on the composition. Charge may be carried by much less mobile divalent ions, or by hydroxyl ions incorporated into the glass during melting, or by electrons. The latter type of conduction is particularly evident in glasses containing transition metal oxides, V_2O_5, Fe_2O_3, CoO, Mn_2O_3 or their appropriate reduced or oxidized states in the glass structure.

Table 2.7.3 Minimum resistivity levels in insulating ceramics

IEC class	Material Type	Minimum resistivity ($\log_{10}\Omega m$) in:					
		IEC 672, d.c.			BS 1598[1], d.c.		
		20°C	200°C	600°C	20°C	300°C	600°C
Ceramics:							
C–110	Porcelains, siliceous	11	6	2	11	5	2
C–111	Porcelains, pressed	10	6	2	11	5	2
C–112	Porcelains, cristobalite	11	6	2	—	—	—
C–120	Porcelains, aluminous	11	6	2	11	6	3
C–130	Porcelains, aluminous	11	6	2	—	—	—
C–210	Steatite, low-voltage	10	7	3	11	7	5
C–220	Steatite, normal	11	8	5	—	—	—
C–221	Steatite, low-loss	11	9	5	11	9	6
C–230	Steatite, porous	—	8	5	—	—	—
C–240	Forsterite, porous	—	9	5	—	—	—
C–250	Forsterite, dense	11	9	5	—	—	—
C–310	Titania	10	—	—	—	—	—
C–410	Vitreous cordierite	10	6	3	9	5	2
C–420	Celsian, dense	12	11	7	—	—	—
—	Zircon, dense	—	—	—	11	7	3
C–500	Electrical refractories	—	7	3	—	—	—
C–530	Electrical high alumina	—	8	4	—	—	—
C–610	Mullite	11	9	4	—	—	—
C–620	Mullite	11	9	4	—	—	—
C–780	Alumina, 80–86%	12	10	5	11	7	5
C–786	Alumina, 86–95%	12	10	5	11	7	5
C–795	Alumina, 95–99%	12	10	6	11	8	5
C–799	Alumina, >99%	12	10	6	$\{\,12^2$ 12^2	$—^2$ $—^2$	5^2 $6^2\,\}$
C–810	Beryllia	12	10	7	12^2	$—^2$	6^2
C–820	Magnesia, porous	—	—	—	—	—	—
C–830	Zirconia, stabilized	9	—	—	—	—	—
Glasses:							
G–110	Alkali-lime-silica	10	5	—	—	—	—
G–111	Alkali-lime-toughened	10	5	—	—	—	—
G–200	Borosilicate	12	7	—	—	—	—
	Silica	—	—	—	—	—	—
Other ceramics:							
	Sapphire	—	—	—	—	—	—

[1] The types of material to which the specifications of the various classes of BS 1598 apply are presumed on the basis of other properties.

[2] These requirements are from BS 4789:1972, *Ceramic components for use in envelopes for vacuum tubes.* Class 1 is the first set, class 2 the second set. Requirements are also set for 200°C and 400°C. Materials in IEC class C–795 may also meet these standards, but in general those of still lower alumina content do not. In addition, a requirement is set that the room-temperature resistance is not reduced below the specified level by firing in vacuum or in hydrogen. Class 3 is intended for beryllia products with the same resistivity requirements as for Class 2.

In purely crystalline materials, resistivity is determined by the concentration of defects, such as vacancies and impurities in solution and at grain boundaries, which control the mobility of ions, particularly oxygen and some divalent species. At high temperatures, the atmosphere, especially the partial pressure of oxygen, can affect the equilibrium concentration of defects like oxygen ion vacancies. This phenomenon is used to advantage in enhancing the conductivity of thread and tape guides based on TiO_2 to avoid electrostatic charging. Firing under reducing conditions renders the material sub-stoichiometric with respect to oxygen and greatly enhances its electron semi-

DIN 40685[3], a.c. 50 Hz, at						ASTM, d.c., at				
20°C	200°C	400°C	600°C	800°C	1000°C	25°C	300°C	500°C	700°C	900°C
9	5	3	2	—	—	—	—	—	—	—
9	5	3	2	—	—	—	—	—	—	—
—	—	—	—	—	—	—	—	—	—	—
9	5	3	2	—	—	—	—	—	—	—
—	—	—	—	—	—	—	—	—	—	—
—	—	—	—	—	—	—	—	—	—	—
9.7	8	5	3	—	—	12[4]	5	3	2	1
10	9	7	5	4	3	12[4]	8.7	7	5	4
—	—	—	—	—	—	—	—	—	—	—
—	—	6	5	3.7	3	—	—	—	—	—
—	9	7	5.7	4	3	—	—	—	—	—
—	—	—	—	—	—	—	—	—	—	—
9	6	4	2	—	—	—	—	—	—	—
—	—	—	—	—	—	—	—	—	—	—
—	—	4.7–5	3–3.7	2–2.7	1.7–2	—	—	—	—	—
—	—	5	4	3	2	—	—	—	—	—
—	7	4	3	2	1	—	—	—	—	—
—	—	7	5	3.7	2	12[5]	8	5.6	4.6	3.6
—	—	8	6	4.7	3.3	12[5]	8	5.3	4.3	3.3
—	—	9	6	5	3.7	12[5]	8	5.9	4.8	3.9
—	11.7	10	7.3	5.5	4	12[5]	8.75	6	5	4
—	—	—	—	—	—	13[6]	10	9	7	6
—	—	—	—	—	4	—	—	—	—	—
9	—	4	—	—	1	—	—	—	—	—

[3] The nearest equivalent classification is used. There are differences in the range of Al_2O_3 content of alumina ceramics between this and IEC 672.

[4] ASTM D2757 contains four categories of material based on mechanical properties and dielectric loss. Figures for Type I (lowest quality) and Type IV (highest quality) materials are given against C-220 and C-221 respectively.

[5] As specified in ASTM D2442 for four categories of ceramics that differ in alumina content from those of IEC 672, but are broadly equivalent.

[6] As specified in ASTM F356 for Type II (>98% BeO) and Type III (>99% BeO) materials, Type I (>95% BeO) being a factor 10 lower at all temperatures.

conducting properties. Similarly, the conductivity of stabilized zirconia is related to oxygen pressure at high temperatures, and this is used as the basis for oxygen meters to measure O_2 partial pressures in gas mixtures, such as exhaust gases from cars or boilers.

The majority of oxide ceramics dealt with in this Handbook are not so markedly affected as TiO_2 or ZrO_2, but still show changes which may be as great as one or two orders of magnitude with changes in oxygen potential. No ceramic can be considered to give good insulating performance at temperatures above 1200°C, with implications for the safety of electrically heated equipment. At higher temperatures, diffusion of oxygen in particular can render otherwise gas-tight materials permeable to oxygen with consequences for use in conditions where low oxygen pressures have to be maintained.

With alumina ceramics (and probably others as well), the firing atmosphere, or refiring atmosphere during subsequent processing, affects resistivity values to some extent, with firing in hydrogen producing a significant reduction in resistivity in many commercial products (see, for example, Binns, D B (1965) in the Bibliography) although this should not be treated as always being the case.

A term frequently used in Standards and manufacturers' brochures is the so-called 'T_e' value, expressed in °C. This is the temperature at which the volume resistivity has fallen to a figure of 10^4 Ω m. IEC 672 uses the expression 't_{k1}' for the same point, and also employs 't_{k100}' as the temperature for a resistivity of 10^6 Ω m. Although these temperatures can be obtained simply by interpolation on a resistivity versus temperature plot, they are often quoted specifically because they give a direct indication of the maximum temperature to which one can use the material and still retain some useful

Figure 2.7.1
Resistivity, d.c., (measured one minute after application of test voltage) as a function of temperature for a range of insulating ceramics in single-phase form, demonstrating the maximum that is likely to be achieved under any circumstances.

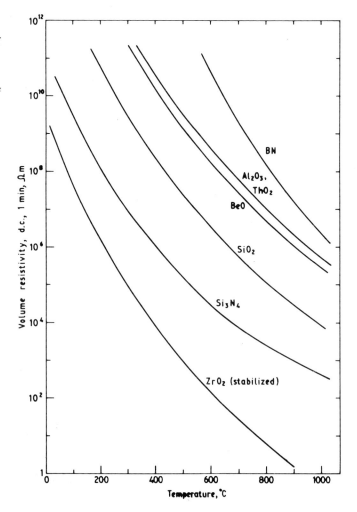

insulating character. Figures for T_e are not included in Table 2.7.3 because their approximate value can be obtained by inspection.

Figure 2.7.1 illustrates typical curves of d.c. resistivity versus temperature for pure single-phase ceramics. These curves are typical of the best performance likely to be obtained in any commercial product. The most resistive material is boron nitride, followed by alumina, thoria and beryllia. Figure 2.7.2 shows the curves interpolated from the minimum performance specification in IEC 672 (draft). Most products will meet this specification or be of higher resistivity. See the individual data sheets in Part 2 for more detailed data.

Clearly any individual product is subject to some variation in performance depending on precise composition, particularly with regard to alkali metal impurities. If a minimum resistivity in use is essential it is important to ensure that the conditions of measurement are appropriate to the conditions of use, i.e. with respect to a.c. or to d.c. conditions and, if a.c., the frequency. It may be necessary to have tests done under simulated use conditions rather than rely on predictions from one-minute d.c. tests.

Figure 2.7.2
Resistivity, d.c., (measured one minute after application of test voltage) as a function of temperature specified as minimum performance in IEC 672 (draft) for a range of ceramic materials in common usage. Arrows correspond to temperatures in the IEC specification.

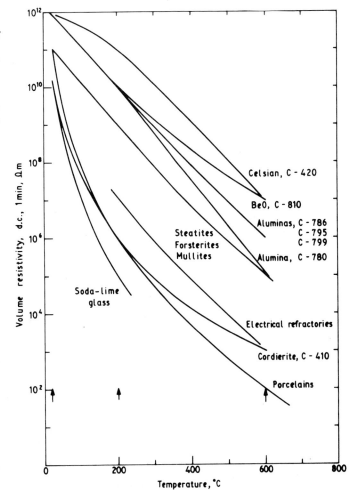

169

2.7.1.4 Dielectric breakdown

The precise nature of dielectric breakdown in insulators is not well understood, and views differ as to whether resistance to breakdown is or is not an intrinsic physical property of the material or an extrinsic property depending on test-piece preparation and test method. However, it now seems to be generally agreed that short-term testing to initiate failure in say one minute of application has uses as a quality-control tool but may not model behaviour over long periods of time at lesser voltage gradients.

Three types of breakdown are recognized:

1. 'Intrinsic breakdown' is conventionally measured in a laboratory test such as that described in BS 1598:1964, where a high voltage is placed across a thinned section of material. The geometry is such that breakdown occurs across the thin section rather than around the surface.
2. Breakdown from external discharges can cause general erosion at surfaces which may develop into deep pitting and the production of a discharge path through the material.
3. Thermal breakdown can be caused by conduction or dielectric loss in a material so that its temperature is raised. In most ceramics this leads to a decrease in resistivity and thus the temperature can continue to rise until equilibrium is reached with the surroundings. Under these conditions, material degradation may lead to breakdown.

In most ceramic materials, intrinsic breakdown is usual because the high refractoriness limits degradation sufficiently to prevent the other types of failure. Many extrinsic factors also influence breakdown, particularly those associated with component design, environment and liability to obtain surface discharge, etc.

In complex microstructures, it is thought that voids and grain edges can act as field concentrators, and thereby influence the voltage differential required to effect breakdown. Thus the breakdown voltage gradient must be expected to vary, even when other physical properties are reproducible since failure is likely to result along the path presenting the least resistance to breakdown, determined by the distribution of voids and grain edges or corners.

Because the voltage required to cause breakdown through a plate of ceramic material is not in direct proportion to the thickness of the plate, test data are usually obtained on a standardized thickness of material, preconditioned appropriately to remove moisture, tested in oil, and subjected to defined rates of application of voltage. Tests are conducted and results are quoted in various forms:

BS 1598:1964 is an a.c. pass/fail test at a specified r.m.s. voltage with rapid application of full voltage, the specimen being a disc with a thin central section 2–3 mm thick sandwiched between a flat and a spherical electrode. All six specimens tested are required to pass.

ASTM D116 employs specimens 6.35 mm thick with flat electrodes under oil using an a.c. voltage progressively increasing at 1 kVs^{-1} until failure. The result is expressed either as the breakdown voltage or as the dielectric strength (voltage gradient through the sample thickness).

DIN 40685 employs a similar specimen to the BS test with central depression of final wall thickness 1.5 ± 0.15 mm. This is tested under oil between a flat and a ball electrode, increasing the applied a.c. 50 Hz voltage to specified

Table 2.7.4 **Dielectric breakdown** (See text for definition of test practices.)

IEC class	Material type	IEC minimum withstand		DIN with-stand	BS[1] with-stand	ASTM[2] minimum
		kVmm^{-1}	kV	kV	kV	kVmm^{-1}
Ceramics:						
C–110	Porcelains, wet	20	30	30	25	—
C–111	Porcelains, pressed	—	—	—	5	—
C–112	Porcelains, cristobalite	20	30	—	—	—
C–120	Porcelains, aluminous	20	30	30	25	—
C–210	Steatite, low-voltage	—	—	—	—	7.13
C–220	Steatite, normal	15	20	20	20, 25	7.45
C–221	Steatite, low-loss	20	30	34	20, 25	7.45
C–230	Steatite, porous	—	—	—	—	—
C–240	Forsterite, porous	—	—	—	—	—
C–250	Forsterite, dense	20	30	30	—	—
C–310	Titania	8	15	15	—	—
C–410	Cordierite, dense	10	15	15	5, 25	—
C–420	Celsian, dense	20	30	—	—	—
C–500	Electrical refractories	—	—	—	—	—
C–610	Mullite	17	25	26	5, 25	—
C–620	Mullite	15	20	26	—	—
C–780	Alumina, 80–86%	10	15	18	} 25, 25	{ 9.85
C–790	Alumina, 86–95%	15	18	18		9.85
C–795	Alumina, 95–99%	15	18	18		9.85
C–799	Alumina, >99%	17	20	20		9.85
C–810	Beryllia	13	20	—	—	11.9
C–820	Magnesia, porous	—	—	—	—	—
C–830	Zirconia, stabilized	—	—	—	—	—
Glasses:						
G–110	Alkali-lime-silica annealed	25	25	—	—	—
G–111	Alkali-lime-silica toughened	25	25	—	—	—
G–200	Borosilicate	30	30	—	—	—
—	Silica	—	—	—	—	—

[1] Neither BS 1540 nor BS 1598 is specific about material types that fall into each of their classes based on qualifying levels of properties. However, based on the quoted physical properties it is possible to judge what would be required of some types of material to qualify for each class, and the data in the Table reflect this judgement. Where two figures are given, the first is for pressed products and the second for plastic products of presumably lower porosity levels.

[2] Specifications for alumina ceramics are from ASTM D2442 for a thickness of 3.175 mm. For beryllia they are from ASTM F356 for the same thickness. For steatite there are four categories in ASTM D2757, with a test thickness of 6.4 mm.

levels within 10–20 s. No failures are to occur in 5 specimens. For porous materials, the test is done in air after drying the specimen at 100°C.

IEC 672 offers two methods, one broadly equivalent to DIN 40685 but with a conductive layer on the hemispherical recess surface. The other employs a flat plate 2.5 ± 0.5 mm thick between spherical electrodes. The test at 50 Hz is carried out under oil, increasing the voltage at a rate sufficient to cause puncture in 10–20 s. The mean of five tests is expressed as the breakdown voltage gradient. Alternatively, for a pass/fail test, the voltage may be raised rapidly to the required value and maintained for one minute, and the result quoted as a minimum withstand voltage.

It is therefore clear that in interpreting results for dielectric breakdown tests, the test method must be taken into account. As shown particularly in

Group A data sheets for alumina ceramics in Part 2, the dielectric strength (volts per mm thickness) decreases markedly with increasing thickness. Furthermore, there is evidence that d.c. breakdown levels are rather higher than the peak a.c. levels for the same material. The reasons for this are unclear, but the higher d.c. resistance of insulators may give lower internal currents prior to breakdown.

Table 2.7.4 shows the minimum specifications on dielectric breakdown stated in various Standards. Note should be made of test conditions.

2.7.1.5 Insulating materials

Table 2.7.5 gives a guide to the types of insulating ceramic materials commonly employed for various applications or devices. The choice is often based not simply on electrical properties but also on other physical properties relevant to the application, on cost related to performance, and on the ability to achieve sizes or shapes of component. For example, large high-tension insulators would be very expensive and often physically impossible to make in any material other than plastic-processed porcelain, and heavy-duty fuse

Table 2.7.5 Insulating applications and materials typically used

Application	IEC class	Material type	Notes
Structural power insulators	C–110 C–112 C–120	Siliceous, cristobalite and aluminous porcelains.	Usually plastic processed, impermeable, glazed.
Low tension insulators	C–110 C–111 C–210	Siliceous porcelains Steatites	Plastic or pressed, not necessarily impermeable, usually glazed.
Cable cleats	C–120	Aluminous porcelains	High strength needed.
Vacuum leadthroughs	C–795 —	Alumina ceramics Glass-ceramics	Commonly metallized. Directly bonded from melt or preforms.
Coil formers: low-power	C–110 C–120 C–220	Siliceous porcelains Aluminous porcelains Steatite	Often glazed.
high-frequency precision	C–221 C–780 C–786 C–795	Low-loss steatite High-alumina ceramics High-alumina ceramics High-alumina ceramics	
high-temperature	C–500	Electrical refractories	For wire heating elements.
Fuse bodies	C–410 C–780 C–786 C–795	Vitreous cordierite High-alumina ceramics High-alumina ceramics High-alumina ceramics	For high power. For small low power.
Microwave windows	C–799 C–810 —	High-alumina ceramics Beryllia. Glass-ceramics	See BS 4789:1972. For tailored properties.
High power vacuum devices	C–795 C–799	High-alumina ceramics High-alumina ceramics	For controlled metallizing.
Electronic packaging	C–786 C–795 C–799	High-alumina ceramics High-alumina ceramics High-alumina ceramics	
Heat sinks for electronics	C–810	Beryllia	For high thermal conductivity.

bodies require not only electrical insulation, but also thermal shock resistance and improved mechanical properties to survive when the fuse blows. In dealing with a material specification for an insulator, these other factors should be borne in mind.

2.7.2 Electrically conducting ceramics

Most of the ceramics that have significant electrical conductivity from room temperature upwards are outside the scope of this Handbook because they are specialized materials used for electrical purposes only. However, some are of more general use, and are discussed briefly in this Section.

Electrical conduction through ceramic materials can result from a number of different mechanisms, depending on the type of material. It can occur by the conduction of electrons, as in semiconducting ceramics, or by the passage of ions. The ability to conduct electrons is usually described in terms of an electronic energy band structure. For metals, there is always some electron occupancy in the conduction band, and electronic conduction is always present. For semiconducting materials, the occupancy of the conduction band is temperature and composition dependent. For insulators, the conduction band is unoccupied, and it requires high energy levels to cause conduction, e.g. by dielectric breakdown. Most oxide ceramics covered by this Handbook are electronic insulators at ambient temperature, but are ionic conductors at elevated temperatures. Some conduct ions very readily, and this property is put to use in applications as sensors and batteries. Many ceramics are, or can be induced to be, electronic semiconductors.

2.7.2.1 Electronic semiconductors

In a semiconductor, some electrons are loosely bonded to sites in the crystal lattice, usually some form of defect, such as a vacancy or an impurity. Under the effect of a driving voltage these electrons are mobile and drift from site to site. The conductivity produced is determined by the concentration of the sites and their electron energy levels. Examples include silicon carbide, molybdenum disilicide and lanthanum chromite, all used for electrical heating elements. In this application, silicon carbides tend not to be deliberately doped with impurity species to control conductivity, and this lends some variability in resistivity (typically of the order 10^{-4} Ω m), encountered at temperatures below 500°C. Lanthanum chromite is usually doped with calcium to produce an n-type semiconductor with a similar resistivity to that of silicon carbide.

Titanium diboride is a semiconductor with resistivity typically of the order 10^{-7} Ω m. Because of its resistance to attack by aluminium, it is used for resistively heated boats for aluminium evaporation, in which case the resistivity is normally increased by controlled additions of boron nitride and/or aluminium nitride, both good insulators which also assist in the hot-pressing process used for fabrication.

Thread-guides based on titania may be made conducting to allow discharge of static electricity generated more especially by synthetic yarns. This is done by firing in reducing conditions so that some Ti^{4+} ions are reduced to Ti^{3+}, creating n-type semiconduction. Tin oxide is another n-type semiconductor used as an electrode material in glass tanks.

These are the major materials relevant to the coverage of the Handbook, but specialist materials with specific semiconducting properties may be designed for specific applications, such as jet engine igniters. Many of these materials contain transition metal oxides which can exist in more than one valence state. Control of composition and firing conditions can yield a broad range of electrical properties.

2.7.2.2 Ionic conductors

As noted earlier, in the absence of electronic conduction, ionic conduction becomes the principal mode of charge transfer. Ionic mobility in insulators depends upon the ion type, and upon temperature. The higher the temperature, the more mobile the ions become, in parallel with the increasing rate of thermal diffusion of atomic species. In oxide ceramics, the principal conducting species are alkali metal ions, which are usually present as impurities in all raw materials, or may be deliberately added, as with feldspars in porcelains. The purer the system, the more resistive the material. However, oxygen conduction becomes significant at high temperatures, and so all oxides conduct to some extent at temperatures above 1000°C.

Of special interest is stabilized zirconia, which shows oxygen conduction at temperatures above about 500°C due to the highly disordered cubic structure caused by the stabilizing additions. This material is used as an oxygen pressure sensor. The conductivity depends on the rate at which oxygen can be supplied to the negative electrode and passed into the material to maintain electrical charge neutrality. The sensing surface therefore has a porous electrode, usually of platinum, to allow the passage of oxygen to the ceramic. The ionic current is then related to the partial pressure of oxygen, and to the temperature of the ceramic. Much development work is concerned with investigation of materials and performance, especially long-term operation at elevated temperatures where destabilization of zirconia may occur. Yttria-stabilized material seems to be the most resistant to degradation of performance.

Stabilized zirconia has also been used as an electrical heater. However, there are some drawbacks due to the need to maintain all parts of the ceramic, including end connections, at a temperature in the range 1000–1200°C, to keep the resistivity sufficiently low, typically 10^{-1}–10 Ω m, for useful heat to be generated. The heater geometry and thermal design require particular care. Nevertheless, at present zirconia offers the only practical method of electrical resistance heating for temperatures in excess of 1800°C in air.

Fast ion conduction is of special interest in the development of solid electrolyte materials for new types of battery. Many of the materials reported in the scientific literature are of academic interest only as either performance is not adequate for economic storage of power, or there are severe engineering problems in the manufacture or life of cells employing them. The material that has created most interest is beta-alumina, considered suitable for the high energy density sodium/sulphur battery. This material has a nominal composition $Na_2O.11Al_2O_3$, and is an ionic conductor of sodium with useful properties for cell operation in the temperature range 350–400°C. It is presently being developed in several countries to optimize conductivity and cell lifetime.

Most glasses are ionic conductors, more especially those containing alkali metal species which are relatively mobile compared to network-forming species. This makes it possible to melt some types of glass by the use of immersed electrodes, using the glass as the resistive medium. Tin oxide is usually used as the semiconducting electrode material, having limited solubility in silicate glasses.

2.7.3 Piezoelectric materials

Some types of assymmetric crystals generate potential differences between opposing faces when compressed in various crystalline directions, and conversely, when subjected to a voltage gradient undergo mechanical distortion. Alpha-quartz is one such material, commonly used for the primary elements in clocks and watches. Other materials are outside the scope of this Handbook.

2.7.4 Magnetic ceramics

None of the materials covered by this Handbook have useful magnetic properties.

2.8

Optical properties

For the majority of applications of technical ceramics, optical properties are of no consequence. Most ceramics are opaque in bulk, although some are translucent to varying degrees. Very few are sufficiently transparent for optical uses. In this last category are single-crystal oxides such as sapphire and alpha-quartz, polycrystalline materials such as transparent glass-ceramics, translucent alumina and some hot-pressed oxides, and of course technical glasses. Since it is not the intention of this Handbook to deal in depth with optical characteristics of technical glasses, this Section is brief, and is limited to discussion relevant to materials covered by this Handbook.

2.8.1 Optical transmission

Transmission of light by solid media depends upon there being little absorption or scattering of the incoming beam. Low levels of absorption are obtained in frequency ranges well away from those where atomic bonds interact with the radiation, and thus absorption behaviour is essentially determined by chemistry. Most oxides, including silicates, are transparent in the visible range, but show varying cut-off frequencies in transmission in the infrared and ultraviolet regions. Good transmission in the middle infrared ($>6\ \mu$m wavelength) is obtained only with some halides, sulphides, selenides and elemental materials such as silicon and germanium. Materials containing OH^- ions, such as fused quartz, many glasses and some minerals, show marked absorption in the near and middle infrared. Most carbides, borides and nitrides, especially those of a semiconducting nature, have very poor transparency. Transparent films of silicon nitride have been made, but bulk materials are opaque.

In addition to absorption and scattering by the crystal lattice, the microstructure of polycrystalline materials plays an important role. Discontinuities such as grain boundaries, second phases, porosity and crystal defects (especially those associated with impurities) can all scatter incoming radiation to an extent determined by their size and distribution relative to the wavelength of the radiation. Features small compared to the radiation wavelength do not scatter strongly, whereas those of similar size do. For example, in a polycrystalline alumina ceramic containing no second phase, transmission in the visible range is controlled by grain size and by porosity. Coarse-grained varieties ($>15\ \mu$m mean grain size) with no porosity show high levels of transmission. Such products are used for sodium vapour lamp envelopes. In fine-grained varieties ($<5\ \mu$m mean grain size) with no porosity, translucency only is obtained in thin sections, as there are enough small grains to scatter the radiation. In both fine- and coarse-grained materials with more than perhaps 0.2% porosity, translucency is lost because scattering is enhanced by the numerous small pores.

When a second phase is present, such as a glassy phase, refractive index mismatches at interfaces cause scattering and loss of transmission. The greater the mismatch, the greater the opacity of the material. In glasses, glazes and enamels, deliberately-added opacifiers, such as TiO_2, are often added to reduce transmission through thin sections. Most oxide ceramics are multiphase and are therefore opaque.

Most oxide glasses are transparent in the visible range because grain boundaries and porosity are absent. Transmission at a given frequency depends on lattice absorption effects; impurities can cause coloration and transmission cut-offs in the infrared (e.g. OH^-) and in the ultraviolet.

The transmitted intensity is usually related to the spectral absorption coefficient, k, where the incident intensity I_o is attenuated to I by a material thickness x, according to the relationship:

$$I = I_o \exp \{-kx\} \qquad\qquad 2.8.1$$

Measurements are normally made in a spectrophotometer. The same instrument can be used to measure other related optical characteristics at any incident angle, including diffuse transmission and reflection caused by scattering from the surface and the bulk. Figure 2.8.1 shows the spectral absorption coefficients for various forms of fused silica. Table 2.8.1 summarizes some optical properties of materials covered by this Handbook which are used for optical purposes.

Figure 2.8.1
Absorption spectra from various types of silica products (data from Thermal Syndicate PLC).

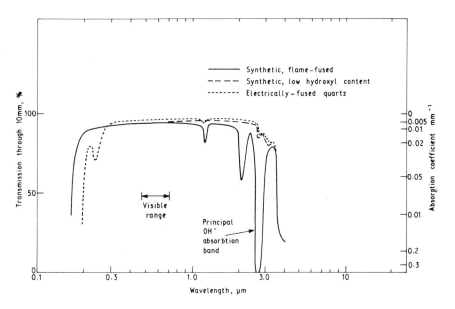

2.8.2 Refractive index

When light crosses a boundary between different media its velocity changes. The refractive index, μ is the ratio of the velocity in vacuo to that in the medium:

Table 2.8.1 Optical properties of some ceramics and glasses

Material/orientation	Refractive index, 25°C at			Absorption coefficient, mm^{-1}, at			Useful range of optical transmission (>10% for 2 mm transmission)	
	0.4 μm	0.65 μm	3.0 μm	0.4 μm	0.65 μm	3.0 μm	min, μm	max, μm
Sapphire ordinary	1.787	1.765	1.710	$\ll10^{-3}$	$\ll10^{-3}$	$<10^{-3}$	0.15	7.5
ordinary at 1200°C	—	—	—	0.004	0.001	0.001	0.1	5.0
Alpha-quartz ordinary	1.557	1.542	1.484	$\sim10^{-3}$	$\sim10^{-3}$	$\sim10^{-2}$	0.18	4.0
extraordinary	1.567	1.550	—					
'Zerodur' glass-ceramic (Schott)		1.542 (mean)		0.07	0.02	0.8	0.37	3.0*
Soda-lime Float glass		1.517 (mean)		0.016	0.024	0.03	0.35	3.0*
Borosilicate glass ('Pyrex')		1.474 (mean)		$\sim10^{-3}$	$\sim10^{-3}$	$\sim10^{-3}$	0.30	3.5*
Fused quartz (typical)	1.470	1.457	1.418	$\sim10^{-3}$	$\sim10^{-3}$	0.02	0.18	4.0*
Calcium fluoride (single-crystal)	1.441	1.431	1.414	$\sim10^{-3}$	$\sim10^{-3}$	$\sim10^{-3}$	0.13	12.0

*Flame-fused materials have a strong absorption band at 2.7 μm wavelength due to the presence of OH$^-$ in the materials. Electrically fused quartz and synthetically produced material using water-free methods have much reduced absorption.

$$\mu = \frac{v_{vacuo}}{v_{medium}} = \frac{\sin i}{\sin r} \qquad\qquad 2.8.2$$

where i and r are the incident and refracted angles of the beam to the surface normal. μ is a function of frequency and temperature. The reflective properties of the surface are also determined by the refractive index.

The majority of oxides in common use have values of μ between 1.3 and 2.0 in the visible spectrum, tending to fall in the infrared and to rise in the ultraviolet parts of the spectrum. Those containing high atomic number species, such as Ti, Zr, Th, etc., have rather higher values of refractive index, which is why some of them are used as opacifying agents in enamels and glasses.

2.8.3 Colour

Colour in oxide ceramics and glasses is produced by impurity atoms in the lattice. Particular frequencies are absorbed by the electronic structure associated with the impurity site, and this gives reduced transmission in parts of the spectrum, most obvious in the visible region. Transition metals, particularly V, Cr, Mn, Fe, Co, Ni, and Cu and combinations of these, are most effective in producing colour by the interaction between these species and the surrounding matrix, particularly in glasses. The colour may also be dependent on the atmosphere used in firing or melting because the valency state of many of those listed above may be altered, and this changes the electronic configuration and hence the absorption spectrum.

Opaque carbide, nitride or boride ceramics are generally grey or black in colour. Some types of silicon carbide are greenish, depending on the impurities they contain, while boron nitride in hot-pressed form is white to pale grey.

Although the colour of oxide-based technical and engineering ceramics can be changed deliberately by the addition of secondary oxides of various types, this is usually done for commercial reasons. Deliberate coloration gives some identity to a product, e.g. pink-coloured aluminas, and may disguise small colour variations within a component due to iron spots or sensitivity to firing atmosphere (note that brown or black aluminas contain ingredients necessary for the fabrication process; see the appropriate Data Sheets in Part 2). In some instances, dark-coloured oxide ceramics are advantageous in the end use, e.g. substrates for photo-electronic devices, and thread guides where thread visibility is required. Mostly, however, colour is a cosmetic factor of little importance.

Properties are altered insignificantly by the small amount of added colouring oxide, the addition usually being incorporated within the primary crystalline phase.

Iron is a very common impurity in all raw materials, and produces coloration from slight creaminess through to orange in otherwise white products. 'Whiteness' is often preferred because products tend to sell better, but this requires more expensive processing, purer raw materials, and perhaps even reduction firing, to keep iron in the ferrous state in which it tends to cause a dead white rather than a yellow colour. In amounts of more than about 0.5%, iron can cause a reduction in refractoriness, which is why high purity is required for the most refractory of products.

2.8.4 Emissivity

2.8.4.1 Definitions

At high temperatures, the emissivity of a material has significant consequences for its rate of heating and cooling under radiation conditions, and therefore on its thermomechanical performance. The same is true, of course, at lower temperatures, but is less significant compared to heat transfer by fluid contact. The subject is mathematically complex, and only a brief summary is given here. For full definitions and development of radiation theory, the reader is referred to texts cited in the Bibliography.

The emission of radiation from a surface depends on many factors:
temperature
bulk composition
surface composition (impurities, coatings, oxide layers, etc.)
optical transparency
surface profile
optical wavelength
observation angle.

In the following derivations, the subscript 'b' is used to denote a black body, or perfect emitter, the subscript 'total' to denote over all wavelengths, the superscript $'$ to denote directional properties, and no superscript to denote hemispherical integrated properties.

A perfect emitter or black body emits radiation according to its surface temperature through the Planck radiation equation:

$$E_b(\lambda) = c_1 \lambda^{-5} \{\exp (c_2/\lambda T) - 1\}^{-1} \qquad\qquad 2.8.3$$

where $E_b(\lambda)$ is the hemispherical radiant power from unit area at temperature T for unit wavelength interval centred on wavelength λ, and where c_1 and c_2 are constants, 3.742×10^{-16} Wm^2 and 1.439×10^{-2} m.K respectively. The radiant power into unit solid angle from unit area at angle θ from the surface normal follows the Lambert cosine law:

$$E_b'(\theta,\lambda) = E_b'(0,\lambda) \cos \theta \qquad\qquad 2.8.4$$

where the prime refers to directional emission, and $E_b'(0,\lambda)$ refers to emission normal to the surface. Integration of $E_b'(\theta,\lambda)$ over the hemisphere gives the relationship:

$$E_b(\lambda) = E_b'(0,\lambda) \qquad\qquad 2.8.5$$

The total radiant power into a hemisphere is found by integrating Equation 2.8.3 over all wavelengths:

$$E_{b,total} = \int_0^\infty c_1\lambda^{-5}\{\exp\ (c_2/\lambda T) -1\}^{-1}d\lambda$$

$$= c_3T^4 \qquad\qquad 2.8.6$$

where c_3 is Stefan's constant, 5.670×10^{-8} Wm^{-2}K^{-4}.

These relationships apply to a perfect emitter. For real surfaces, they have to be modified according to emitting power, and this is conventionally done by inserting the emissivity factor into the equations. Taking the most fundamental relationship, the emission in unit wavelength range at wavelength λ into unit solid angle at angle θ from the surface normal and angle ϕ of rotation about the normal is given by:

$$E'(\theta,\phi,\lambda,T) = \epsilon'(\theta,\phi,\lambda,T)\ E_b'(\theta,\lambda,T) \qquad\qquad 2.8.7$$

where $\epsilon'(\theta,\phi,\lambda,T)$ is known as the *directional spectral emissivity* at temperature T. Angle ϕ may have to be taken into account for a real surface because there may be directional topography, whereas emission from a black body is by definition independent of ϕ. Because of the angular dependence of ϵ', real surfaces do not necessarily obey the Lambert cosine law, Equation 2.8.4, and each case has to be treated on its own merits.

To reduce the complexity in calculating the total power radiated, the emissivity has to be averaged, either over all wavelengths or over all angles. Averaging over wavelengths using Equations 2.8.5 and 2.8.6 gives the *total directional emissivity:*

$$\epsilon'_{total}(\theta,\phi,T) = \frac{E'_{total}(\theta,\phi,T)}{E'_{b,total}(\theta,T)} \qquad\qquad 2.8.8$$

where $E'_{b,total} = c_3T^4\cos\theta/\pi$ for the black body.

Averaging over angles gives the *spectral hemispherical emissivity:*

$$\epsilon(\lambda,T) = \frac{E_\lambda(\lambda,T)}{E_b(\lambda,T)} \qquad\qquad 2.8.9$$

Averaging over both wavelengths and angles gives the *total hemispherical emissivity:*

$$\epsilon_{total}(T) = \frac{E_{total}(T)}{E_{b,total}(T)} = \frac{E_{total}(T)}{c_3T^4} \qquad\qquad 2.8.10$$

where E_{total} can be expressed as an integral over the hemisphere including either $\epsilon'(\theta,\phi,\lambda,T)$ or $\epsilon'_{total}(\theta,\phi,T)$ or $\epsilon(\lambda,T)$.

It is clear from this that caution should be exercised in the interpretation of the term 'emissivity' and in the use of data from various sources.

Emissivity should be defined completely, but often is not. Measurement systems which compare the emission from a test-piece to that from a black body vary widely in their design and response spectrum, and consequently results are reported in various forms. One of the most commonly quoted figures is the total normal emissivity, i.e. in a direction perpendicular to the surface ($\theta = 0$). This may be different from the total hemispherical emissivity because of the angular dependence of emissivity in non-black bodies.

2.8.4.2 Effect of surface finish

A black body surface emits according to the Lambert cosine law. In practice, this condition is met fairly closely by matt black surfaces where surface roughness is greater than the wavelength being considered, such as porous fine-textured carbon. For the surfaces of bulk ceramic materials there are usually varying degrees of roughness, perhaps with some directionality from the surface grinding process which causes the spectral directional emissivity to have the (θ, ϕ) dependence, and which results in departure from the cosine law. Each case will be different. Emissivities also vary with wavelength, and the wavelength dependence may also be surface dependent.

At high temperatures surface profiles may change as a result of recrystallization, thermal etching, volatilization or oxidation, with changes in resulting emissivity. The same applies to coatings applied to components to change emissivity characteristics. Contamination of surfaces, more particularly by carbon, metals and transition metal oxides, may alter emissivity in service.

2.8.4.3 Effect of optical transparency

Most oxide ceramics are transparent to a degree in the infrared and visible wavelength ranges. Emission therefore is not purely a surface effect. Account has to be taken of the thickness of the material involved compared to the thickness required for effective optical opacity at all wavelengths. If this condition is not met, then the nature of the rear surface of the material and of materials behind it will affect the measured emission and, conversely, care must be taken in the use of emissivity data on thick materials in applications involving thin sections. Absorption of incoming radiation will similarly be affected.

2.8.4.4 Data

Because of the factors described above, emissivity data are subject to considerable variation from source to source depending on measurement conditions. Data from any one source pertain to the geometry and wavelength range of measurement, and to the type and surface finish of the test-piece used. The Data Sheets in Part 2 contain relevant data on particular products, together with references to sources. Here, only broad bands are given to demonstrate good and bad emitters at 1000°C. Most materials show some temperature dependence of emissivity. Above 1000°C, emissivity tends to fall in many products, both oxides and non-oxides, but not usually by more than about 20% up to 1800°C. Below 1000°C, behaviour varies, emissivity either rising or falling with increasing temperature.

Table 2.8.2 Typical total normal emissivity figures

Range of total normal emissivity at 1000°C, $\epsilon'(\theta = 0)$	Materials with emissivity in range
>0.9	Carbons, graphites Silicon nitride (reaction-bonded)
0.7–0.9	Silicon carbide (most types) Silicon nitride (hot-pressed, dense sintered) Hot-pressed TiC, WC 'Pyroceram 9608'
0.3–0.7	Most alumina ceramics BeO Mullite Most glass-ceramics Hot-pressed TiB_2, ZrB_2, $MoSi_2$ Pyrolytic graphite Fused quartz
0.1–0.3	Pure alumina ceramics MgO ZrO_2 ThO_2
<0.1	none

Note: This Table indicates typical results on polished specimens. Composition, porosity distribution and specimen thickness can all influence the result on a particular product. Most emissivity data show a temperature dependence, either increasing or, more typically, decreasing with increasing temperature. Some materials show a maximum at around 1000°C.

2.9

Chemical properties

Note: The text and tables in this Section contain specific numbered references to sources of information. These references are given in the Bibliography that follows the Section.

2.9.1 Introduction

One of the outstanding advantages which ceramics have over metals and alloys is their high degree of chemical inertness. This property is especially valuable at high temperatures and means that ceramics can be considered for use in severely corrosive environments in which the performance of metals is no longer satisfactory.

The successful use of ceramics to solve materials problems involving severe conditions covers a wide range of applications and industries. In the chemical industry, vitreous silica and aluminosilicate materials are widely used for plant requiring acid resistance, and aluminas are used where hardness is also required, e.g. for components used in acid pumps. Large quantities of ceramic crucibles and tubes are used for handling molten metals, and must be inert not only towards the metal, but also to the operating atmosphere and to the refractories they touch in use. High-pressure sodium lamps require a translucent material resistant to sodium vapour at high temperatures, and this requirement was satisfied by the development of a high-purity grade of alumina, free from reducible constituents. In the development of high-performance non-oxide ceramics with potential for applications in high-temperature engines, the candidate materials need to resist degradation due to oxidation and corrosion by fuel combustion products, e.g. sulphur, sodium and vanadium compounds, in addition to having reliable thermal and mechanical properties.

In spite of the advantages of ceramics in providing solutions to materials problems in corrosive environments, their potential as engineering materials is far from being realized. This is partly due to the shortage of reliable comparative information on the resistance of different classes of ceramics to chemical corrosion. Consequently, it is difficult to make a good choice of material without extensive tests. One reason for this is the fact that a chemical name such as 'alumina', or 'silicon nitride', or 'silicon carbide', may be applied to a number of products, formulated in a variety of ways, and consequently having a wide range of compositions. The resistance of a material to a corrosive environment does not depend solely on the major component, but is critically dependent on the nature, concentration and distribution of minor components, and these of course depend on the fabrication process and resulting microstructure.

The aims of this Section are to discuss some of the factors which influence the corrosion resistance of ceramics, and to give an impartial comparison of the characteristics of materials used for engineering applications. Claims for any one material can then be seen in perspective. The most common types of corrosive environment and the ceramics most likely to withstand them, are also considered. Finally, the information available is summarized in comparative tables. More detailed descriptions of the performance of materials are included in the relevant Data Sheets of Part 2 and in the references cited in the Bibliography.

The comments and descriptions given in this Section apply to the properties of strong fine-grained ceramics intended for load-bearing applications. Although some of the comments are relevant to an understanding of coarser, porous materials, the corrosion resistance of heavy refractories towards molten glasses, fluxes, metals and slags is not discussed here.

2.9.2 Factors determining corrosion resistance

2.9.2.1 Chemical inertness of major components

Clearly the chemistry of the major component will play a major part. Alumina is the most versatile of the oxides in resisting attack by acids, alkalis, molten metals, fused salts and oxidizing and reducing gases at high temperatures. Other ceramics have superior properties under specific conditions, and so may be preferred for demanding applications, e.g. spinel is considered to be more resistant to alkaline solutions and melts, and zirconia is considered more suitable for melting reactive metals.

2.9.2.2 Chemical inertness of minor components

Ceramics are not usually pure compounds, but contain minor phases which may be glassy or crystalline. These may be formed from impurities in the raw materials, or from deliberate additions which are essential for the fabrication process employed (see Section 2.2). *They are often much less resistant to attack than the major components, and so have a considerable influence on overall corrosion resistance, even when they are present at low concentrations.* The way in which they are distributed in the ceramic is a contributory factor. If during sintering they become concentrated at grain boundaries, corrosion can occur by intergranular attack; however, if they form solid solutions, or are situated within the crystals, their influence may be much less significant. As an example, high-alumina ceramics commonly contain a small proportion of MgO which inhibits grain growth during sintering and produces a uniform fine-grained structure. However, if basic oxides accumulate in sufficient quantities at grain boundaries during firing, the ceramic will be vulnerable to acid attack, even though the alumina grains are not affected. Intergranular attack can make the body weaker, softer, porous and more prone to wear. Some suppliers of alumina ceramics formulate compositions with minor phases which have high resistance to acids for applications requiring this property, primarily because the usual

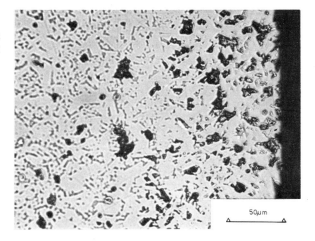

Figure 2.9.1
Intergranular leaching of the glassy phase in a 95% alumina ceramic after 3 days immersion in concentrated HCl at 20°C. This material is not designed for corrosion resistance.

50μm

types of product developed for electrical properties or strength are readily corroded (Figure 2.9.1). Another example is that of silicon carbides containing free silicon. The free silicon may be corroded by species which do not react with silicon carbide itself and the result is degradation of properties with the surface becoming porous.

2.9.2.3 Surface texture and porosity

The corrosion resistance of a ceramic is influenced by the surface area exposed to the corrosive agent. A body having a smooth surface will initially be more resistant than one having a rougher surface texture, and impervious bodies are obviously much more resistant than porous ones in which the corroding agent can penetrate the bulk and gain access to a much larger surface area for attack. Rather than simply corroding away from the external surface, open-porous bodies are weakened throughout. Some materials may be impermeable only by virtue of a dense as-fired skin protecting a porous interior. This situation sometimes occurs with chemical stoneware.

2.9.2.4 Formation of protective layers

The corrosion of a ceramic depends not only on the reactivity of its constituents towards the environment but also on kinetic factors, since the reaction products may form a barrier which can retard further attack. The oxidation of non-oxide ceramics at high temperatures provides an example of this effect. Silicon nitride is thermodynamically unstable in air and is oxidized to silica, but in practice this silica usually forms a protective film on the surface and inhibits further reaction. Similarly, a silica film enables silicon carbide furnace elements to be used above 1500°C in air. However, an inert gas containing only a small proportion of oxygen can cause more damage than air[1]; a continuous film of silica is not formed, and the reaction forms only volatile silicon monoxide, SiO. If this occurs, the bonding between the silicon carbide grains is slowly destroyed and the elements fail prematurely.

The presence of corrosive agents which react with a protective film can lead to accelerated reaction. For example, silicon nitrides and carbides are severely corroded by molten Na_2SO_4 in air, and the corrosion is believed to start by dissolution of the silica layer produced by the oxidizing atmosphere[2]. In the absence of oxygen, the materials are little affected. More generally, the conditions of use determine whether the reaction products are removed, causing continuous reaction, or remain to form a barrier and so limit the extent of attack. Reactions between metals and oxide ceramics at high temperatures under vacuum are generally much more extensive than in air since volatile species (e.g. lower oxides) are removed from the system, or alloy directly with the metal.

2.9.2.5 Temperature

One would expect the corrosion of ceramics to become more severe with increasing temperature, and usually this is the case, but there are some exceptions. Aqueous solutions generally become more reactive with increasing temperature, and the greater solubility of reaction products, together with increased agitation, lead to more effective exposure of fresh surfaces and so to increased attack. When the application involves exposure to a corrosive agent over a range of temperature in both liquid and vapour forms, the liquid form may cause more corrosion so that less attack will occur at higher temperatures. An example of this behaviour is found in the corrosion of cordierite heat exchangers by sulphuric acid[3].

Another example is the oxidation of porous silicon nitride, which is commonly much more extensive at temperatures around 1100°C than at temperatures above about 1200°C. At lower temperatures a continuous protective film of silica is not formed, and oxidation takes place internally. At higher temperatures where the film produced is continous, the initially more rapid reaction slows to a rate less than that at lower temperatures because flow of oxygen to the interior becomes greatly restricted.

2.9.3 Behaviour of various types of ceramic

2.9.3.1 Oxides

Alumina

Alumina is by far the most important oxide ceramic and is the most versatile in resisting corrosion. In the pure form, alumina has good resistance to attack by acids and fairly good resistance to alkalis. It is a very stable compound, resistant to oxidation and reduction, and so may be used in oxidizing and reducing atmospheres and for handling reactive molten metals. With impure materials, the inertness depends on the composition of the minor phase or phases, as well as on the method of manufacture and the grain structure achieved. Some of these materials have been studied at NPL with regard to acid attack, and the test results demonstrate that, even with only 0.5% of minor components, resistance to attack is determined by the precise composition of the minor grain boundary phase (Figure 2.9.2).

For applications involving exposure to acids, some suppliers make small additions of oxides such as MgO and SiO_2 so that the bonding glassy phase

Figure 2.9.2
Bars 8 mm × 5 mm of various
high-alumina ceramics
fractured after 3 days
immersion in boiling 6N HCl
followed by dye penetrant.
The darkened surface is an
indication of the varying extent
of penetration, determined by
minor-phase composition.

produced during firing has greater resistance to intergranular attack than the
general purpose materials formulated without this property in mind. On the
other hand, alumina used for precious metal thermocouple insulators and
tubes should be free from reducible oxides such as silica which could cause
embrittlement of the thermocouple wires under reducing conditions.

These examples illustrate the need to consult the suppliers of high-alumina
ceramics to ensure that the product under consideration has the properties
needed for the duty the component is intended to perform.

Silica

Pure silica is used extensively in the molten metal handling industries
primarily for its excellent resistance to thermal shock. The vitreous form is
used, either the dense or the porous sintered type, rather than the crystalline
types, because phase transformations in the latter cause problems in thermal
cycling conditions.

Silica has good resistance to acids with the exception of hydrofluoric, and
is widely used in the chemical industry. It is attacked under strongly alkaline
conditions, and this property is utilized in the casting of metals and alloys
to form complex shapes. The most important application of this technique
is for the production of air-cooled gas turbine blades for jet engines from
nickel alloys. The porous silica preforms have sufficient inertness to enable
the alloys to be cast around them at temperatures near 1500°C, but can
subsequently be removed by dissolution in alkaline solution.

Silica is not especially resistant to reducing conditions at high temperatures,
since it becomes sub-stoichiometric and under severe conditions may form
volatile SiO.

Aluminosilicate ceramics, porcelains

The properties of porcelains vary widely and depend on the compositions
and proportions of the constituent phases (see Section 2.2.1), but generally

they have quite good resistance to acids, either hot or cold. They are corroded under strongly alkaline conditions, but to a lesser extent than pure silica ceramics.

Chemically-resistant materials are available for applications involving exposure to acids at moderate temperatures. 'Chemical stoneware' is a coarse-textured material used for large vessels and tower packings. It may be impervious only by virtue of a non-porous as-fired skin. 'Chemical porcelain' has a much lower iron content and a finer texture, and is more like a conventional high-quality electrical porcelain when intended for use as heavy laboratory ware and process plant components. When greater thermal shock resistance is required for laboratory ware, the microstructure may be highly glassy and essentially quartz-free. See Part 2 for further details.

For high-temperature applications, some 'aluminous porcelains' may be used up to 1500°C, and bodies formulated to give a large proportion of mullite crystals in a siliceous glassy matrix but with a low level of alkali components, i.e. 'impervious mullites', can even be used to 1700°C. These high-temperature ceramics have good resistance to slags, glasses, fluxes and metal oxides, and are used for thermocouple protection tubes and furnace tubes. Their inertness towards hot gases enables them to be used in analysis, e.g. for combustion tubes. They also have good resistance to acids.

Glasses

The corrosion resistance of glasses depends very much on the composition. Even water can produce a degree of surface attack as a result of leaching of ions from the glass. The higher the alkali metal content, the greater is the susceptibility to surface attack and the formation of a surface deposit. However, this is a simplified approach, and the durability of a glass can be improved substantially by the incorporation of small amounts of modifying oxides such as CaO and Al_2O_3. In this way, soda-lime glass of suitable composition has sufficient resistance to corrosion to enable it to be used for containers for storage of concentrated acids at room temperature. The inner surface becomes depleted of sodium ions after a short time, and the rate of attack slows down. Glasses of even greater chemical resistance usually have a low alkali metal content, and are often based on borosilicates, like the 'Pyrex' type. Resistance to acid solutions is usually good, and such compositions are used for large-scale vessels and piping for chemical processing plant for temperatures up to 100°C. Resistance to alkaline solutions is less good, but is often adequate at up to 50°C. No glass is resistant to hydrofluoric acid. Glasses are generally not suitable for applications such as the containment of melts of various types, as they are prone to attack and in any event are not especially refractory. Better performance is obtained from high-silica or pure silica glasses (see above).

Zirconia

Zirconia is one of the most thermodynamically stable ceramic materials and is appreciably more refractory than alumina. Because pure zirconia undergoes phase transformations on cooling from the firing temperature, it is necessary to include a small proportion of CaO, MgO or Y_2O_3 to stabilize the cubic structure. Of these, CaO is most widely used, but the presence of a base does make the ceramic somewhat more vulnerable to acid attack. In reducing environments ZrO_2 becomes slightly substoichiometric, but the oxygen-deficient structure is stable, and stabilized zirconia may be used for melting most metals without causing contamination. It can be used for platinum metals and alloys and even for iridium (melting point 2450°C). It can also be used for vanadium, chromium, manganese and titanium (which is highly reactive). It is fairly stable towards slags and glasses of acidic and basic types because of limited solubility in melts, and is considered more suitable than alumina for melting glasses containing phosphates and borates.

Magnesia

Although magnesia is used on a large commercial scale in refractories for steel and cement manufacture, it is not widely used in a dense sintered form. It is basic in character, and is therefore readily attacked by acids, but has good resistance to alkalis. Magnesia is a valuable ceramic for handling molten metals, being resistant to the reactive alkali metals and sufficiently refractory for containing high-purity iron and iron alloys, platinum, uranium and thorium at temperatures up to 2300–2400°C. Care is needed in use under vacuum because the vapour pressure of the oxide becomes significant above about 1600°C.

Spinel

Spinel is similar to alumina in heat resistance, but is reported to be more resistant to basic melts and slags, even to highly aggressive ones such as lead oxide.

Beryllia

Beryllia is amphoteric like alumina but is in general more basic and less inert. It is attacked by strong acids and strong alkalis, but is reported to be resistant to molten basic slags. The high toxicity of beryllium compounds means that precautions must be taken in manufacture, and that use in corrosive environments may be hazardous. Beryllia can be used at very high temperatures, and has good chemical stability. These properties enable it to be used for melting and alloying metals, including reactive and refractory ones.

Thoria

Thoria has a melting point of about 3300°C, and is the most stable oxide known. It is difficult to manufacture, and therefore expensive, and is slightly radioactive; for these reasons it is little used. Nevertheless, since it is chemically stable and refractory, nearly all metals can be melted in it without any danger of contamination, even reactive ones such as lithium and sodium. Its chemical behaviour is similar to that of zirconia, i.e. it is fairly readily attacked by acids but has good resistance to alkaline melts.

Titania

Titania ceramics are used for applications which utilize their electrical properties, but have not found uses where resistance to corrosive attack is required. Titania is fairly resistant to acids but is attacked by alkalis. It is not especially stable towards reducing agents, and is therefore unsuitable for use in contact with molten metals.

Tin oxide

Tin oxide in ceramic form is reported to have very good resistance to corrosion by molten glass[4], and is used as an electrode in the melting of lead-containing glasses.

Chromium oxide

Chromium oxide has been prepared as a pure ceramic but is readily attacked by acids and alkalis and so is unsuitable for use in most corrosive environments. However, it has limited solubility in molten glass and slags, and is used as a refractory in contact with such melts.

2.9.3.2 Non-oxides

Silicon nitrides

Silicon nitride is manufactured by two principal methods: reaction-bonding (RBSN) and hot-pressing (HPSN). The former process leads to a porous, but essentially single-phase material, whereas the latter gives a fully dense material but with significant amounts of grain boundary phases formed from the hot-pressing additive. The latter form is more expensive to produce, but has better resistance to oxidation and chemical attack owing to its much lower surface area. Both types have good resistance to acids, but are prone to attack under strongly alkaline conditions. Silicon nitride is resistant to wetting by most metals and can be used under reducing conditions in the production and handling of many alloys, including those of aluminium, zinc, brasses and bronzes[5]. However, care must be exercised because in assessing silicon nitride for an application involving contact with a molten metal, it is necessary to consider the possibility of reaction not only with the metal, but also with any oxides or slags which may be present. An oxide may react to form a silicide, or under oxidizing conditions may dissolve the protective silica film on the ceramic and so lead to breakdown of the structure by oxidation. As an example, copper is reported to attack Si_3N_4, probably through the oxide.

Other classes of silicon nitride and sialon[6] ceramics are being developed using sintering technology to achieve impervious materials without the usual recourse to hot-pressing (see Section 2.2.3.2). Such materials contain sintering aids, and the corrosion resistance will in many instances be controlled by the composition of the second phase produced. These materials have some potential advantages over conventional silicon nitrides, principally easier fabrication than the hot-pressed types and better oxidation resistance than the reaction-bonded types. They have also given promising results in molten metal tests, showing good resistance to aluminium, copper and iron. As yet there is little information on their behaviour with acids and alkalis, but this can be expected to be controlled by the nature of the secondary phases.

Silicon carbides

Impervious silicon carbide ceramics may be produced by reaction-sintering, by hot-pressing and recently by pressureless-sintering with additives. The first process gives a product containing a small proportion of free silicon, which influences resistance to oxidation and chemical corrosion to a marked degree. The second process leads to the production of a small amount of an oxide-

Figure 2.9.3
Leaching of the silicon phase of a reaction-bonded silicon carbide by 7 days' immersion in 10% KOH solution at 80°C, showing
(a) the depth of penetration, and
(b) the attack front within the material.

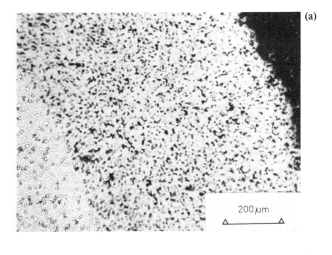
(a)

200 μm

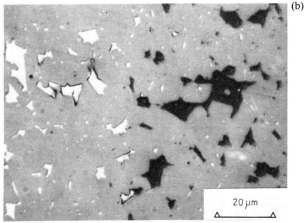
(b)

20 μm

based grain boundary phase, whereas the third method produces an essentially single-phase material. Overall, silicon carbides have very good resistance to acid solutions and melts but are prone to attack under severe alkaline conditions (Figure 2.9.3). In alkaline solutions the rate of attack may be low enough for the ceramic to be used successfully, e.g. for wear-resistant parts in alkali process plant and paper mills, but corrosion by molten alkalis in an air atmosphere is very severe. In contact with molten metals, and even with solid metals at high temperatures, the free silicon in the reaction-bonded varieties tends to form alloys or silicides and the ceramic becomes degraded. Reference to phase diagrams for binary metal/Si alloys is useful in assessing whether severe attack is likely to occur, e.g. as with platinum.

Boron nitride

Boron nitride ceramics are generally prepared by hot-pressing and usually contain a small proportion of boric oxide, an impurity which improves the pressing characteristics. They are reported to be attacked by strong acids, but to be stable towards alkalis, although this is surprising in view of the presence of the acidic boric oxide. The non-wetting character of boron nitride may account for this behaviour. A purer pyrolytic form made by chemical

191

vapour deposition may be more resistant to attack, but is available only as thin-walled articles. Boron nitride starts to oxidize at about 700°C, but can be used up to about 1000°C in oxidizing atmospheres. In inert or reducing atmospheres it is said by manufacturers to be usable to 2750°C. Some grades tend to be degraded by absorption of moisture from the atmosphere.

The most valuable characteristics of boron nitride are its resistance to wetting by metals, alloys, salts, slags and glasses, and its high level of chemical inertness. Its resistance to wetting and its lubricating properties stem from the crystal structure which resembles that of graphite. It has been used for melting a wide range of metals such as Al, Na, Cu, Fe, Au, Mn and Sn. It has also been used for melting non-metals, especially where high purity is required, as in the preparation of semiconductor materials, e.g. Si, Ge, Ga, In, As. It is inert to a number of corrosive molten salts, e.g. alkali halides, lithium borate, and cryolites, and has good resistance to molten glasses. However, it does react with molten alkali carbonates and hydroxides.

Boron Carbide

Hot-pressed boron carbide is resistant to mineral acids but is attacked by fused alkalis. It oxidizes in air above 1000°C. It is expensive, and so is little used as a corrosion-resistant component.

Titanium Diboride

Titanium diboride can be produced by hot-pressing or by sintering a cold-pressed component in vacuum or an inert atmosphere. It can be heated in air to about 1200°C without excessive oxidation. It is resistant to concentrated acids at room temperature, but is attacked by fused bases and some salts. It has good corrosion resistance towards molten metals, although it is attacked by some of the more reactive ones, such as cobalt, nickel and titanium. It does not react with graphite up to about 2200°C. A titanium diboride/boron nitride composite is widely used as a material for aluminium evaporator boats.

Carbons and Graphites

Many carbons and graphites are commercially available with a wide range of properties. The majority of them are open-porous as manufactured, and in order to seal them against liquid ingress they have to be impregnated with a resin or polymer of suitable type. Corrosion resistance is therefore determined by the nature of the material. Generally, carbons and graphites are resistant to attack by non-oxidizing acids and by alkalis. At higher temperatures, resistance to corrosion depends on the absence of oxygen, since oxidation occurs freely from about 400°C upwards. Many materials are not wetted by glasses, slags, and molten salts, and thus find extensive use as crucible materials, linings for reactors, etc. However, many metals form carbides in the presence of free carbon, so there are limitations in molten (or even solid) metal handling. In addition, many products contain small amounts of non-carbonaceous material, such as siliceous slag, and this may react with or contaminate melts.

Vitreous carbon

Vitreous carbon is produced by the controlled thermal degradation of certain phenol-aldehyde plastics in an inert atmosphere. It is more inert than graphite towards corrosive chemicals, due to its glassy structure and high purity. It has made its greatest impact in the semiconductor industry for processing compounds of elements such as gallium, arsenic and phosphorus without contamination. It has been successfully applied in chemical engineering where its resistance to alkalis is especially useful, and for a wide range of laboratory equipment. It has been used in the glass industry as a mould for lenses, and for a variety of glass-working tools and fixtures.

2.9.4 Attack by various types of corrosive environment

In this Section the most common types of corrosive environment are considered, and the most resistant classes of ceramic for each type are indicated.

2.9.4.1 Acids

Silica and borosilicate glasses have good resistance to acids at moderate temperatures and are widely used in chemical plant, but are attacked by hydrofluoric acid, even at room temperature. Aluminosilicate ceramics such as porcelains also have quite good resistance to acids, and since they are harder and stronger than glasses, they also have greater wear resistance. High-alumina ceramics can be specially formulated to have excellent resistance to acids, and these materials are suitable for applications requiring resistance to wear and corrosion, but care should be exercised in selection because many general purpose or electrical materials are not formulated for corrosion resistance and are weakened and become porous on exposure to acids. As described above, acid-resistant varieties are available, but since all alumina ceramics except those of highest purity contain SiO_2, all are attacked by hydrofluoric acid. NPL tests have demonstrated that the best acid resistance is obtained in materials of the very highest purity.

The impervious engineering grades of silicon carbide have excellent resistance to acids, even HF, and give good wear resistance. However, silicon-containing products are attacked by HF/HNO_3 mixtures which dissolve the silicon phase and leave a porous, weaker material.

Ceramics containing the more basic oxides either as major or minor constituents, e.g. magnesia, beryllia, and lime-stabilized zirconia, are more vulnerable to acid attack.

2.9.4.2 Alkali solutions and fused alkalis

Silica and siliceous glasses are prone to attack by caustic alkali solutions and are severely attacked by fused alkalis. Aluminosilicate ceramics are also attacked under these conditions but to a lesser extent, the higher-alumina compositions being more resistant. High-alumina ceramics are affected to only a slight extent by caustic alkali solutions, but significant attack occurs in fused alkalis, potassium hydroxide being more corrosive than sodium hydroxide. The impervious grades of silicon carbide have been successfully used in alkali solutions since the level of attack is slight, particularly in those with no free silicon phase, but reaction is appreciable in hot solutions and is severe in fused alkalis. Silicon nitrides are also severely attacked by fused alkalis under oxidizing conditions.

2.9.4.3 Fused salts, oxides, slags and glasses

The extent of reaction between a melt and a ceramic depends on many factors, which include viscosity, acidity or basicity, the nature and solubility of reaction products and the chemistry of the major and minor components of the ceramic. Very little systematic information is available on this topic, and it is difficult to generalize or make predictions about the likelihood of attack. For example, Figure 2.9.4 shows an example of the phenomenon of melt-line attack, where the interface between melt, container and atmosphere suffers more severe attack than at the interface between melt and container only. This may be caused by a number of factors, including surface tension and density gradients which lead to more rapid removal of reaction products at the melt-line. Prediction of behaviour under such conditions is difficult.

Figure 2.9.4
Melt-line attack of a 99.7% alumina crucible (seen here in cross-section) by a borax melt at 1000°C for 24h.

10mm

High-alumina ceramics are probably the most resistant to attack overall, but even they are heavily attacked by melts of Na_2O, $Na_2S_2O_7$, Na_2O_2 and KOH. Other ceramics may be preferable for particular melts, e.g. spinel is reported to be more resistant to basic slags while zirconia is preferred for melting glasses containing phosphates and borates.

Fused sodium carbonate attacks most ceramics to some extent, but aluminas are among the most resistant. Fused sodium sulphate attacks silicon carbides and reaction-bonded silicon nitrides in air, but has little effect on alumina. Boron nitride has exceptionally good resistance to molten salts and glasses. This is probably due to its resistance to wetting.

2.9.4.4 Molten metals

When choosing an oxide ceramic for handling a molten metal, the reactivity of the metal towards oxygen and the stability of the ceramic oxide are important factors, since reduction of the ceramic will cause contamination of the metal. Many oxide ceramics are suitable for low-melting, fairly unreactive metals, whereas for the more reactive ones, such as the alkali metals, silicon and titanium, it is necessary to use the most suitable compositions, e.g. CaO-stabilized zirconia, and to ensure that they are free from reducible constituents such as silica.

Some of the non-oxide ceramics have good resistance to molten metals, and have been used for metal and alloy-handling applications. Silicon nitride is resistant to wetting by most metals, and is used in the production of light alloys including those of aluminium and zinc. It resists attack by brasses and bronzes but is attacked by copper in air. Boron nitride is another ceramic which is resistant to wetting by most metals and alloys, and is widely used as a container for liquid metals.

Impervious silicon carbides resist corrosion by low-melting, fairly unreactive metals, e.g. tin and lead, but since most metals can react with silicon to form silicides, ceramics containing free silicon are unsuitable for handling the more reactive ones.

Vitreous carbon shows good resistance to molten metals and alloys and has been used for processing aluminium, zinc, silver and some precious metals. It is, however, attacked by alkali metals.

2.9.4.5 Hot gases

In general, oxide ceramics are the most stable in air and oxidizing atmospheres, but in some cases they are attacked by reducing gases at high temperatures. Alumina is one of the most satisfactory for a variety of atmospheres and remains unaffected by air, water vapour, nitrogen or vacuum up to about 1700°C. At higher temperatures there is some reaction with water vapour and reducing gases resulting in vaporization as suboxides. Beryllia is similarly inert in air, nitrogen and vacuum up to 1700°C, but reacts with water vapour at high temperature to form the volatile $Be(OH)_2$. Zirconia is stable to high temperatures in oxidizing atmospheres, but tends to lose some oxygen in reducing conditions and is attacked by water vapour above 1800°C.

The non-oxide ceramics are prone to degradation at high temperatures in oxidizing atmospheres, but the severity of attack depends on many factors, including porosity, purity and the formation of protective layers of reaction products. Silicon nitride, silicon carbide and molybdenum disilicide become oxidized to silica, and this often forms a protective film which retards further attack. On the other hand, boron nitride forms volatile boric oxide on oxidation which is unable to afford protection, carbon and graphite form gaseous CO and CO_2, and many other types of non-oxide form discontinuous non-protective oxide layers.

Several of the oxide ceramics, e.g. alumina, beryllia, magnesia, and zirconia, are reported to be unstable at high temperatures in halogen- and sulphur-containing atmospheres, although the mechanism of attack is uncertain.

Table 2.9.1 Some criteria for determining attack

Criterion	Test	Applicability
Loss or gain of section	Simple immersion, weighing and/or dimension measurement before and after. Attack expressed as weight change, mg/cm^2 or cut-back rate mm/h.	Severe corrosion, large changes in section, especially melt-line attack and oxidation of non-oxides. Quantitative. Unsuited to minor phase dissolution and penetration. Weight change unsuited to liquid attack where medium adheres, especially with porous materials.
Penetration	Simple immersion, wash, dry, dye penetration and fracture. Measure penetration depth.	Many ceramics where minor phase is attacked by aqueous or gaseous media. Unsuited to initially porous materials. Quantitative.
Loss of strength	Immersion of bend test specimens, dry, fracture, compare strength before and after.	Limited to test pieces rather than components. Useful for aqueous and gaseous media. Quantitative for given specimen size. Unsuitable when deposits are formed.
Loss of hardness	Immersion of components, suitable scratch or macro-hardness test (e.g. HR45N) before and after.	Indicates penetration of medium and potential loss of section. Nondestructive. Hardness tests quantitative but unsuitable when deposits are formed.
Increase in wear rate	Wear test in appropriate medium, measure weight loss or cut-back rate. Ball mill test simple alternative for ranking, compare weight loss with medium and with water.	Suited to simulation of use on components or test pieces. Quantitative. Suited to aqueous-based tests only.

2.9.5 Determining resistance to corrosion

It is not always clear what is implied by 'corrosion-resistant'. The term often appears in manufacturers' literature, but usually insufficient information is given to enable one to determine whether resistance is adequate for a proposed use. The relevant criteria depend upon the application, and are summarized in Table 2.9.1. If attack is likely to be rapid and the component is to be considered as a consumable, simple loss-of-section tests may be adequate to determine the best material. Weight loss is preferred if corrosion is slow. However, both these measurements can be misleading if grain boundary attack occurs, leaving the material damaged although it shows little change in dimensions or loss of weight. A weight gain may even be recorded. In such cases dye penetration, strength or hardness tests will reveal changes that might otherwise not be observed.

If in addition mechanical erosion is likely to occur, this will remove soft attacked or penetrated layers and speed up attack, perhaps by several orders of magnitude. In such cases, a suitable wear test in the medium is appropriate. A simple alternative is to ball-mill the material in the corroding medium, weighing the material before and after and comparing the result with that obtained with water only. Even scratching the surface with a pen-knife after exposure will indicate whether a problem could arise.

It is necessary in reporting results to specify the criteria of attack and the environmental conditions of the test where relevant:

   temperature
   duration (attack is often non-linear with time)
   concentration and/or pressure of the medium
   whether oxidizing or reducing
   whether the medium is static or flowing, of fixed volume or continually
       replenished.

These points should be specified as well as material composition and micro-structure. The picture is therefore extremely complex, and in this respect the user must expect to have to undertake tests that closely model his own use conditions. Information other than the purely qualitative is seldom available from the suppliers or from the technical literature. In some cases accelerated tests may be possible, but consideration should be given to the mechanisms of attack because changing the conditions (e.g. temperature) may change the mode of attack as well as the rate.

2.9.6 Comparative tables

Tables 2.9.2 to 2.9.6 are intended to give comparative information on the resistance to attack of different types of ceramic under corrosive conditions. The materials included are limited by available space and detail but cover the principal oxides and non-oxides in pure impervious form (i.e. containing

Table 2.9.2 Maximum working temperatures of refractory ceramics
(See also Section 2.6 where more materials are included.)

Material	Temperature of fusion or decomposition °C	Approximate maximum working temperature, °C		
		Oxidizing atmospheres	Reducing or inert atmospheres	Remarks
Silicates:				
Silica, vitreous	1710	1050	~ 500*	Can be used for short periods to 1350°C in oxidizing conditions.
Impervious mullite	~1900	1650	uncertain	
Oxides:				
Beryllia	2570	1900	**	
Magnesia	2850	2300	1700	Easily reduced at high temperatures.
Spinel	2100	1950	~1800	
Alumina	2050	1900	1900	
Titania	1840	1600	< 800	Easily reduced at high temperatures.
Zirconia (CaO stabilized)	2550	2200	**	
Tin oxide	1500 (sublimes)	1400	—	Easily reduced, volatile above 1500°C.
Thoria	3300	2500	~2000	
Non-oxides:				
Silicon carbide	2600 (decomposes)	1650	2320	Oxidation at low partial pressures of O_2 more severe than at higher pressures.
Boron carbide	2450	800	2000	
Tungsten carbide	2750 (decomposes)	550	2000	With metallic binders softens at about 800°C.
Silicon nitride (reaction-bonded)	1900 (sublimes)	1200	1850	
Boron nitride	2300	1200	1870	In solid form can be used to 1600°C in air for short periods.
Titanium diboride	2980	800	>2000	
Molybdenum disilicide (glass-bonded)	1870	1700	1350 (in dry hydrogen)	Above 1500°C the glass phase is fluid and the material deforms.
Graphites	3600 (sublimes)	450	2500	Plastic deformation and vaporization begin above 2500°C.
Vitreous carbon	3600 (graphitizes)	550	2500	Performance depends on manufacturing conditions.

*Depends on medium. Can be used in argon to >1000°C.
**Depends on medium.

Table 2.9.3 Resistance to acids, alkalis and halogens

Reagent	Silicates		Oxides				
	Silica, vitreous	Mullite	BeO	MgO	MgAl$_2$O$_4$	Al$_2$O$_3$	ZrO$_2$
Acids:							
General inorganic	A[8]	—	B[12]	C[12]	A[12]	—	B[12]
HCl	A[8]	A[14]	—	C[12]	A[12]	A[15]	A[12]
HNO$_3$	A[8]	A[14]	—	C[12]	A[12]	A[15]	B[12]
H$_2$SO$_4$	A[8]	A[14]	—	C[12]	A[12]	A[15]	B[12]
H$_3$PO$_4$	B[8]200	B[14]	—	B[12]	A[12]	A[15]	B[14]
HF	C[8]	C[14]20	—	B[12]	B[12]	A[12]	B[12]
Alkalis:							
General	—	—	—	A[12]	A[12]	—	—
Hot alkali solutions	B[8]	—	—	A[12]	A[12]	B[12]	—
Hot KOH solution	C[14]80	B[14]80	—	A	A	A[14]80	A[14]80
Fused alkali carbonates	—	—	B[12]1200	A[12]	A[12]	B[12]	—
Fused Na$_2$CO$_3$	C[14]900	C[14]900	—	A[15]900	B[15]900	B[14]900	B[14]900
Fused alkalis	C[8]	C[14]500	B[12]	A[12]	A[12]	C[12]	C[12]
Fused KOH	C[14]500	C[14]500	—	C[15]500	B[15]500	B[15]500	A[15]500
Halogens:							
Fluorine	C[8]	C[26]	—	C[26]	—	A[12]	C[26]
Chlorine	A[4]500	B[26]>700	—	B[12]	—	A[12]	A[26]
Bromine	A[22]400	—	—	—	—	A[12]	—
Iodine	A[8]	—	—	—	—	A[12]	—

Key: A — Resistant to attack up to temperature (°C) indicated (often not given in technical literature).
 B — Some reaction at temperature indicated.
 C — Appreciable attack at temperature indicated.

Table 2.9.4 Resistance to fused salts and oxides

Reagent	Silicates		Oxides				
	Silica, vitreous	Mullite	BeO	MgO	MgAl$_2$O$_4$	Al$_2$O$_3$	ZrO$_2$
Salts:							
Fluorides	C	C	—	C[27]	C[27]	C[12]	C[12]
KF	C[14]900	C[14]900	—	—	C[15]900	C[14]900	C[14]900
Chlorides	—	—	—	B[27]	—	A[12]1200	B[27]
MgCl$_2$	B 1200	—	—	—	—	—	—
BaCl$_2$	C[15]1000	A[15]1000	—	—	A[12]1350	B[12]1350	B[15]1000
Nitrates	B[17]	—	—	—	—	A[12]	—
Sulphates	—	—	—	—	—	A[12]	—
Na$_2$SO$_4$	—	A[14]1000	—	—	—	A[14]1000	A[14]1000
Bisulphates	—	—	—	—	—	B[12]	B[12]
Phosphates	B[17]	—	A[12]	—	—	A[12]	—
Borax	C[15]1000	C[15]1000	A[12]	—	—	C[15]1000	C[15]1000
NaVO$_3$	C[15]800	C[15]800	—	—	—	B[15]800	A[15]800
PbO	C[15]1000	C[15]1000	—	A[15]1000	C[15]1000	B[15]1000	B[15]1000
V$_2$O$_5$	B[14]800	C[14]800	—	—	—	C[14]800	C[14]800

Key: A — Resistant to attack up to temperature (°C) indicated.
 B — Some reaction at temperature indicated.
 C — Appreciable attack at temperature indicated.

SiC reaction-bonded	Si$_3$N$_4$ reaction-bonded	Si$_3$N$_4$ hot-pressed	BN hot-pressed	TiB$_2$ hot-pressed	Vitreous carbon
A[7]	A	A	B[4]	—	A[18]
A[7]200	A[5]	A[14]	—	A[11]	A[18]
A[7]226	A[5]	A[14]	B[11]	A[11]	A[18]
A[7]200	A[5]	A[14]	B[11]	A[11]	A[18]
A[7]226	A[14]	B[14]	B[11]	—	A[18]
A[13]	B[5]	C[14]20	B[11]	—	A[18]
A[13]	B[5]	—	A[4]	—	A[18]
B[7]	B[5]	—	A	—	A
B[14]80	A[14]80	A[14]80	A	—	A
—	—	—	B[9]	—	B[18]
C[14]900	C[14]900	C[14]900	—	—	—
C[14]	C[5]	C[14]500	B[9]	—	B[18]
C[14]500	C[14]500	C[14]500	—	—	—
{ A[7]400	—	—	—	—	A[18]
C 800 } A[5]900		—	C[11]980	—	A[18]
—	—	—	—	—	A[18]
—	—	—	—	—	—

Superscript — Reference number to list of cited sources.
No reference indicates expected behaviour.

SiC reaction-bonded	Si$_3$N$_4$ hot-pressed	BN hot-pressed	TiB$_2$ hot-pressed
—	B[5]	A[4]	A[27]
C[14]900	C[14]900	A[28]1060	—
B[7]900	A[5]	—	B[27]
B[7]900	—	—	—
C[15]1000	C[15]1000	—	—
—	A[5]	A[15]350	B[11]
—	—	—	—
C[14]1000	C[14]1000	C[15]1000	—
—	—	—	B[11]
—	—	—	—
B[15]1000	A[15]1000	B[15]1000	—
C[15]800	C[15]800	—	—
B[15]1000	C[15]1000	C[15]1000	C[15]1000
C[14]800	C[14]800	—	—

Superscript — Reference number to list of cited sources.
No reference indicates expected behaviour.

Table 2.9.5 Resistance to some metals and non-metals

Element	Melting point °C	Silicates		Oxides				
		Silica, vitreous	Mullite	BeO	MgO	MgAl$_2$O$_4$	Al$_2$O$_3$	ZrO$_2$
Li	109	B[8]250	C[14]400	A[25]400	B[25]400	C[25]400	C[25]400	B[12]
Na	98	C[14]500	C[14]500	A[32]800	B[32]600	A[27]815	B[12]	B[12]
K	64	B[29]M	—	A[32]800	B[32]600	—	A[16]	B[12]
Be	1277	—	—	A[12]	B[17]1800	—	B[17]800	A[12]1800
Mg	650	B[8]800	B[26]	C[32]900	C[26]	B[12]	B[12]900	B[12]
Ca	838	B[8]600	—	B[12]850	—	B[12]	B[12]	B[12]
Sr	768	B[29]M	—	—	—	B[12]	A[12]	A[12]
Ba	714	B[29]M	—	—	—	—	A[12]	B[12]
B	2300	B[29]M	—	—	—	—	B[12]1300	—
Al	660	C[8]800	C[14]800	B[12]	B[26]	—	B[12]1500	B[12]
C	3727 (sublimes)	B[8]1000	—	B[12]1800	B[12]1600	B[12]	B[12]1600	B[12]1300
Si	1410	A[30]1400	—	B[12]1800	B[12]1800	—	B[12]1800	A[28]1450
Ge	937	—	—	—	—	—	A[28]1100	—
Sn	232	A[8]	A[28]1300	—	A[12]	—	A[10]	—
Pb	327	A[21]700	A[26]	A[32]800	A[12]	A[28]1400	A[21]700	A[26]
As	817	—	—	—	—	—	A[12]M	—
Sb	631	—	—	—	—	—	A[12]M	—
Bi	271	—	—	—	A[27]1000	—	A[12]	A[27]1000
Ti	1668	—	—	C[12]1800	C[17]1800	—	B[17]1800	B[12]1800
V	1900	—	—	A[12]	—	—	A[12]1700	A[12]
Cr	1875	—	—	A[12]	A[26]2100	—	A[12]	A[12]
Mn	1245	—	—	B[12]	A[12]	A[28]1710	A[12]1250	A[12]
Fe	1536	—	A[26]	A[12]	A[12]M	—	A[12]1500	A[10]M
Co	1495	—	—	—	—	—	A[12]1500	A[28]1550
Ni	1453	—	—	A[12]1800	A[12]1800	—	A[17]1800	A[17]1800
Cu	1083	—	A[28]1300	—	A[12]	—	A[28]1843	—
Zn	420	A[8]	A[28]1300	—	A[12]	—	A[10]	A[26]M
Zr	1852	—	B[12]1800	C[17]1800	—	B[12]1800	A[12]1800	—
Nb	2415	—	—	B[12]1800	A[16]1800	—	A[17]1800	A[12]1800
Mo	2610	A[8]	—	A[12]1800	A[17]1800	A[12]	A[12]1900	A[12]1800
Rh	1966	—	—	—	—	—	A[10]	A[26]
Ag	961	A[8]	—	—	A[12]	A[28]1550	A[33]M	—
Cd	321	A[8]	A[28]1300	—	—	—	—	—
Ta	2996	—	—	A[12]1600	A[17]1800	—	A[12]1700	A[17]1600
W	3410	A[8]	—	A[12]1800	A[17]2000	A[12]	A[12]1900	A[17]1600
Ir	2454	—	—	—	—	—	A 1800	A
Pt	1769	A[8]	A[31]750	A[26]M	A[12]	A[31]1600	A[10]M	A[26]M
Au	1063	A[8]	—	—	A[12]	A[28]1897	—	—
Hg	− 38	A[8]	—	A[32]300	A	A	A[34]300	A[32]300
Ce	795	B[8]800	—	B[24]	—	—	—	—
Th	1750	—	—	B[24]	A[12]M	—	—	—
U	1132	—	—	—	A[12]M	—	A[34]1200	—

Key: A — Resistant to attack up to temperature (°C) indicated.
     B — Some reaction at temperature indicated.
     C — Appreciable attack at temperature indicated.
     M — Denotes element in molten state (presumably near melting point).
Superscript—Reference number to list of cited sources.
No reference indicates expected behaviour.
s.s. - steel, mild or stainless, may also be a suitable crucible material.
m.p. - melting point.

| ThO$_2$ | Non-oxides | | | | | Suitable container for melting at melting point |
	SiC reaction-bonded	Si$_3$N$_4$ hot-pressed	BN hot-pressed	TiB$_2$ hot-pressed	Vitreous carbon	
B[12]400	C[14]400	C[14]400	A[25]400	—	B[18]	BeO, Al$_2$O$_3$, BN
B[12]1400	C[14]500	C[15]500	A[7]M	—	B[18]	s.s.
B[12]1400	—	—	—	A[27]871	B[18]	BeO, Al$_2$O$_3$, s.s.
A[17]1800	—	—	B[7]1280	—	—	BeO, ZrO$_2$, ThO$_2$
B[12]	—	B[5]750	—	A[11]M	—	C, TiB$_2$
B[12]	—	—	—	—	—	C
A[35]	—	—	—	—	—	Al$_2$O$_3$
A[35]	—	—	—	—	—	most at m.p.
—	—	—	A[7]M	—	—	BN
A[32]1000	C[14]800	A[5]900	A[7]M	A[11]M	A M	most at m.p.
A[12]	—	B[5]1050	B[39]>1700	A[11]2200	A	—
B[17]1800	—	A[37]M	A[7]M	B[11]M	—	ZrO$_2$, BN
—	—	—	A[11]M	—	—	Al$_2$O$_3$
—	A[15]600	A[5]300	A[7]M	A[11]M	A[18]	most at m.p.
—	A[15]600	A[5]400	A[27]815	A[11]M	—	most at m.p.
—	—	—	A[38]M	—	A[18]	Al$_2$O$_3$
—	—	—	A[7]M	—	—	Al$_2$O$_3$, C
A[27]1000	A[7]600	—	A[7]M	A[11]M	—	most at m.p.
A[17]800	—	—	—	B[11]M	—	ThO$_2$
—	—	—	—	—	—	Al$_2$O$_3$
—	—	—	B[39]1650	A[39]M	—	BeO, ThO$_2$
—	—	—	—	—	—	Spinel, Al$_2$O$_3$
A[28]1550	—	B[5]1450	A[7]M	—	—	Al$_2$O$_3$, ZrO$_2$
—	—	—	—	B[11]M	—	Al$_2$O$_3$, ZrO$_2$
A[17]1800	—	—	B[7]1460	B[11]M	—	Al$_2$O$_3$, ZrO$_2$
—	A[7]	C[5]1150	A[7]M	A[39]M	—	C, mullite, Al$_2$O$_3$
—	A[7]600	A[5]550	A[9]M	A[11]M	A M	Mullite, Al$_2$O$_3$
A[17]1800	—	—	—	—	—	Al$_2$O$_3$, ThO$_2$
B[17]1800	—	—	—	—	—	Al$_2$O$_3$, ZrO$_2$
A[17]1900	—	—	—	—	—	ThO$_2$
—	—	—	—	—	—	MgO, ThO$_2$
—	—	A[5]M	A[38]M	A[11]M	A M	most at m.p.
—	—	—	A[7]M	A[11]M	A M	most at m.p.
A[17]1900	—	—	—	—	—	—
A[17]2200	—	—	—	—	—	—
—	—	—	—	—	—	ThO$_2$
A[31]1100	C[15]1100	—	B[7]1770	—	—	Al$_2$O$_3$, ZrO$_2$
—	—	—	A[38]M	—	—	most at m.p.
—	A[15]20	—	—	—	—	most at m.p.
—	—	—	B[26]M	—	—	CeS
A[36]M	—	—	—	—	—	MgO, ThO$_2$
A[36]M	—	—	B[7]1140	—	—	CeS, MgO, ThO$_2$

Table 2.9.6 Resistance to attack by hot gases

Gas	Oxides					
	Silica, vitreous	BeO	MgO	Al$_2$O$_3$	ZrO$_2$	ThO$_2$
Air	A 1700	A[16]1700	A[16]1700	A[16]1700	A[16]2400	A[16]3000
Steam	A[8]	B[16]	—	A[16]1700	C[10]1800	—
Argon	A	A[16]1700	A[16]1700	A[16]1700	A	A
Nitrogen	A[8]	A[16]1700	A[16]1700	A[16]1700	B[37]2200	A
Vacuum	—	A[16]1700	A[16]1700	A[16]1700	A	A
Carbon monoxide	A[30]	A[16]1700	A[16]1700	A[16]1700	—	—
Hydrogen	A[8]	A[16]1700	A[16]1700	A[16]1700	—	—
Sulphur-containing	A[8]	B[16]	B[16]	A[26]	B[16]	B[16]
Hydrogen sulphide	—	—	—	—	—	—
Fluorine	C[8]20	—	C[26]	A[12]	C[26]	—
Chlorine	A[4]500	—	B[12]	A[12]	A[26]	—
Halogens	—	B[16]	B[16]	—	B[16]	B[16]

Key: A — Resistant to attack up to temperature (°C) indicated.
  B — Some reaction at temperature indicated.
  C — Appreciable attack at temperature indicated.
Superscript—Reference number to list of cited sources.
No reference indicates expected behaviour.

greater than about 99.7% of the major phase or phases). Materials that are less pure tend to be corroded more rapidly, but performance can vary widely with minor-phase composition and conditions of exposure. The results, from a variety of sources, are expressed in qualitative terms. It is not possible to be certain of the validity of the information because frequently there is insufficient experimental detail in the original references. For example, a material may be described as 'resistant to acids', with no mention of types, concentrations, temperatures, periods of exposure or methods used to detect attack. For this reason the Tables can only give a rough indication of resistance to attack, are intended only as a guide, and must be used with caution. Because the information is mostly unchecked by NPL, the standard format of the Handbook is broken in order to include references to the sources of information. Many references concern specific products rather than general categories of material or research studies. The Bibliography (Section 2.10) contains full details of the references.

If a ceramic is described as 'resistant to attack' up to a given temperature, this does not necessarily mean that there has been no reaction at all, but that no gross change has been observed within the time-scale of the observation, which is usually not given. It may be that the examination was not sufficiently thorough to detect attack. It is quite possible for the physical and mechanical properties of a ceramic to be greatly changed by corrosion without any visible change in appearance. Further, the temperature quoted may not be the highest one at which the term 'resistant' might be applied; it may simply be the highest used in the test cited. In some cases the references give a more detailed account of the nature and extent of attack. Where no reference is given, performance has been judged on the basis of what would be expected chemically. Also, it should be assumed that the quoted information is based on short-term observations at ambient pressure, and that a rating of 'resistant to attack' may not be appropriate for long-term use.

Non-oxides

SiC reaction-bonded	Si$_3$N$_4$ hot-pressed	BN hot-pressed	Vitreous carbon
A[14]1200	B[14]1200	C[7]1200	A[19]550
B[14]220	A[14]220	C[15]220	A[19]1100
A[7]2320	—	A[7]2775	A[19]3000
A > 1400	A[40]1800	A[11]	A > 1000
A > 1000	A[40]900	A[7]2775	A[20]3000
A > 1000	A > 800	A[38]800	—
A[7]1000	—	A[7]2775	A[41]1200
A[13]1050	A[5]1000	—	—
A > 800	A[5]1000	—	A[18]
B	—	—	A[18]
A[7]400	A[5]900	C[11]980	A[18]
—	—	—	A[18]

2.10

Bibliography for Section 2

With the exception of the references to Section 2.9, the intention of this Bibliography is to give the reader who wishes to read around the various aspects of technical ceramics a choice of other sources of information, perhaps dealing with more fundamental points or greater academic detail than those expressed in the text of this Handbook. In the main the references given are to books, but also included are some scientific or technical papers which are of a general or comparative nature.

The Bibliography to Section 2.9 gives a large number of references used to compile the tables in that Section. As expressed earlier, the reason for doing this is that much of the information is proprietary, or on specific products, where the reader may find it relevant to refer back to the original to obtain further detail.

Section 2.2—Composition and Microstructure

Bloor, E C. The composition and properties of electrical ceramics. *Ceramics, a Symposium*, edited by Green, A T and Stewart, G H, British Ceramic Society, Stoke-on-Trent, 1953, 227–83.

Creyke, W E C, Sainsbury, I E J, Morrell, R. *Design with non-ductile materials*, Applied Science Publishers, London, 1982.

Fulrath, R M, Pask, J A (editors). *Ceramic microstructures '76, Proc. 6th Int. Materials Symposium*, Univ. of Berkeley, Calif, Aug. 24–7, 1976, Westview Press, Boulder, Colorado, USA, 1977.

Gitzen, W H. *Alumina as a ceramic material*, American Ceramic Society, Columbus, Ohio, USA, 1970.

Grimshaw, R W. *The chemistry and physics of clays and other ceramic materials*, 4th. edn., Ernest Benn Ltd, London, 1971.

Kingery, W D, Bowen, H K, Uhlmann, D R. *Introduction to ceramics*, 2nd. edn., John Wiley and Sons Inc., New York, 1976.

McMillan, P W. *Glass-ceramics*, 2nd. edn., Academic Press, London, 1979.

Waye, B E. *Introduction to technical ceramics*, MacLaren and Sons Ltd, London, 1967.

Section 2.4—Thermal Properties

Burnett, S J. Properties of refractory materials, *Report AERE-R 4657*, HMSO, 1967.

Kubashewski, O, Evans, C B, Alcock, E LL. *Metallurgical thermodynamics*, Plenum Press, Oxford, 1970.

Thermophysical Properties of Matter, IFI Plenum, New York, of which the following are relevant to ceramic materials:

Volume 2 – Thermal conductivity, non-metallic solids, authors Touloukian, Y S, Powell, R W, Ho, C Y, Klemens, P G, 1970.

Volume 5 – Specific heat, non-metallic solids, authors Touloukian, Y S, Buyco, E H, 1970.

Volume 10 – Thermal diffusivity, non-metallic solids, authors Touloukian, Y S, Powell, R W, Ho, C Y, Nicolaou, M C, 1973.

Volume 13 – Thermal expansion, non-metallic solids, authors Touloukian, Y S, Kirby, R K, Taylor, R E, Lee, T Y R, 1977.

Wachtman, J B (editor). *Mechanical and thermal properties of ceramics*, NBS Special Publication 303, 1969.

Section 2.5—Mechanical Properties

Bortz, S A, Lund, H H. The brittle ring test. *Mechanical properties of engineering ceramics*, edited by Kriegel, W W, Palmour, H, Interscience Publishers, New York, 1961, 383–404.

Braiden, P M. Techniques for stress analysis of ceramics. *Proc. Brit. Ceram. Soc.*, 1982, **32**, 315–32.

Clinton, D J, Morrell, R. Hardness testing of alumina ceramics. *Proc. Brit. Ceram. Soc.*, 1984, **34**, 113–27.

Creyke, W E C, Sainsbury, I E J, Morrell, R. *Design with non-ductile materials*, Applied Science Publishers, London, 1982.

Davidge, R W. *Mechanical behaviour of ceramics*, Cambridge University Press, 1979.

Evans, A G, Langdon, T G. Structural ceramics. *Prog. Mater. Sci.*, 1976, **21**(3/4).

Jayatilaka, A de S. *Fracture of engineering brittle materials*, Applied Science Publishers, London, 1979.

Koester, R D, Moak, D P. Hot hardness of selected borides, oxides and carbides to 1900°C. *J. Amer. Ceram. Soc.*, 1967, **50**(6), 290–6.

Kriegel, W W, Palmour, H. *Mechanical properties of engineering ceramics*, Interscience Publishers, New York, 1961.

Moore, M A, King, F S. Abrasive wear of brittle solids. *Proc. Int. Conf. Wear of Materials 1979*, **2**, April 16–18, Dearborn, Michigan, Amer. Soc. Mech. Engrs., New York, 1979, 275–85.

Proceedings of the British Ceramic Society, 1975, **25** edited by Davidge, R W; 1978, **26** edited by Godfrey, D J; and 1982, **32** edited by Davidge, R W; British Ceramic Soc., Stoke-on-Trent, Staffs.

Shook, W B. Critical survey of mechanical property test-methods for brittle materials, *Tech Rpt. ASD–TDR–63–491*, 1963, AD–417621.

Stanley, P, Sivill, A D, Fessler, H. The unit strength concept in the interpretation of beam test results on brittle materials. *Proc. Inst. Mech. Eng.*, 1976, **190**(49/76), 585–95.

Wachtman, J B (editor). *Mechanical and thermal properties of ceramics*, NBS Special Publication 303, 1969.

Westbrook, J H. The temperature dependence of hardness of some common oxides. *Rev. Hautes Temp. et Refr.*, 1966, **3**(1), 47–57.

Wiederhorn, S M. Reliability, life prediction and proof testing of ceramics. *Proc. Conf. Ceramics for High Performance Applications*, Hyannis, Mass, 1973, Brook Hill Pub. Co., Chestnut Hill, Mass., USA, 1974, 635–64.

Section 2.6—Thermomechanical Properties

Boley, B A, Weiner, J. *Theory of thermal stresses*, John Wiley, London and New York, 1960.

Hasselman, D P H. Thermal stress resistance parameters for brittle refractory ceramics, a compendium. *Bull. Amer. Ceram. Soc.*, 1970, **49**(12), 1033–7.

Morrell, R. Thermal stress and thermal shock in ceramics – a survey of industrial problems and a review of test methods and thermal stress theory. *NPL Report CHEM66*, 1977.

Levin, E M, Robbins, C R, McMurdie, H F. *Phase diagrams for ceramists, Vol. 1*, 1964; *Vol. 2*, 1969; *Vol. 3*, 1975; *Vol. 4*, 1981 (edited by Roth, R S et al.); *Vol. 5*, 1983 (edited by Roth, R S et al.); American Ceramic Society, Columbus, Ohio, USA.

Roark, R J, Young, W C. *Formulas for stress and strain*, 5th. edn., McGraw Hill, New York, 1975.

Section 2.7—Electrical Properties

Binns, D B. Results and discussion of testing programme. *The use of ceramics in valves*, edited by Popper, P, British Ceramic Research Association Special Publ. 46, 1965, 167–89.

Bloor, E C. The composition and properties of electrical ceramics. *Ceramics, a Symposium*, edited by Green, A T and Stewart, G H, British Ceramic Society, Stoke-on-Trent, 1953, 227–83.

Hench, L L, Dove, D B. *Physics of electronic ceramics*, Parts A and B, Marcel Dekker, New York, 1971.

Jaffe, B, Cook, W R, Jaffe, H. *Piezoelectric ceramics*, Academic Press, 1971.

Kingery, W D, Bowen, H K, Uhlmann, D R. *Introduction to ceramics*, 2nd. edn., John Wiley and Sons Inc., New York, 1976.

Kohl, W H. *Handbook of materials and techniques for vacuum devices*, Van Nostrand/Reinhold, New York, 1967.

Snelling, E C. *Soft ferrites: properties and applications*, Iliffe Books Ltd, London, 1969.

Section 2.8—Optical Properties

Driscoll, W G, Vaughan, W (editors). *Handbook of optics*, McGraw Hill Inc., New York, 1978.

Moses, A J. *Handbook of electronic materials, Vol. 1: Optical materials properties*, IFI Plenum, New York, 1971.

Siegel, R, Howell, J R. Thermal radiation heat transfer, Vol. 1, The blackbody, electromagnetic theory and material properties. *Report NASA SP–164*, 1968.

Touloukian, Y S, DeWitt, D P. *Thermophysical properties of matter, Vol. 8: Thermal radiative properties, nonmetallic solids*, IFI Plenum, New York, 1972.

Whitson, M E. Handbook of the infra-red optical properties of Al_2O_3, carbon, MgO, and ZrO_2. *Report TR-0075(5548)–2*, Vols. 1 and 2, SAMSO-TR-75-131-Vol1 and -Vol2, AD-A013722 and AD-A013723 respectively, 1975.

Section 2.9—Chemical Properties

General references:

Lay, L A. *Corrosion resistance of technical ceramics*, HMSO, 1984.

Morey, G W. *The properties of glass*, 2nd. edn., Reinhold Publishing Corp., New York, 1954.

Levin, E M, Robbins, C R, McMurdie, H F. *Phase diagrams for ceramists, Vol. 1*, 1964; *Vol. 2*, 1969; *Vol. 3*, 1975; *Vol. 4*, (edited by Roth, R S et al.) 1982; American Ceramic Soc., Columbus, Ohio, USA.

Numbered references in text:

1. Product literature, Morgan Refractories Ltd.
2. Tressler, R E et al. Molten salt corrosion of SiC and Si_3N_4 ceramics. *J. Am. Ceram. Soc.*, 1976, **59**(9-10), 441-4.
3. Day, J P. A study of the chemical reactivity in ceramic heat exchangers. *Trans. A.S.M.E., A*, 1979, **101**(2), 270-4.
4. Fisher, D J. The resistance of ceramics to chemical corrosion. *Chem. Soc. Special Publication* No. 30, 1977, 1-11.
5. Product literature, Advanced Materials Engineering Ltd.
6. Product literature, Lucas-Cookson-Syalon Ltd.
7. Product literature, The Carborundum Company.
8. Product literature, Thermal Syndicate PLC.
9. Product literature, Borax Consolidated Ltd.
10. Product literature, Friedrichsfeld GmbH.
11. Product literature, Kawecki Berylco Industries.
12. Ryshkewitch, E. *Oxide Ceramics*, Academic Press, New York and London, 1960.
13. Product literature, British Nuclear Fuels Ltd.
14. Lay, L A. The resistance of ceramics to chemical attack. *NPL Report CHEM 96*, 1978.
15. Lay, L A. Unpublished NPL results.
16. Kohl, W H. *Handbook of materials and techniques for vacuum devices*, Van Nostrand-Reinhold, New York, 1967.
17. Kohl, W H. *Materials and techniques for electron tubes*, Chapman and Hall, New York, 1962.
18. Product literature, The Fluorocarbon Company.
19. Anon. Comparative properties of vitreous carbon with other materials. *Design Eng.*, March 1970.
20. Anon. Glass-like vitreous carbon resists heat and corrosive chemicals. *Product Eng.*, July 1977.
21. Asher, R C, Davies D, Beetham, S A. Some observations on the compatibility of structural materials with molten lead. *Corrosion Sci.*, 1977, **17**(7), 545-57.
22. Gafni, G, Aladjem, A, Vahalom, J. Behaviour of materials in contact with bromine. *Reviews on coatings and corrosion*, 1977, **2**(2-3), 173-86.
23. McKee, D W, Chatterji D. Corrosion of silicon carbide in gases and alkaline melts, *J. Am. Ceram. Soc.*, 1976, **59**(9-10), 441-4.
24. Product literature, Consolidated Beryllium Ltd.
25. Tuohig, W D, Battles, J E. Ceramics in lithium alloy metal sulphide batteries. *Workshop proceedings on Ceramics for energy applications*, held at Batelle Columbus Labs., Ohio, USA, 1975, edited by Schorr, J R.

26. Campbell, I E, Sherwood, E M. *High temperature materials and technology*, John Wiley, New York, 1967.
27. Berry, W E. *Corrosion in nuclear applications*, John Wiley, New York, 1967.
28. Bockris, J O'M, White, J L, MacKenzie, J D (editors). *Physicochemical measurements at high temperatures*, Butterworths Scientific Publications, London, 1959.
29. Lawson, W D, Nielson, S. *Preparation of single crystals*, Butterworths Scientific Publications, London, 1958.
30. Product Literature, Heraeus Quartzschmelze GmbH.
31. Elwell, D, Scheel, H J. *Crystal growth from high-temperature solutions*, Academic Press, London, 1975.
32. Lyon, R D (editor). *Liquid metals handbook*, Atomic Energy Commission, Department of the Navy, Washington DC, USA, 1952.
33. Lyman, T (editor). *Metals handbook*, American Society of Metals, Cleveland, Ohio, USA, 1948.
34. Gitzen, W H. *Alumina as a ceramic material*, American Ceramic Society, Columbus, Ohio, USA, 1970.
35. Product Literature, Elektroschmelzwerk Kempten GmbH.
36. Richardson, H K. Small cast thorium oxide crucibles. *J. Amer. Ceram. Soc.*, 1935, **18**, 65–9.
37. Lynch, J F, Ruderer, C G, Duckworth, W H (editors). *Engineering properties of selected ceramic materials*, American Ceramic Society, Columbus, Ohio, USA, 1966.
38. Archer, N J. The preparation and properties of pyrolytic boron nitride. *Chem. Soc. Special Publication* No. 30, 1977, 167–180.
39. Thompson, R. Borides: their chemistry and applications. *Royal Institute of Chemistry Lecture Series* No. 5, 1965, 1–40.
40. Product Literature, Associated Engineering Developments Ltd.
41. Product Literature, Le Carbone Lorraine.

SECTION 3

Design in ceramics

3.1

Introduction

This Section is intended as a review of some of the factors that need to be considered in the design and use of a ceramic component. Since ceramics are used for a very wide range of applications it is possible to make only general points, illustrated with some examples.

Engineering ceramics have advantages in certain respects over other materials such as plastics, metals and natural materials, wood, stone, etc. These advantages may be in properties for end use, or simplicity or cheapness of the manufacturing process. On the other hand, a property advantageous for a particular application may entail less favourable side-effects. Changing the material specification may improve one property while degrading others. This is demonstrated in general terms in Table 3.1.1, where most of the advantages are accompanied by corresponding disadvantages when seen from alternative angles, emphasizing the need to understand how to optimize design in ceramics.

Sometimes a ceramic is the material of choice, for example for insulating characteristics at high temperatures. More often, a switch to ceramics becomes necessary because the materials chosen initially do not perform adequately. Sometimes, but only rarely, a switch is made to reduce costs of materials or of machining. In the main, the choice of material depends on meeting requirements for the end use without excessive cost penalty.

The design of the component depends on its application or on the application of the assembly of which it is part, and on how localized the particular property requirements are. The aim of the designer must be to give a technically and a commercially viable product. For example, if a long component requires a high-temperature capability only at one end, or if improved abrasion resistance is required in the single bore of a large component, then one obvious solution is an assembly of a metal and a ceramic part. This will probably be much more cost-effective than simply replacing the whole metal component by one of similar design in ceramic. However, when considering such assemblies, due attention must be paid to the design of the joint and the duty expected of it. Conversely, it may be possible to combine two existing parts into one ceramic part if the properties of the ceramic are suitable, for example, if a combination of electrical insulation and high strength or refractoriness is required.

The component shape depends not only on nominal properties and the duty of the component, but also on manufacturing feasibility. This is dealt with technically in this Section, and is an extremely important aspect of design since it affects all others, even the nominal properties of the product.

Table 3.1.1 Advantages and corresponding disadvantages of engineering ceramics in general terms

For	Against
Wide range of sizes can be made, 0.2 mm to 3 m possible.	Severe limits in some materials, determined by manufacturing techniques required. Small sizes are mechanically weak.
Dimensional stability.	Cannot cold-work. Local stresses cannot relax.
High hardness, abrasion-resistant, wear-resistant.	Difficult to machine after firing. Abrasive.
Electrical insulation.	All lose insulating properties at very high temperatures.
Electrical conductivity in special materials.	
Strength, especially in compression.	Brittle, especially in tension and shear. Failure stress variable.
Strength at high temperatures.	
Wide range of thermal conductivity and expansion coefficient available.	Thermal shock limitations for low thermal conductivity and high expansion coefficient materials.
Impervious, or controlled pore structures.	In most materials, residual porosity limits surface finish achievable.
Corrosion resistant.	Some products are not designed for resistance to corrosive media. Non-oxides may oxidize at high temperatures.
Low density compared to most metals.	
Transparency or translucency.	
Cheap raw materials in many cases.	Expensive tooling and secondary shaping operations. Some raw materials are quite expensive.
Non-toxic.	Beryllia is toxic as a dust.
Many specialist manufacturers of some types of material.	Limited availability of some varieties of material, limited engineering expertise, limited understanding of performance.

In particular, it affects the cost of the component. Small quantities required for experiment or limited-scale applications would normally be manufactured by machining in the unfired state, followed by additional machining after firing to the surface finish or tight tolerances required. This would give a relatively high unit cost, but low tooling costs. On the other hand, large quantities for a production run would normally be manufactured with special-purpose tooling to minimize the labour costs of each unit. In this case the tooling costs would be high but would be amortized over many thousands of units, and give a net low unit cost. With the use of special tooling, many useful features can be introduced into a component design at almost no extra cost to increase its cost-effectiveness, for example, specified radii on corners, curved shapes instead of straight edges, variations in thickness profile. It may be cheaper, for example, to make a number of short interlocking tubes by die-pressing in a special die than the equivalent length of extruded tube followed by machining.

Aspects such as these will be developed in this Section, but as a check list for those unfamiliar with working with ceramics, the following can be considered as the major steps involved:

1. Initially, choose materials in the low to medium cost bracket which would seem to fulfil technical requirements and which should do the job from the property point of view. It must be emphasized that in many cases the actual cost of the ceramic material is very small compared to the cost incurred in secondary machining operations. Some costs in the production of ceramic components may be reduced by using established design and technical experience in manufacturing organizations.

2. Consider the technical requirements, particularly those that apply only to a small part of the component. It may be better to use a small component in an assembly to meet such a local requirement than make the entire existing component in ceramic. Conversely, look at the original function of the design, because it may be possible to combine appropriate components or their functions into a single ceramic component. This is particularly advantageous if the component is to be made by one of the mass-production techniques.

3. Consider the means of joining or fitting the ceramic component to the rest of the system in relation to its expected duty under all conditions. Pay particular attention to the undesirability of undue stress concentrations on the ceramic, including those brought about by a change in temperature when expansion coefficients are mismatched.

4. Give serious consideration to the quantities of material or components required at each stage of product development, i.e. for material approval, application tests, prototypes, pre-production, and production.

5. Contact likely manufacturers, experts and research organizations. Be prepared to change designs according to the discussion. Do not resent change, because while you may have the greatest understanding and technical expertise in the design and function of your assembly, you may not be an expert in the design of the one ceramic component in the system. There is a wealth of ceramic-orientated knowledge in the organizations that deal with ceramics routinely. Do not ignore this valuable source of advice.

6. Ensure that the material and the manufacturer's process will give you properties and tolerances to do the job. Awareness of the influence of manufacturing methods on properties and sizes is useful here. Be as flexible as possible on tolerances.

7. Assess some trial pieces if appropriate. Tests on hardware mean so much more than staring at a drawing board. Consider any necessary changes of design. Consider whether you need special quality-control procedures, such as checking dimensions or overload proof-testing.

8. Establish clearly the ownership of the design that results from external help. This will clearly involve commercial, technical and patent appraisal of the design.

9. Place your order according to a specification agreed with the manufacturer at all stages of design and development from the initial trials on materials through to the final production quantities of the finalized design. Do not omit to specify quality-control procedures to ensure acceptable dimensions and surface finish. Do not omit to specify special protective packaging if required.

This type of sequence should enable the user to build up a good working relationship with the manufacturer. If you do not act flexibly and with an open mind, you may find yourself with a very large bill for something that might not work as well as it should. Once a design has been committed to production, changes may involve heavy expenditure on retooling at the customer's expense.

The following Sections give background information for the inexperienced user on some aspects of:

1. manufacturing methods (to enable him to appreciate the ways in which articles are made and how these may influence available sizes and properties)
2. how manufacturing methods influence the design of small components
3. complex design and trouble-shooting
4. methods of joining ceramics to other materials
5. quality control and testing of components.

3.2

Manufacturing methods

The vast majority of ceramics are made by shaping an appropriate powder mass, with a binder if necessary, and then subjecting the shape to a high-temperature process which converts it to a ceramic. In general, unlike most metals, ceramics cannot be shaped cheaply after the firing stage. It is therefore usual to try to achieve the required dimensions at the powder-shaping stage by making due allowance for firing shrinkage. Since manufacturers would see their expertise as lying in the areas of shaping and firing, it is usual to buy the component in the required shape direct from the manufacturer. It is therefore necessary to plan rather differently with a ceramic component than with the equivalent in almost any other material.

Consider first the primary methods of producing a shape prior to firing. The type of shape, the material and the capabilities of a particular manufacturer determine how this is done. Table 3.2.1 summarizes the major methods, and these are described more fully in the following Sections.

3.2.1 Wet shaping methods for ceramics

One of the traditional methods within the pottery trade is the moulding of a clay-like mass of the required composition, usually a mixture of clays, a flux and a filler. This is sometimes termed *jolleying* when performed by machine, and is the method for making largish objects with axial symmetry such as plates, bowls, dishes etc. Some clayware items may be shaped by hand. In the technical ceramics field this tends to be restricted to large pieces of electrical porcelain which would be difficult to shape by other means.

The feed material for this process is normally wet-mixed and filter-pressed to a fairly compliant mass which may then be de-aired and extruded to form blanks ready for shaping.

If the shape required has cylindrical symmetry, one of the easiest ways of making it is by *extrusion* through a suitably shaped die. Again the compliant mass from filter-pressing may be used if this is readily mouldable as is usually the case with clay-based materials. For clay-free materials, or materials with only small amounts of clay, plasticity needs to be enhanced with the addition of a binder, which may be entirely organic or may be inorganic (e.g. boehmite, a very sticky hydrated form of alumina), to suit the process. Extrusion may be continuous or intermittent depending on the type of equipment available, and the plastic mass is de-aired before being passed through the die.

The process of *slip-casting* has its origins in the pottery industry. A heavy suspension of the precursor powders in a liquid, usually water, is poured

Table 3.2.1 Primary shaping methods for ceramic materials

Route	Materials	Shapes
Plastic shaping, jolleying etc.	Porcelains and clay-based materials.	Largish shapes with axial symmetry, hand-shaped pieces.
Extrusion	All clay-based materials, steatite. With additional plastic binders, many non-clay-based materials, such as aluminas, some non-oxides.	Long thin rods, tubes, multibore tubes and other sections. Turning may be done on extruded blanks.
Slip-casting	Clay-based materials, some high-alumina ceramics, some silicon nitrides, silicon carbides, some refractory materials, such as magnesia, etc., used for crucibles.	Irregular shapes to coarse tolerances, thin-walled components, small-quantity production for prototypes.
Tape-casting	Alumina ceramics	Simple shapes such as rectangular plates cut from sheet.
Semi-dry pressing (of granulated filter-pressed cake)	Clay-based materials, steatite, some aluminas.	Wide variety of short rods, tubes and other shapes with some profiling in pressing direction.
Dry pressing (of spray-dried powder or of dried granulated cake)	Some clay-based materials, steatite, alumina ceramics Most oxide and non-oxide ceramics.	Wide variety of small shapes pressed uniaxially with limited profile in the pressing direction.
Isostatic-pressing: (a) dry bag on to a mandrel (b) wet bag on to solid shape or on to a mandrel	Oxide and non-oxide ceramics.	(a) Long runs of simple shapes, e.g. spark plug bodies and nozzles (b) Large blanks for subsequent machining, internal surface reproduced from mandrel.
Injection-moulding	Glass-bonded mica (performed hot), most ceramics (performed warm with a plastic or wax binder).	Complex irregular shapes with holes, curves and twists in three dimensions.
Hot-pressing	Specialized products from oxides and non-oxides.	Limited to simple flat plates or cylinders of dimensions limited by size of press.
Hot isostatic pressing (a secondary process using high external gas pressure)	Tungsten carbide, some advanced ceramics for certain applications.	Any size, limited only by the scale of the equipment. Specialized manufacture.
Electrophoretic deposition	Some oxides. Some enamels and glazes.	Thin-walled shapes and coatings. Seldom used for monolithic components.
Plasma-spraying	Some oxide and non-oxide materials.	Thin-walled shapes and coatings.
Chemical vapour (pyrolytic) deposition	Some non-oxide materials, boron nitride, silicon carbide etc.	Thin-walled shapes and coatings.

into a plaster mould. As the liquid is drawn out of the suspension into the plaster by capillary action, the solid particles segregate at the plaster surface. The process is allowed to continue until the layer of rigid material is built up to the required thickness or, for solid shapes, until the mould is full. Excess slip is poured off, and the mould and its contents are left to dry. On splitting the mould the shape is removed and dried completely. Slip-casting requires the slip to have the correct pH to keep the particles in suspension, and the correct particle size distribution to give strength to the cast shape when it is dry. Since no pressure is applied in the process, slip-cast shapes may have a lower bulk density ('green' or unfired density) than mechanically-shaped components and hence rather higher firing shrinkage. Bubbles in the slip can leave voids in the casting. This method is used extensively for thin-walled ware, tubing, crucibles, trays, etc., which would be difficult to press from powder.

In these wet shaping methods, where the shaping depends on the rheological properties of the wet mass, it is often possible to combine two or more parts produced by the primary shaping method to make a composite component by joining them while still wet with a small amount of ceramic slip as an adhesive and then blending the joint to eliminate external evidence. Examples of this are the fitting of handles or spouts to hollow-ware, and the closure of one end of an extruded tube by hand working. In critical conditions, such joints tend to be sources of weakness, and manufacture in one piece is to be preferred.

In many cases, because of the relatively low cost of tooling for slip-casting and extrusion, these processes may be economically viable for making prototypes and for small batch production. When larger quantities are required, the most economic route would normally be by die- or isostatic-pressing, but this can lead to changes in properties.

Tape-casting is a specialized method of producing thin, flat, uniform strip which can subsequently be cut into rectangular tiles. A thick slip, often using an organic vehicle for quick drying, is cast on a belt to a specified thickness and allowed to dry before being cut up. The method is used almost exclusively for the production of thin electronic substrates where control of surface finish and flatness is of overriding importance.

3.2.2 Dry shaping methods for ceramics

Powder pressing is the most widely used method of shaping a ceramic powder mass. This is usually performed on automatic or semi-automatic presses, and is a relatively fast operation enabling long runs of components to be made. It is usual to make the pressed shape as close to the final required shape as possible, with due allowance for firing shrinkage. Surprisingly complex shapes can be made, limited only by the cost of the mould or die and the ingenuity of the die maker. In fact the cost of the die is usually a significant factor determining the cost of the component, and complex dies would not normally be employed except for long runs, say upwards of 5000 depending on component size and complexity. For shorter runs, or for shapes that cannot be directly moulded, it is common practice to press a blank and then machine it to the required shape prior to firing. The pressed blank is usually strong enough to withstand gentle handling, and hand shaping is not uncommon, particularly for difficult edges or profiles and for the removal of flash.

Die-pressing is a uniaxial process, with the die cavity filled with a metered quantity of powder feedstock. With clay-based materials, the filter cake may be dried further than required for extrusion, and then granulated to form particles 1-5mm across which readily deform and adhere to each other under pressure. Although it is not strictly a dry shaping method, the water content being typically around 10% and the pressed shapes requiring further drying before firing, the shaping technology is the same as for completely dry pressing of materials not containing clay. For this latter category, it is usual to add an organic binder to the mix during the wet mixing stages. The mix is then dried and granulated (often spray-dried) to form a free-flowing powder.

Die-pressing has some limitations. Regard has to be paid to the ability to fill the mould with powder feedstock, and to the ability to transmit pressure to all parts of the mould cavity so that the pressed shape has uniform density and no weak edges. Variations in pressed (or 'green') density lead to variations in fired density, and uneven firing shrinkage leads to distortion. For these reasons there are limitations on the ratio of length in the direction of pressing to diameter or wall thickness of various parts of the shape. This subject is discussed more fully in the next Section. Some variation of properties from point to point can be expected. Discussion with manufacturers on these aspects can be fruitful, and perhaps lead to the use of a pressed blank followed by machining, as described earlier, to ensure good properties in critical areas. An example might be an edge requiring a specified surface finish and hardness for wear resistance.

A technique which to some extent overcomes the problems of uneven density found in die-pressing is *isostatic-pressing*, in which pressure is applied hydrostatically. There are two main versions of this process. In 'wet bag' pressing a rubber mould bag, sometimes with an inserted pin or mandrel to produce a shaped bore, is filled with powder and placed in a chamber of pressure-transmitting fluid, which is then pressurized. The applied pressure on the powder mass is more or less hydrostatic, and compaction is uniform (on the mandrel if this is included). 'Dry bag' pressing is a variant of the process, used for production of standardized shapes, in which there is no contact between operator and pressurizing fluid. The rubber tooling set forms part of the pressurizing system in the press, and the shape is normally pressed on a suitable mandrel which facilitates its removal from the tooling set after compaction. 'Dry bag' pressing is used for the manufacture of insulators for vehicle spark plugs because the process is capable of being run automatically and continuously to produce very large numbers of pieces. 'Wet bag' processing by comparison is very slow, and tends to be used primarily for the production of large blanks of pressed powder for subsequent machining, or for small runs of large pieces. Pressed, or 'green' density tends to be lower than in die-pressing, but is more homogeneous.

Injection-moulding is a process complementary to all others in that it is a method of making complex irregular shapes that would defy simple uniaxial pressing and would be difficult to machine from blanks. The powder mass is mixed with sufficient plastic binder to enable the mixture to be injected under pressure and at raised temperature into a cooler mould cavity in which it solidifies. After a short time, the mould is opened and the shape is ejected. More binder is normally needed than with almost any other process, and this leads to low green bulk density and larger shrinkage on firing, as well as problems of dealing with noxious fumes from the binder. Complex shapes such as terminal blocks, pigtail thread guides and cores for casting turbine blades are made in this way. The technique is used mainly for well-established shapes because of high tooling costs. Furthermore, because the filling of the mould depends on the transient rheology of the injected mass, there can be variations in density and defect content from point to point, especially in high-strength type materials.

3.2.3 Firing of ceramic materials

Nearly all ceramic materials are subjected to high-temperature processing to convert the shaped powder or mineral mass into a rigid hard ceramic. This occurs in part by chemical reaction of the constituents, and in part by redistribution of solid and liquid phases by one or more physical processes, but with the result that the shape usually densifies and shrinks as the pore space between the precursor particles is progressively removed. The raw materials for a particular product are chosen by the manufacturer so that they can be mixed, shaped and then processed at high temperature to produce the required microstructure and properties. For oxide- and mineral-based materials the firing process is usually one of simply heating in air (or the exhaust gases resulting from fuel combustion) for the required length of time. For non-oxide materials, rather more specialized processing is required, often specific to a given product.

3.2.3.1 Mineral- and oxide-based ceramics

For firing these materials, pieces are normally stacked in or on systems of refractory kiln furniture, either on flat plates separated by pillars, or in refractory boxes (termed 'saggers'). Precautions have to be taken in firing long rods and tubes and large heavy pieces because at the firing temperature most ceramics can distort under their own weight. Specially-shaped kiln furniture may be required to retain shape. Frictional forces produced between the piece and its support during shrinkage can be enough to cause distortion and even cracking. Large heavy pieces may be fired sitting on a blank disc of the same material, the disc providing a support that shrinks at the same rate as the piece, which thereby does not suffer frictional drag from the kiln furniture. Refractory tubing may be fired hanging from a ceramic pin or rod to keep it as straight as possible. This poses a limitation on the length and diameter of high-quality tube because of the size of furnace required and the difficulty of maintaining a uniform temperature over the length of the piece. Clearly, upper size limits are imposed on ceramic articles by the scale of the firing facilities available to the firm, and this may be determined by the type of work they normally undertake. Manufacturers cannot be expected to scale up in size beyond existing levels unless it is very much worth their while!

For wet-processed materials, the first step in the firing process is the removal of excess water at a temperature of 100–120°C. This is usually done in drying ovens before the high-temperature firing. The main firing may be done in intermittent kilns or in continuously fired tunnel kilns, depending on availability. The initial stages of firing have to be carefully controlled for materials containing temporary organic binders which have to be burned out under oxidizing conditions without disrupting the pressed shape. This process is usually complete by 300–400°C. On heating further, natural minerals lose combined water up to about 600°C, and reaction between all the anhydrous components begins above 700°C.

Where components have to be machined or treated in special ways, it is often necessary to give a low-temperature fire (a pre-fire) to the ceramic. This is done to burn out all the organic binders used in the primary green manufacturing process and to consolidate the powder to an extent where it is handleable and machinable by normal lathe or drilling tools, but not densified to the extent that diamond machining is required.

The maximum temperature and hold time to complete the densification process are chosen to suit the material and to achieve the required grain structure. Firing temperatures clearly vary according to the type of material, and in particular to the composition and particle size of raw materials. As a rough guide:

Simple claywares	1150–1250°C
Electrical porcelains	1200–1300°C
Refractory porcelains, steatites	1250–1500°C
Alumina ceramics, <96%	1350–1650°C
Alumina ceramics, >96%	1550–1800°C
Magnesia, zirconia, beryllia, thoria	1500–1900°C

Recent developments have involved the use of fast firing, in some cases to cheapen the firing cycle, and in others to achieve sintering to a dense body before grain growth occurs. In both cases, such processing tends to limit the size of component that can be reliably fired. The main problem is the temperature gradients in the material as it begins to shrink. If shrinkage is uneven, it can lead to cracking. At present the method is restricted to clay-based articles such as thin wall tiles, and to some of the fine-grained newer ceramics such as 'zirconia-toughened alumina'.

The residual porosity may be open (i.e. the component may be permeable to gases or liquids) or closed (i.e. impermeable to gases or liquids). In materials designed to be impermeable, simple firing in air leaves typically 0.5–5% closed porosity in the form of microscopic closed voids. In the main these do not affect the functioning of the component for the majority of applications. If the ultimate in fine grain size, strength or surface finish is essential, these pores can be substantially eliminated by subjecting the material to external pressure while it is in a relatively soft state during firing. This process, known as *hot-pressing*, is advantageous in enhancing densification without grain growth, but carries a heavy cost penalty and shape limitation. There are two variants of hot-pressing:

1. direct hot-pressing of a pressed powder blank in a die
2. isostatic hot-pressing of a prefired shape.

These methods are little used commercially for *oxide* ceramics. Direct hot-pressing is used for the production of some alumina ceramic tool pieces, and for research purposes. Isostatic hot-pressing uses high-pressure gas at high temperatures to eliminate most residual porosity. It is usual to prefire the ceramic component to an impervious state, so that the porosity is not connected to the surface. The pressure differential between the surface and the residual porosity gives the driving force for its elimination. There are some developments in progress on the use of isostatic hot-pressing on open porous ceramic shapes, or on 'green' pressed blanks, in which the surface of the component is sealed with an impervious layer, usually a glass or a metal foil.

3.2.3.2 Non-oxide ceramics

Most non-oxide ceramics are fired under rather different conditions to the simple vitrification or sintering methods employed for clay-based and oxide materials. Many non-oxides are very reluctant to sinter without pressure at easily attainable temperatures, and all require inert or non-oxidizing atmospheres. Nevertheless, the basic points about support of components during firing mentioned in the previous Section are relevant here also.

Pressureless-sintering is normally used for cermets (hardmetals) based on tungsten carbide using vacuum and a temperature of 1300–1400°C but, in the field of non-oxide ceramics, it is used only for what might be termed development materials. Alpha- and beta-silicon carbide can be sintered using a suitable dopant at temperatures between 2050 and 2200°C. Boron carbide can similarly be sintered. Silicon nitride can be sintered with suitable oxide additives at temperatures between 1700 and 1800°C in a nitrogen atmosphere (at higher temperatures it would dissociate to silicon and nitrogen). 'Sialon' materials (silicon aluminium oxy-nitrides) can also be sintered with suitable oxide additions in a similar temperature range. In all these instances, the primary phase would not sinter without the described additions, which are optimized for individual properties.

Sintering of such materials is enhanced by pressure, and many non-oxides can be produced by *hot-pressing*. However, it is an expensive process compared to sintering, and is limited to simple shapes, or to blanks which require subsequent machining. Since some of the materials with advantageous properties are also very hard, the combination of hot-pressing plus machining increases the expense; hence the attempts to develop sintering routes in which there is much less restriction on shape. Materials which are routinely hot-pressed on a commercial basis include silicon nitride, boron carbide, boron nitride, and titanium diboride/boron nitride composites. As a material under development, hot-pressed silicon carbide is also available. Hot-pressing is usually performed in a graphite die, sometimes lined with boron nitride to prevent reaction of the component with the graphite, and components are generally limited in size to about 100–150 mm or even less.

The most commonly employed method of bonding a non-oxide is by *'reaction-bonding'*. In this process, the required ceramic phase is formed in situ by reaction between chemical components. This has the advantage of being a relatively low-temperature, pressureless firing route, with the added attraction in some cases of very little change in dimensions between the green and fired states. The processes tend to be individual to given products, and some of them are described below.

'REFEL'* silicon carbide is produced by infiltrating a powder compact of silicon carbide and graphite with molten silicon under vacuum. The powder compact is first shaped by one of a variety of techniques, the binder is removed, and under slightly oxidizing conditions the carbon in the surface skin is removed. The greater porosity of the surface then acts as a wick to help the molten silicon rise up the component from the reservoir to penetrate the compact. The reaction between carbon and silicon produces fresh silicon carbide on the precursor grains and bonds them together. Control of compact density results in essentially no size change during this process, but the maximum size of component is limited by two factors. Firstly, the reaction is exothermic, and there is a risk of cracking due to thermal transients in cross-sections greater than about 20 mm. Secondly, although the capillary rise is more than adequate for practical purposes, the length of components is limited by the scale of plant required to contain the process at a fairly uniform temperature.

Other types of reaction-bonded silicon carbide employ vapour-phase reactions using either SiO or Si to effect the reaction with free carbon. In all products some free silicon remains, filling what would otherwise be porosity. The same type of process is used to convert the surface of graphite into one predominantly of silicon carbide for improved wear resistance.

Reaction-bonded silicon nitride (RBSN) is produced by nitridation of a

---

* A trademark of British Nuclear Fuels Ltd.

silicon powder compact under controlled conditions. Much fundamental work, now well documented, has been performed to understand the process and the influence of temperature, atmosphere and impurities in the precursor silicon. To go to completion, the process needs to be conducted slowly at temperatures near the melting point of silicon (1410°C) so that the silicon compact does not melt to form large globules within the component. Even so virtually all materials contain a small amount of free silicon, as well as some silica (SiO_2) from the original silicon particle surfaces. There is very little size change in the process (less than 1%), the increase in volume during reaction tending to fill the porosity in compact. RBSN is always open-porous because of the need for nitrogen gas to penetrate to achieve reaction. Sizes tend to be limited more by the capacity for producing silicon compacts than by the reaction-bonding process itself, although items greater than about 20 mm wall thickness require rather longer processing times than thin-walled items to allow gas penetration and to avoid uncontrolled exotherms during reaction.

Carbon and graphite products are also essentially reaction-bonded. The pressed blank of carbon or graphite particles, with a carbonizable binder, often a tar or a resin, is fired under reducing conditions. During this process the binder chars and decomposes and the free carbon produced binds the precursor particles together. The higher the firing temperature, the greater the degree of conversion of amorphous carbon to graphite and the stronger the bond. The same type of process may be used for carbon fibre reinforced carbon composites.

The processes described above are those used to manufacture fine-grained, homogeneous ceramics of high strength where crystal-crystal bonding is the aim. For technical ceramics of lower grade, and for refractory products, only silicon carbide is of significance, and for these purposes direct bonding between the carbide grains is not always essential. There are two main methods used to produce ceramic shapes. Clay-bonding requires no specialized chemical reaction. The product is fired in a suitably non-oxidizing atmosphere, and is not especially refractory. Nitride-bonding relies on the reaction between nitrogen gas and free silicon to produce a refractory bond of silicon nitride between the silicon carbide grains, and is essentially a reaction-bonding process. Some refractory products use a silicon oxynitride bonding process. The products as a general rule are fairly coarse-grained, and are used for kiln furniture and furnace parts at temperatures in excess of the capability of silicate-based products, say above about 1300–1350°C. Large pieces pose less of a manufacturing problem than with the cleaner, finer-grained engineering ceramics because firing shrinkage and distortion are usually low, limited by the coarse grain size, and fine tolerances are not usually required. Other methods of bonding have been reported, using silicon carbide (produced by reaction-bonding) and alumina.

3.2.4 Specialized shaping methods for ceramics

3.2.4.1 Vitreous carbon

Most graphite and carbon products are produced by pressing a suitable powder mix and firing under inert conditions to carbonize a binder and produce a porous product which is partly graphite, partly amorphous carbon, depending on the firing conditions. In contrast, vitreous carbon is a variety of carbon made by carbonizing a cross-linked polymeric material that has already been moulded to the required shape. The cross-linking appears to prevent graphitization of the carbon, which remains as an amorphous black glassy-looking material. It is of low density, but has no open porosity, and is useful as a crucible or lining material which has the chemical inertness of carbon and is also impermeable. It is mostly restricted to thin-walled shapes.

3.2.4.2 Chemical vapour deposition (c.v.d.) ceramics

It is possible to produce ceramics from volatile compounds of their chemical constituents. For example, silicon- and carbon-containing gases, such as the chlorides, may be reacted with hydrogen at high temperature to deposit silicon carbide and give HCl as the exhaust gas. In this way, ceramic coatings may be laid down on suitable substrates to produce either coated components, or thin-walled complete components after removal of the substrate. The term 'pyrolytic' is also used.

This is a specialized process not yet in common usage. Materials that can be made by this route include graphite and carbon fibre composites, silicon carbide, silicon nitride, titanium carbide and boron nitride. The microstructure produced tends to depend very much on deposition conditions, i.e. proportions of gaseous components, rate of gas flow, type of substrate, temperature and pressure, and this has limited its commercial use. Tungsten carbide tools are being coated with titanium carbide by such methods, and boron nitride crucibles are available commercially.

3.2.4.3 Flame and plasma spraying

This is an adaptation of the ceramic spray-coating process whereby thin-walled oxide ceramic components can be made by flame or plasma spraying a fine precursor powder or powder mix on to a heated substrate. In the spraying process, the particles are heated above their melting point, and are essentially splat-cooled on hitting the substrate. Some residual open porosity can be expected, and subsequent firing of the component may be recommended to improve density and remove stresses introduced by the quenching process. The types of material that can be processed in this way tend to be limited to stable oxides, such as alumina, zirconia, magnesia, thoria, silica etc. which will not degrade in air. Even so, metastable phases may be produced, such as occurs with alumina, and a subsequent firing is needed to produce a stable phase.

3.2.4.4 Electrophoretic deposition

With certain ceramics it is possible to manufacture a slip or suspension of ceramic particles in water or other electrolyte. These particles become electrically charged by virtue of their structure and/or by the use of surface active agents, and can therefore be deposited onto a pre-shaped electrically conducting former by a voltage gradient. After electro-deposition, the built-up skin on the former is removed, dried and fired in the usual way. This method can be very precise in dimensions and has been used for making specialized thin-walled components such as wave-guide windows. It is not, however, in general use in the ceramic manufacturing industry, but is frequently used for deposition of thin coatings, such as enamels on metals.

3.2.5 Manufacture of glasses and glass-ceramics

Glass melts are produced by fusing a batch of mixed raw materials in the required weight proportions. Melting conditions are important in achieving homogeneous bubble-free material, and compositions tend to be optimized to have good working characteristics if this is important, and to give resistance to devitrification (crystallization) during working.

3.2.5.1 Sheet glass

Most sheet glass is now made by the 'Float' process developed by Pilkington Brothers PLC, whereby glass from a large melting tank is allowed to form a sheet with a high-quality surface finish by floating it on to a bath of molten tin. This has almost completely replaced traditional drawing methods, except for such applications as greenhouse glazing where optical imaging is unimportant. The glass emerges from the Float production line in the annealed state, and is cut into a range of standard-sized sheets for distribution. Specific sizes are either to special order, or cut from the standard sizes by scribing and snapping.

Some sheet glasses for decorative or glazing purposes are further treated, e.g. some of the solar control glasses.

Thermal strengthening or toughening is used to improve the strength of glass sheet. The glass is heated to a little above the glass transition temperature, and then cooled fairly quickly by controlled air blasts. This causes the surface to become rigid whilst the inner region is still fluid. As the central zone cools and becomes rigid it draws the surface into compression, imparting higher strength to the sheet. Such a material will resist light surface damage unless this is sufficiently deep to enter the tensile central zone. If this occurs the material will craze over suddenly, perhaps without warning. It should be noted that the glass generally has to be held by some form of clamp during this process, and the point of clamping can be a source of incorrect toughening and subsequent failure. The manufacturer should be consulted about the risks involved.

Chemical strengthening can also be used, inducing surface compression by 'stuffing' the surface with additional ionic species, usually by immersion in a molten salt bath. Strength levels can be extremely high, but the compressive layer is very thin and can readily be damaged, in which case the strength is no greater than that of ordinary sheet glass.

Sheet glass can be shaped to a limited curvature after manufacture by allowing it to sag to the shape of a mould, e.g. car windscreens and decorative glazing. This is done prior to any thermal or chemical toughening process (see BS 952).

Rod and tubing are normally drawn from the melt, either vertically upwards, or down through an orifice in the tank bottom (over a mandrel in the case of tubing). Small-bore tubing is normally drawn down from a larger diameter. Specialist manufacturers can advise on their capability in terms of size and wall thickness ranges, since these vary between different types of glass. Precision-bore tubing can be made by shrinking oversize tubing on to a removable precision mandrel.

3.2.5.2 Moulded glassware

Molten glass from the main melting tank is allowed to cool to the required temperature at which its viscosity is correct for the particular moulding process. As the glass comes through an orifice in the base of the tank, 'gobs' or large droplets of glass are sheared off and are fed to the moulding process in synchronization with the moulding machinery. The moulding operation may include such processes as pressing, extruding and blowing into a mould or series of moulds. In this way automatic moulding of glassware is a relatively cheap process per unit of production, but quantities have to be very large. Typical products include bottles, ash-trays, ovenware, some laboratory glassware, glass bricks, TV funnels and face-plates, chemical plant components and insulators.

The whole moulding process is one that requires careful control of conditions. It is very much a transient process, relying on the setting of the glass as it cools to hold the shape made in the liquid state. As a consequence it is not an accurate shaping process. Square corners cannot be produced, and should not be specified. Uniformity of wall thickness or flatness of surfaces cannot be guaranteed. Clear holes cannot easily be made, but a blind hole can be introduced by moulding a hollow cap which is later cut off. Screw threads to large tolerances can be moulded on to outside surfaces. Moulding faults, such as surface crazing, adherence of mould oxide or lubricants, slumping if over-hot, etc., arise if conditions are not optimized. Quality control checks are important in eliminating optically obvious defects. All moulded glassware has to be annealed at a temperature near the glass transition temperature to remove stresses produced as a consequence of cooling rapidly and unevenly during the moulding process. The articles are otherwise prone to shatter. Thermal toughening can be carried out, but this is usually a subsequent process, perhaps after further machining or shaping.

The size range of blown or moulded glass components depends on the manufacturer's capability and the type of glass involved. Components with length or diameter from 10–500 mm and with wall thickness from 3–30 mm can be moulded automatically. Thinner walls require blowing or blow-moulding. The overall dimensions can be to a tolerance of typically $\pm 2\%$ or better, but wall thickness may need a much greater tolerance, e.g. ± 1 mm, arising from the inaccuracies of hot moulding. Hand moulding of large pieces is generally less accurate. Creyke et al. (see Bibliography) give further information on this subject.

Components need to be designed so that they can be readily removed from the mould (or vice versa). Tapers in the direction of mould movement ease the removal of the hot component, taper angles being typically 1–5° depending on component size.

3.2.5.3 Flame-worked glassware

Most glasses, providing they are resistant to devitrification, can be flame-worked in the viscous state by various processes. Hand-working is particularly useful for special glassware, for laboratory ware, for special seals to metals or between various materials. For production articles it is clearly most advantageous to flame-work glass by machine, as in the electronic valve and light bulb industry, but this is often not possible. For specialist products or for short runs, skilled craftsmen must be used, with commensurately higher unit costs.

3.2.5.4 Optical and small-batch glasses

Large-scale glass-making is normally undertaken in tanks made from refractory blocks, which have a lifetime of several years but clearly dissolve or are eroded away by the glass. Optical glasses need to be made to rather higher standards of homogeneity and purity, and are usually melted in smaller quantities on a batch basis, using furnaces lined with platinum alloy. Other special glasses and glazes required in limited quantities can also be made in this way but, if purity is unimportant, they may be melted in large refractory pots.

Optical glasses are normally cooled slowly in block form, with particularly long and careful annealing to ensure homogeneity of refractive index, which is a function of fictive temperature (see Figure 2.2.27). Special glasses for other applications are quenched, moulded, cast, drawn, or processed by whatever technique is required for the particular application.

3.2.5.5 Silica glass

Silica glass, without deliberately-introduced network-modifying species that lower the glass transition temperature range and decrease viscosity and working temperature, is relatively refractory and cannot be produced by the normal glass melting methods. A range of different methods of manufacture have been developed by specialist companies in the field, producing different qualities of product.

For lower-quality products where neither transparency nor the complete absence of closed porosity is important, such as trays for material processing, boats and dishes for chemical analysis, and heating element tubes and mantles, high-quality sand is fused around a carbon electrode until a sufficiently thick layer of viscous melt is produced. The electrode is removed, and the melt, with unmelted material adhering to it, is blown into a mould which consists of a number of the required shapes. When cold, the shapes are cut out of the moulding, and the rough surface skin is removed by grit-blasting.

For higher-quality products where transparency is an important criterion, a higher-quality melt is produced from graded crystal quartz by fusing to higher temperatures to produce billets. These billets are then drawn into tubing or rod in carbon or tungsten rod furnaces under a protective atmosphere.

For optical-quality material, silica is usually produced synthetically by oxidation of silicon tetrachloride in an oxy-hydrogen gas flame. Silica is deposited as a billet which is slowly withdrawn from the furnace. Titania-silica glasses are produced in the same way. There are alternative methods which lead to a lower hydroxyl ion (OH^-) content in the silica, such as hydrogen-free plasma deposition.

Clear silica can be flame-worked at high flame temperatures, but care needs to be taken to ensure that volatile silicon monoxide is removed from the vicinity of the operator. The glass must be clean and free from alkali deposits otherwise devitrification to cristobalite will be enhanced.

A glass of about 96% SiO_2 can be produced by the 'Vycor' process in which a borosilicate glass is made by normal glass-melting processes, and is then heat-treated to cause it to separate on a very fine scale into two interpenetrating phases. One of these contains about 96% SiO_2, and the other contains most of the boron and sodium as well as some SiO_2. The latter phase leaches readily in acid, and a honeycomb of the 96% SiO_2 glass is produced. This is densified by heat-treatment to a translucent high-silica glass which has vestigial porosity.

3.2.5.6 Sintered glasses

Glass powder or grit produced by crushing bulk glass can be shaped and fired to a modest temperature a little above the transformation range to produce a porous sintered material. In this way, narrow sieve fractions of glass powder can be used to produce a range of filter materials of various pore sizes. Finely powdered glasses can be shaped by many conventional dry and wet shaping methods. Die-pressing can produce fairly accurate shapes with thin walls and small holes and with a dimensional accuracy which would be impossible with use of molten glass. One material in fairly common use is slip-cast, sintered fused silica which has an open porosity level of typically 10–15% of bulk volume. It is fairly easily machinable by tungsten carbide tools because of its friability. The same type of material made by injection moulding is used for precision cores for casting turbine blades where a high degree of thermal shock resistance is required in a complex shape but where open porosity is needed to facilitate removal by chemical dissolution (Figure 2.2.28).

3.2.5.7 Glass-ceramics

This class of material (also known by the Russian name 'sital') is manufactured mainly by routes that reflect a glassy origin. A glass-ceramic commences life as a glass melt which is usually cast or moulded to the required shape. However, since the precursor glasses are designed to devitrify on a fine scale within the temperature range between the transformation, T_g, and the liquidus, T_L, they cannot generally be worked satisfactorily in the glassy state as can normal, relatively devitrification-resistant materials. This poses a time/temperature limitation on the shaping process which may limit the complexity of the component further than is often the case with a simple glass.

Following the moulding process, the glassy components are subject to a heat treatment designed to nucleate and grow crystals on a fine scale, sometimes known as 'ceramming', converting the material to a polycrystalline form usually with some residual glassy intercrystalline material. Crystallization is exothermic, and compositions are designed to be tolerant to the thermal runaway this can produce in large shapes.

Research has produced many varieties of glass-ceramic, each of which has to be treated in a different way, and has individual limitations on shaping procedures. The applications for such materials tend to be rather individual, and a particular commercial composition may have been designed to suit a particular aspect of assembly of a component, or a seal, or to show particularly desirable properties such as zero coefficient of expansion.

Monolithic glass-ceramics (i.e. for free-standing components) are usually designed to 'ceram' with the minimum of distortion due to slumping (viscous sag above T_g) and to volume changes on crystallization. On the other hand, in making glass-ceramic to metal fusion seals, substantial viscous flow and wetting may be desirable before crystallization greatly increases the effective viscosity. This may be more easily done during a moulding operation from the melt than by subsequently heating a blank from cold. Each application may require a different ideal composition to achieve both the desired thermal expansion properties and the process requirements. These same points are equally true in sintered devitrifying solder glasses, such as that used to seal TV face plates to the funnel.

In comtemplating using a glass-ceramic for an application other than one in which a pre-cerammed blank is machined to shape, the user is advised to work closely with the manufacturer of the glass-ceramic to develop both composition and process to a satisfactory conclusion.

3.3

Dimensional tolerances and surface finish

There is much misunderstanding of dimensional tolerances and surface finish of ceramic materials. This arises primarily because routine machining of a metal component to say ± 0.02 mm (0.001″) poses no difficulty in a machine shop, whereas such a level of tolerance requires relatively expensive diamond grinding with almost all ceramics. A second consideration is that the manufacturing methods with metals and to some extent with plastics ensure that geometric properties such as straightness, squareness and roundness, and consistency of material from one piece to the next, are for most purposes taken for granted. The properties of the material are in the main in the stock shapes such as bar, strip, sheet, etc., and the process of manufacture only produces a shape from the pre-prepared material. This is not the case with ceramics because each component is made individually from the starting powder, and variation is possible in every stage of manufacture through to the final product. For example, there may be variations in chemistry and in physical properties which result from variations in shaping technique and in the total 'heat work' experienced in firing. There may be variations in shape due to different degrees of sag while the components are soft in firing. Strict quality control procedures are required to minimize such variation, but nonetheless each piece will be individual, and this individuality has to be taken into account in design and specification. This Section discusses factors affecting simple design and dimensional tolerance for situations where high stresses are unlikely to occur in service. Much of the discussion is applicable also to glass products, except the Sections on shaping from powder which are relevant only to sintered glasses. Generally speaking, moulding tolerances on glassware have to be rather larger than the overall tolerances on as-fired ceramics.

3.3.1 General points

For most sintered technical and engineering ceramics, shrinkage during firing is typically 10–20% on linear dimensions. The precise level of shrinkage depends on 'green' (unfired) density and on final fired density. Both depend on the shaping method, the raw materials and the firing schedule. Such a level of shrinkage inevitably means that fired dimensions of a shaped component are uncertain, usually to about 2%, but sometimes less depending on how easy it is to achieve process control in a long run. In addition, a level of distortion will result from slumping due to gravity. This tends to be most significant in long pieces of thin section which do not have sufficient rigidity to maintain shape. Small pieces may have moulding flash and furnace dirt cleaned off by tumbling in a mill or by vibro-energy milling with scrap components or milling media. Often termed 'rumbling', this process tends to round off external corners, and reduces dimensional accuracy further. However, rounded corners are useful in avoiding local chipping in handling and use, and rumbling is the easiest way of achieving them. BS 1598:1964 Appendix N shows a table of typical manufacturing tolerances in the as-fired state.

For technical glassware, even greater tolerances on as-moulded shapes are required. Precision-bore tube is available, produced by shrinking on to a precision mandrel, but otherwise tolerances must be ample since shaping is done in the liquid state.

For materials which of necessity must undergo a machining process after initial shaping, tolerances can be extremely small. Grinding is normally required to ensure that a surface is flat or that a cylinder is round to better than 0.02 mm (0.001″). Many ceramic manufacturers can undertake this as a matter of routine. If a ground finish is not fine enough or flat enough, for example for seal faces, lapping can be undertaken, typically to a flatness of better than 0.1 fringes/mm with a finish that depends on the care with which the lapping is done. Lapping of optical glass components can be done to a very high degree of precision. Materials with closed porosity, such as all sintered ceramics, show limitations in surface finish achieved in lapping owing to the tendency for grain tear-out and for relief polishing. Nevertheless, it is probably true to say that *good quality surface finishes to the required surface roughness are more readily obtained and retained in hard ceramics and glasses than in most metals.* Furthermore, the lack of macroscopic plasticity means that the *shaping is generally permanent, with no tendency to distort due to slow stress relief, as with metals,* although some forms of low-expansion glass-ceramic are found to change dimensions slowly as a result of the microstructural stresses associated with the substantial thermal expansion anisotropy of crystalline phases therein (see Sections 2.2.4.3 and 2.4.3.3).

3.3.2 Sources of dimensional variation in as-fired components

Cost is an important factor in the design of a sintered ceramic component. It is advantageous to design so that an as-fired component can be accepted for direct assembly into the application. If this is not done, and tight tolerances (which might be normal for machined metal components) are insisted upon where they are not absolutely essential, the cost of grinding operations could be several times the cost of the as-fired shape.

In designing around as-fired tolerances it is necessary to consider several factors:
1. reliability of making the shape in the green state before firing
2. does the proposed shape have large green density variations which might lead to distortion on firing?
3. size variation that can be expected among the fired components, and the means of accommodating this in mating the component to other items
4. in producing rigid joints, the design should allow for minimizing stress concentrations resulting from contact between non-flat surfaces or from localized gripping.

For glasses, (1) should be read as the reliability of moulding, and (2) is not applicable.

The following Sections discuss these points in more detail using some examples. The intention is primarily to produce a broad picture, and it is essential to seek advice from one or more manufacturers on the suitability of a proposed design. Modifications to simplify production should help the customer with a component that can be more reliably incorporated into the final product. The reputation of a manufacturer depends on his ability to win custom based on the reliability of his product and the guidance he gives to the user.

3.3.2.1 Reliability of shaping in the green state

Shaped ceramic bodies can be handled in the so-called green, unfired state, but they are fragile. They can be machined by turning, drilling, milling, form-grinding and filing, and press flashing can be removed by hand with a cloth. If a component cannot be made in one single press operation, it may have to undergo a number of such machining operations before firing to obtain the required dimensions.

The relative fragility of green ceramic bodies means that:
1. there may be size and shape limitations on what can be directly shaped by die-pressing, and on what can be handled satisfactorily in the factory
2. there may be difficulties in machining in the green state, particularly with hole break-out in drilling and turning thin-walled sections.

Furthermore, die-pressing may be unreliable because fragile die parts may bend, wear or break off and thus affect the geometry of the pressed shape.

Figure 3.3.1 illustrates some of these points. In each case, the manufacturer will appreciate the limitations of his capability, and will be able to advise on such points.

For glasses the reliability of moulding is to be interpreted as the ability to obtain the required quality of moulding free from defects (see BS 3447).

3.3.2.2 Liability to distortion on firing

In addition to the normal shrinkage on firing, shape may be distorted for one or more of the following reasons:
1. The restraining effect of contact with a rigid surface while undergoing shrinkage.
2. Bending or bowing due to creep at high temperatures during firing (particularly in long shapes with small cross-sections).
3. Local distortion due to local variations of starting density (more particularly in die-pressed shapes).

If a component changes in size on firing (most materials shrink linearly at least 15% but silicon carbide and silicon nitride made by reaction-bonding are exceptions), then the top of the component in the furnace has freedom to shrink both laterally and vertically almost without restraint other than that resulting from the part of the component connected to it. The bottom of the component, however, has to support the weight of all the material above it and therefore during shrinkage there will be a frictional drag between it and its non-shrinking support which will tend to restrain movement.

Figure 3.3.1
Design factors affecting
manufacturing reliability.

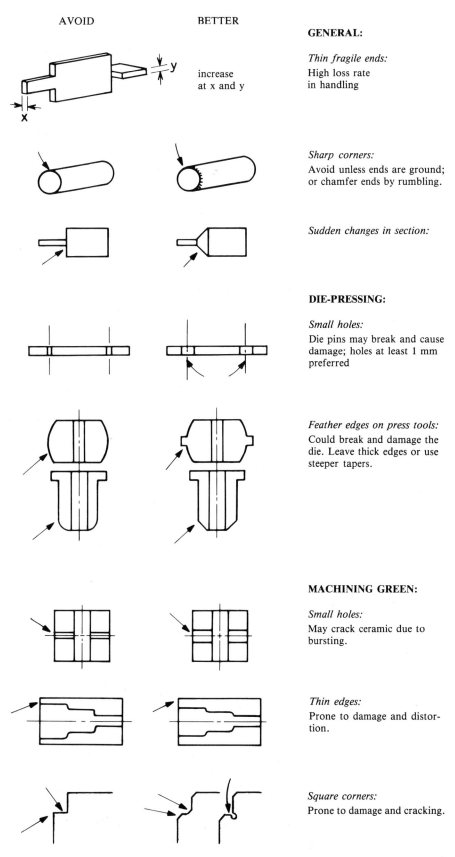

AVOID   BETTER

GENERAL:

Thin fragile ends:
High loss rate
in handling

increase
at x and y

Sharp corners:
Avoid unless ends are ground;
or chamfer ends by rumbling.

Sudden changes in section:

DIE-PRESSING:

Small holes:
Die pins may break and cause
damage; holes at least 1 mm
preferred

Feather edges on press tools:
Could break and damage the
die. Leave thick edges or use
steeper tapers.

MACHINING GREEN:

Small holes:
May crack ceramic due to
bursting.

Thin edges:
Prone to damage and distortion.

Square corners:
Prone to damage and cracking.

Dependent on the material, and on the weight, shape and cross-section of the component, this may result in a lateral shrinkage at the base of the component smaller than at the top, and in extreme cases may result in cracking at the base. Manufacturing techniques to overcome this often involve the use of small inert ceramic particles between the component and its support, but distortion can still occur with large heavy components with a relatively small support area. One solution is to set the component on a tile of the same green material that will shrink at a similar rate in firing and thus avoid most of the drag. However, the purchaser must then expect to pay the cost of the tile as a penalty for the production of the heavy shape he wants.

Another variation of this effect occurs when a component of uneven section is subjected to a fast firing operation and the thin parts heat up and shrink in advance of the thicker parts. When the thick sections finally shrink they distort the previously shrunk thin sections. Manufacturing methods such as the use of closed saggars (refractory boxes to even out the temperature in firing) and slow rates of heating in temperature ranges where rapid shrinkage occurs will help to correct these faults. In cases where fast firing is essential to achieve the required properties, a size or shape limitation may exist.

Bending or bowing distortion during firing results from slump due to gravity, and depends very much on how individual pieces are supported. Shapes that are simple to support, such as flat tiles, may be stacked on a flat base separated by some granular material (sand or alumina for example) which allows lateral movement during shrinkage. Rods, tubes and other extruded sections are normally laid flat unless the manufacturer can suspension-fire them. Distortion can arise in handling material wet from extrusion, and in firing if the support is not perfectly flat. With larger-bore tubes there is always a tendency to sag to an oval cross-section. Manufacturers will normally quote a maximum distortion or bow if requested. If a tight specification is placed on flatness or straightness in excess of the normal operating limits of manufacture, grinding will be required.

'Bow' or, in a plate, 'camber' is defined in ASTM F109–73, as a single 'arch of curvature', which may be expressed as the arch height per unit of component length (see also BS 1598: 1964 Appendix N). For alumina ceramics for electronic applications this might typically be 0.006 mm/mm, but for suspension-fired refractory tubing could well be less. Another term defined by ASTM F109–73 is 'waviness', "a long-order departure from flatness as opposed to sharp discontinuities. Amplitude is in excess of specified surface finish". For any application in which bow or waviness is important, manufacturers' advice should be sought.

Shapes that require expensive support systems to minimize distortion should perhaps be redesigned. In the tableware industry however, it is a matter of routine in firing to support large plates, etc., on 'setters', and the same can be done for technical ceramics.

Local distortion results from uneven shrinkage on firing, and is caused by uneven green density in the shaped product. This is particularly noticeable in die-pressed pieces where die fill and pressing pressure vary from one point to another. It may also occur in slip-cast and in extruded pieces where density, or in some cases the degree of alignment of non-spherical raw material particles, depends on distance from the mould or die face.

Some examples are shown in Figure 3.3.2 which illustrates this point. In

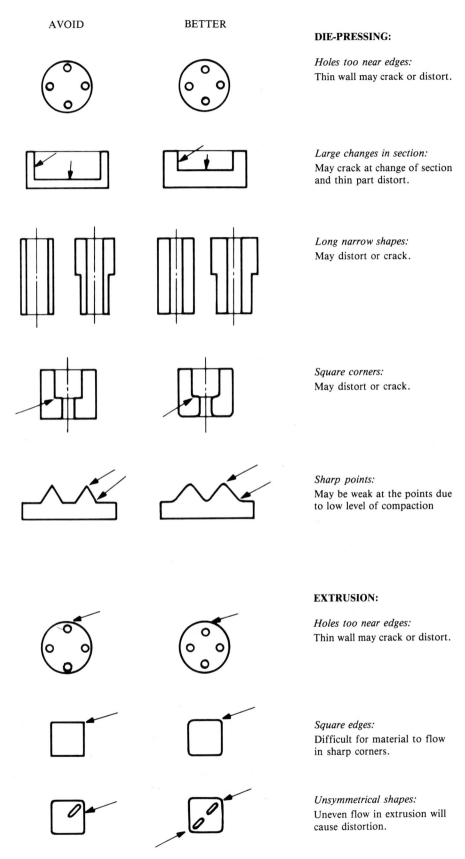

Figure 3.3.2
Designs which induce distortion resulting from uneven green density.

AVOID　　BETTER

DIE-PRESSING:

Holes too near edges:
Thin wall may crack or distort.

Large changes in section:
May crack at change of section and thin part distort.

Long narrow shapes:
May distort or crack.

Square corners:
May distort or crack.

Sharp points:
May be weak at the points due to low level of compaction

EXTRUSION:

Holes too near edges:
Thin wall may crack or distort.

Square edges:
Difficult for material to flow in sharp corners.

Unsymmetrical shapes:
Uneven flow in extrusion will cause distortion.

die-pressing uniform dimensions are desirable. Large changes in section, long thin shapes, narrow gaps between holes and component edges, square internal or external edges and sharp points should be avoided. For example, the variation of die-wall friction in a long thin-walled tube leads to variation of green density along the length, being lowest in the centre which then shrinks more giving a 'waisted' appearance. In extruded sections, sharp corners, holes near walls, excessively thin walls and unsymmetrical shapes are also to be avoided. It is difficult to be specific with respect to slip-casting, but sharp corners are certainly to be avoided. Again the manufacturers advice should be sought.

Distortion of glassware can occur at any stage during manufacture while the temperature is above about 50°C above T_g. Some movement can be expected after removal of hot ware from a mould, or during annealing. These processes are usually optimized to minimize distortion, but in automatic processes this could involve considerable losses until the conditions appropriate to the size and shape of component are found.

3.3.2.3 Size variation between components and size tolerance

Ignoring for the moment the distortion that can occur on firing, there will be a small variation in size between components due to small variations in green density (originating from variable die fill or other process variables). In most materials, particularly those made by machining from pre-pressed blanks, this may be negligible, but for directly-moulded shapes where the amount of material in the die relies on automatic die filling or hand filling without pre-weighing, the variation of mass between pieces, particularly small ones, may be $\pm 1\%$ or more. The average of this variation should lie within say $\pm 1\%$ of the nominal required mass, giving an overall tolerance of $\pm 2\%$. If this mass variation is $\pm 2\%$, then assuming equal distribution of linear tolerances in all three dimensions, the associated linear variation is $\pm 0.67\%$. To this must be added the uncertainty of shrinkage to fired density and any tendency to distort. Manufacturers therefore normally place an overall linear tolerance of $\pm 2\%$ or ± 0.2 mm, whichever is the greater, on what is nominally required, which should encompass size variation between individual pieces. This latter is usually fairly small once production of an item is routine. In addition, if the component is rumbled or glazed, a further tolerance is required, although glazing would not normally be used in areas likely to contact other surfaces, and therefore not in areas requiring accurate sizing.

This overall dimensional tolerance, which may be agreed at a particular level for the purposes of a contractual specification, must always be allowed for in design of the component and of adjacent parts. Take for example a hypothetical component which is clamped to a reference surface and contains two holes which mate with two accurately positioned holes in an associated metal part (Figure 3.3.3). Not only is the tolerance on distance between centres of the respective pairs of holes important, but also the tolerance on hole diameter and the tolerance on the distance between the holes and other locating points. The obvious solution is to ensure that the holes in the ceramic component are sufficiently large to accommodate the combined maximum deviation.

Figure 3.3.3
Allowing for tolerances on dimensions of as-fired ceramic components (schematic and exaggerated).

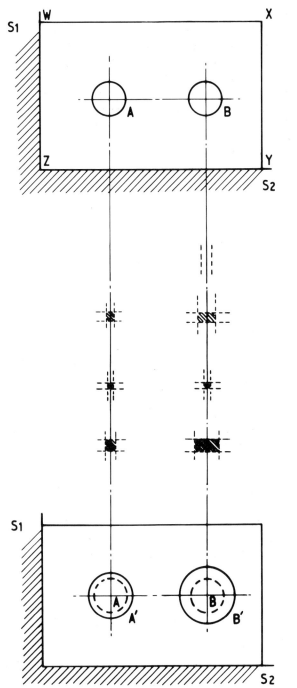

PROBLEM:

A block of ceramic WXYZ to be clamped to reference surfacess S_1S_2 requires holes to line up with A, B in metal bracket, accurately positioned and sized.

TOLERANCES:

(1) on separation of hole centres, e.g. $\pm 2\%$, incorporated in:

(2) tolerances on hole centres relative to reference surfaces S1 and S2. (e.g. $\pm 2\%$)

(3) tolerance on hole diameter (e.g. $\pm 2\%$)

(2) + (3) gives total required allowance to ensure mating with A and B within specified tolerances

SOLUTION:

The ceramic block needs holes A' and B' which are oversize by tolerances (2) + (3) above. In practice both holes would probably be made equally oversize.

Another example would be the clearance required on the inside and outside of a cylindrical ceramic sleeve which acts as an insulating spacer between a metal rod inside a concentric metal tube (Figure 3.3.4). Let us assume the metal component diameters are accurately sized to a tolerance much better than the ±2% of the ceramic. The ceramic sleeve in the as-fired state will require a tolerance of ±2% on inside and outside diameters. The actual variation of wall thickness should be small, only ±2% of thickness as a result of concentricity of the die system used. Depending on the criteria used in an agreed specification, the ±2% tolerance on diameters may or may not allow sufficiently for out-of-roundness caused by slump in firing. This would be a point to check. If the sleeve is of any length, an additional allowance should be made for bow, which is a further point to write into a specification.

This overall tolerance level rather over-simplifies the situation because in practice much lower levels can be achieved with high levels of quality control on well-behaved materials manufactured in large quantities. In addition, there are situations where a whole family of dimensions on a component vary together in the same direction. This subject is dealt with in more detail in Section 3.2.5.

Figure 3.3.4
As-fired tolerances for hollow cylinders (schematic and exaggerated).

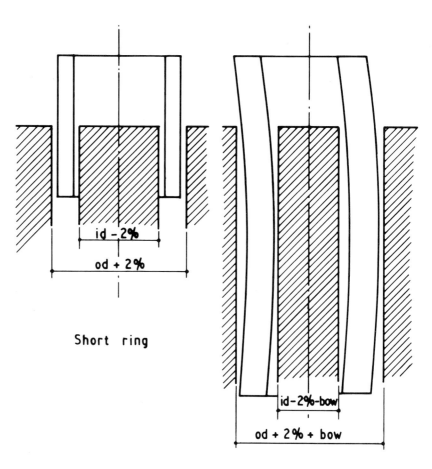

Short ring

Long cylinder with bow

Screw threads can be made externally or internally by form grinding after firing, or by pressing isostatically on to a threaded mandrel, or by turning a blank in the green state (before firing). Because of the need to allow sufficient tolerance on firing shrinkage, those made before firing will never be as accurate as typical standard threads in metals. The threads should be made suitably slack, and should be used only to locate the component and not to clamp it down hard. Threads should be as coarse as possible (< 32 t.p.i. or < 12 t.p.cm.) and not have too sharp an included angle (> 55°, say). The form of the thread should be rounded, not sharp. Any portion of a cylindrical shape left unthreaded should be of diameter less than that of the bottom of the thread (or greater in the case of an internal thread) to allow tool runout. (See also Section 3.5.2).

It is important to discuss tolerance factors with manufacturers. It is often very much cheaper to modify a design to suit as-fired tolerances than to insist on tight engineering tolerance if this involves grinding the component to size. If grinding is essential, then the area to be ground should be minimized.

3.3.3 Machining ceramics and glass to close tolerance

Machining of a ceramic in the fired state is normally undertaken only when it is not possible to achieve the necessary dimensional tolerance, e.g. for mating with other components. It is a relatively expensive process when each item has to be treated individually, but can be surprisingly cheap if the production run warrants setting up automatic or semi-automatic techniques of grinding simple shapes to size. For example, with centreless grinding of short lengths of rod or tube, there is no handling of the individual components, and, subject to the length/diameter ratio and the amount of material to be removed, this can be a relatively cheap operation. The same applies to grinding rods to a defined length and placing flats on surfaces. The limitation is often in gripping the item to get the first reference face, but once this is done the other faces can be ground accurately to close tolerance. Vacuum chucks are frequently used. Checking for dimensions is done on a percentage agreed between manufacturer and customer.

Machining of glasses and some glass-ceramics is much easier than machining most polycrystalline ceramics because of their lower hardness and toughness. It is done much more routinely and is a much faster operation. Most optical components are machined from blocks of material to a rough-ground state before final polishing. Joints of all types in glass pipework and laboratory ware are machined to ensure a good mating fit. The edges of sheet glass are often ground, particularly small pieces such as are used for pressure windows and other technical applications.

Virtually all coarse machining of ceramics and glasses is done with diamond grit impregnated grinding tools rotating at high speed and employing liquid coolant. The surface finish achieved is determined by the wheel type (e.g. peripheral or cup types), grit size, its concentration in the wheel, the bond type (metal or resin), the surface speed, the depth and direction of cut, the type of lubricant, etc. The surface finish determines the surface properties, particularly strength, cleanability, and wettability by coating materials applied subsequently. Thus if the actual surface finish is important, as well as dimensional accuracy, it may be necessary to undertake some trials to obtain optimum machining conditions.

Grinding is not a particularly flexible machining technique (Figure 3.3.5). Flat surfaces and cylinders pose few problems, but intricate shaping should be minimized. In particular, holes should be at least 3 mm in diameter and should be produced undersize before firing, the grinding operation being used only to 'ream' them out to the required dimensions. Direct drilling is difficult, particularly for small holes, although some companies specialize in such work using diamond drills or ultrasonic drills. Internal corners should not be sharp since it is impossible to keep a sharp corner on a grinding wheel. Similarly, closely defined corner radii should be avoided. If a sharp corner is required it should be undercut. Sharp external corners should also be avoided since not only are they readily damaged by impact in handling or use, but also they are liable to chip in machining giving a high rejection rate. Some materials are more prone to chip than others, in particular, glasses, some glass-ceramics, and other materials of low fracture toughness.

The appearance of pieces after grinding critical dimensions only may have to be considered. Figure 3.3.5 shows some examples. The line of intersection of ground and as-fired or moulded surfaces may end up being wavy, due to the variation of shape of the as-fired surface. To avoid this, either both surfaces should be ground, or the design should be reconsidered to relax tolerances, or blending of the surfaces by 'rumbling' or vibro-energy milling should be accepted. Uneven coloration of the exposed machined surface can result with materials with colour variations through the thickness.

The tolerance level achieved by grinding operations tends to depend on the amount of stock to be removed, the rate of removal, the wear rate on the grinding wheel and the precision of the machine, but generally is very close, and probably better than that achievable with metals. 'Burn' does not occur, and very small depths of cut can be made effectively. In this sense grinding of non-metallic materials is easier than with metals. BS 1598:1964, Appendix N gives some general information on tolerances in grinding that are 'in general use'. Tolerances of ± 0.02 mm on a diameter, for example, should pose no problems for the manufacturer. However, some aspects of grinding technique are important. Excessive stock removal rates can overheat the material and can damage the surface either mechanically or by subsequent thermal shock when quenched by coolant. The result is that the surface structure becomes shattered, sometimes with a crazy-paving effect, causing loss of strength, loss of hermetic properties in seals or vacuum applications, difficulties in metallizing, pick-up of dirt and penetration of grinding lubricant. In addition, a large surface area is available for corrosive attack by chemical reagents, and in this respect some grinding fluids must themselves be considered corrosive and should be washed off immediately. This type of defect is fairly easily checked by a test for dye absorption on a clean ground surface. It is essential that this is done before further operations such as lapping or polishing are undertaken.

The ground surface finish may not be appropriate in some applications, and an improvement may be required. Lapping, using diamond paste, is done routinely on shaft seal faces to provide a very finely ground flat surface. Cylindrical lapping of bearing surfaces can be done by some manufacturers. Flatness or roundness tolerances of a fraction of a light fringe per mm are possible.

Figure 3.3.5
Problems in grinding.

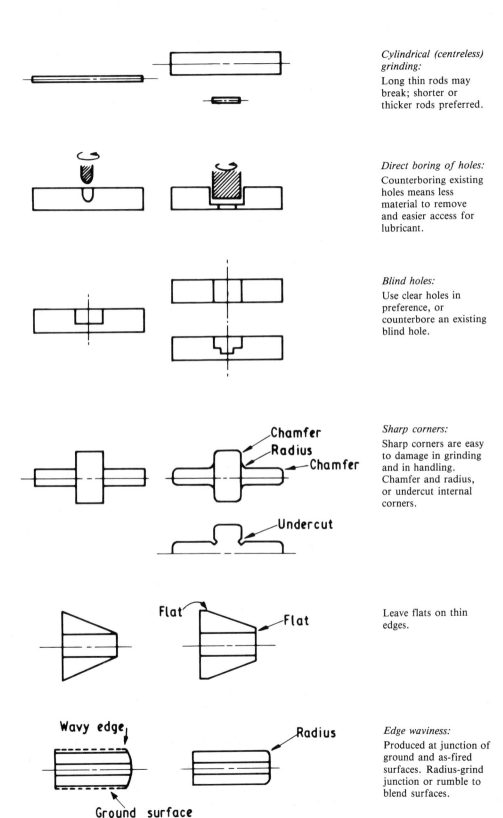

AVOID　　　　PREFER

Cylindrical (centreless) grinding:
Long thin rods may break; shorter or thicker rods preferred.

Direct boring of holes:
Counterboring existing holes means less material to remove and easier access for lubricant.

Blind holes:
Use clear holes in preference, or counterbore an existing blind hole.

Chamfer
Radius
Chamfer
Undercut

Sharp corners:
Sharp corners are easy to damage in grinding and in handling. Chamfer and radius, or undercut internal corners.

Flat
Flat

Leave flats on thin edges.

Wavy edge
Radius
Ground surface

Edge waviness:
Produced at junction of ground and as-fired surfaces. Radius-grind junction or rumble to blend surfaces.

241

A polished finish may be required for some applications where lapping does not achieve a sufficiently smooth surface. However it is difficult to maintain flatness in polishing, and in some materials containing more than one crystalline phase (or additionally a glassy phase) and pores it will prove impossible to obtain the same optical quality as can be achieved on a structurally homogeneous glass. Most glasses, on the other hand, can be polished to a high-quality finish suitable not only for optical use, but even for X-ray use, as in synchrotron mirrors. In this field we depend on the skills of individuals rather than the accuracy of machines to obtain the required flatness or optical figure.

3.3.4 Surface finish

For applications involving friction, light wear or optical reflection, the quality of surface finish is of paramount importance. It may be necessary to specify finish either qualitatively or quantitatively. To give some feel for the variation of surface finish obtained by various treatments, the following Section demonstrates typical results obtained when materials are tested with a surface profile tester such as the 'Talysurf' or 'Talystep' (Rank Taylor Hobson Ltd.), correlated with micrographs obtained on the scanning electron microscope.

3.3.4.1 Surface finish produced on firing

Most ceramic components are either 'rumbled' (a light tumbling or vibratory milling – see Section 3.2.4.2) or machined after firing. Rumbling removes flash and surface contamination (such as furnace packing grit) and rounds off sharp corners, while machining is used to produce accurate dimensions. However, some components are used in the as-fired state, in which surface finish varies greatly according to material type, grain size and composition.

The appearance of clay-based materials depends on the degree of vitrification. Highly-vitrified materials appear glassy, but more refractory and less well vitrified materials appear rather rougher with protruding crystalline material. The roughness is determined by the particle size of the filler and can be considerable in materials with coarse fillers, such as stonewares and kiln furniture.

Sintered oxide ceramics generally show a regular array of slightly faceted grains on the surface. Their apparent average diameter is usually less than the mean grain size measured internally on a polished section.

The as-fired surface of reaction-bonded silicon nitride often appears white, in contrast to the grey interior, due to the formation of a dusty deposit of α–Si_3N_4 needle-like crystals. The high degree of porosity (10–20%) gives the surface a rough appearance which will show traces of the machining procedure used to shape it in the green state (some Si_3N_4 products are now directly moulded, but not many). The as-fired surface of reaction-bonded silicon carbide tends to reflect the microstructure beneath. The coarser the starting silicon carbide grit size, the rougher and more faceted the appearance of the external surface.

Some examples of as-fired surfaces are given in Figure 3.3.6.

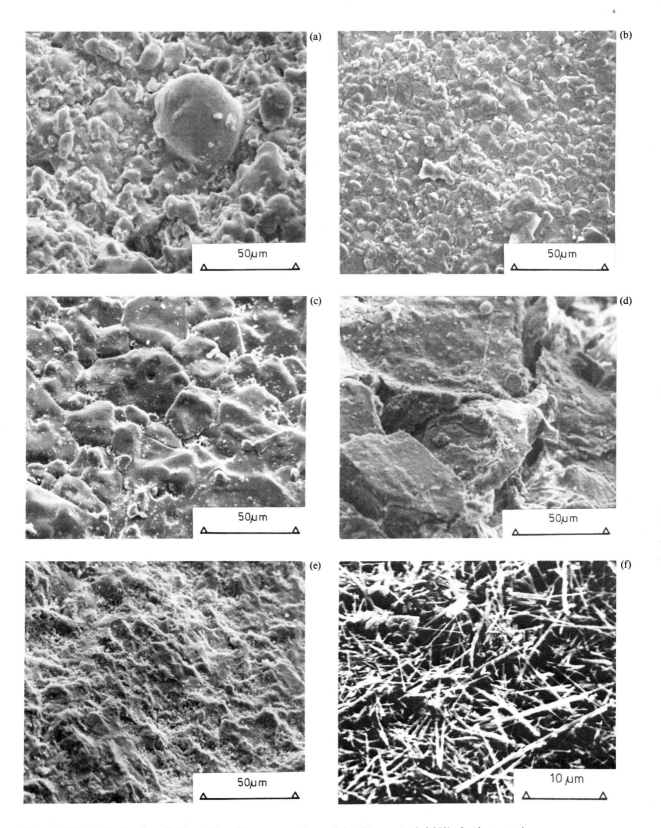

Figure 3.3.6 As-fired surface finish on (a) a siliceous pressed porcelain, (b) an extruded 95% alumina ceramic, (c) a 99.7% recrystallized alumina, (d) a clay-bonded silicon carbide, (e) a silicon-infiltrated fine-grained silicon carbide, and (f) a reaction-bonded silicon nitride.

3.3.4.2 Surface finish produced by machining

Removal of material by rumbling, machining, lapping, etc., destroys the original surface finish, including any 'as-fired skins' resulting from differences in firing conditions or composition. This is usually beneficial in the sense that defects, dirt or unacceptably rough surfaces are removed and replaced by a rather more reproducible finish. Strength is also influenced by machining. If the material is prone to a wide scatter in as-fired strength, removal of surface defects can sometimes narrow the scatter band. If the machining process is severe, the average strength may be reduced. If a high-quality finish, e.g. lapped or polished, is produced, the average strength can be raised. Much depends on just how the finish is produced, in particular the degree of damage introduced by factors such as machining grit size, machining rate, whether sufficient coolant is being applied, machine vibration, etc.

Rumbling (ball milling or tumbling, and vibration milling, done wet or dry) removes material by abrasion and impact attrition leaving a microscopically rough finish, but one which is macroscopically smooth.

Fixed grit diamond machining removes material by a combination of ploughing and chipping, leaving a relatively rough surface with pitting where grains have been torn out, and usually some evidence of plastically ploughed grooves. The finer the grit size and the smaller the advance of the cut, the smaller the scale of the roughness.

Diamond grit lapping of a ground surface removes much of the roughness and leaves a generally flat surface with some relief polishing at grain boundaries and second phases. As with diamond grinding, there is a tendency in some materials for tearout of grains or groups of grains to occur, resulting in a pock-marked surface. It is difficult to distinguish between genuine porosity in cross-section and torn-out grains.

Polishing is a process of progressive removal of surface imperfections and damage introduced by previous machining operations. It is thought to be a plastic ploughing operation, the effect of which depends on the size of grit particles and their hardness compared to the material being polished. The best finishes are obtained by polishing with powders a little harder than the materials being polished. Thus one would tend to use cerium oxide based powders on glass, and diamond on silicon carbide or aluminium oxide.

These surface finishes are altered by refiring the material. The mechanical damage may be annealed out to heal cracks (as in glass) and to remove the surface stress field introduced by the grinding process. In doing this mechanical strength may be altered. Glass is generally strengthened, but in some NPL tests on a 95% alumina it was found that material with finely machined or lapped finish is weakened by refiring. This is explained as being due to removal of a surface compressive stress introduced by machining.

Refiring ceramics with a polished finish reveals the grain boundary and second phase structure. This process, known as thermal etching, results from the high driving force for atomic rearrangement at intersections of grain boundaries with a free surface. Similarly, refiring materials with a ground finish to a sufficiently high temperature can lead to recrystallization of surface grains to the semi-faceted appearance achieved in some as-fired materials. The technique of machine and refire is used to obtain the critically important surface finish found necessary to minimize frictional drag of thread guides for high-speed spinning equipment. In this and similar applications it is usually better to have a surface that gives a minimum of contact area, merely the tops of smoothly profiled grains, rather than a perfectly flat surface. In other words, a surface like that of smooth orange peel is preferred to a lapped or polished surface like that on a billiard ball.

Figure 3.3.7 shows some examples of the surface finish on a 95% alumina ceramic achieved by various types of machining operations, together with surface profile traces which can be used to quantify the roughness in terms of mean deviation from the centre-line average (c.l.a. or R_a). This method has limitations, however, since it does not always provide information on the sharpness of the protruding grains which might be important in applications involving wear. The periodicity of the surface roughness in relation to the amplitude can affect performance in making joints, or in wetting by other materials. Care on specification is needed if these factors are important.

3.3.4.3 Classification of surface defects

British Standard 1598:1964 states that:
"Although it is deemed impractical to set up even general levels of quality for surface defects, since both size and application of ceramic parts are subject to wide variations, the surfaces should not be chipped, blistered, pimpled or speckled so that the life and usefulness of the articles are impaired. It is considered on a commonsense basis rather than by any empirical formula."
Fitness for purpose is the important factor, and if in doubt, this should be subject to some sort of agreement between manufacturer and customer. For many purposes, surface defects such as adhering particles of excess material, contamination spots, small edge chips, variations in colour, surface scratches or ridges may be unimportant and their removal merely cosmetic. Much more important are surface discontinuities that affect the subsequent use of the material, such as the quality of coatings applied to the ceramic when intended for an electronics application, or the shape irregularities which decide whether the component is within tolerances. For mechanical uses, holes, areas of high porosity, cracks (but not necessarily chips) and moulding discontinuities are important in determining strength, and may influence wear resistance. *The user should not demand a higher quality than he needs as this will only raise costs.*

ASTM Standard F109–73 goes rather further than BS 1958:1964 and gives definitions of terms relating to surface imperfections. If there is a requirement on the absence or a minimum level of a certain type of imperfection, this Standard is useful in defining the imperfection. It remains however for purchaser and manufacturer to agree not only a specification but also a means of determining whether it is achieved.

3.3.5 Finalizing specifications, dimensions and tolerances

Once the overall design concept has been decided upon, there is still the problem of putting practical tolerances on a drawing for manufacture, and coming to an agreement with a manufacturer on a specification such that components can be supplied economically and accepted by the customer without further difficulties arising during assembly or use.

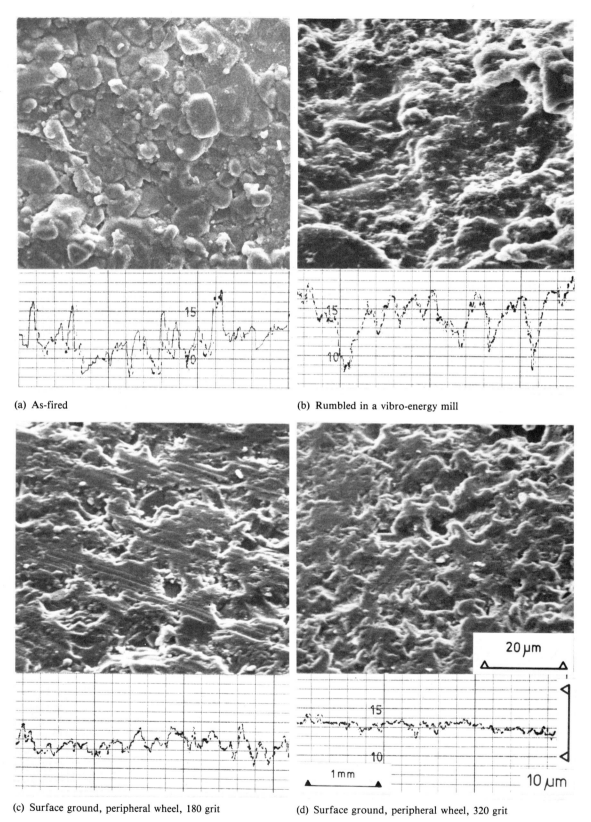

(a) As-fired

(b) Rumbled in a vibro-energy mill

(c) Surface ground, peripheral wheel, 180 grit

(d) Surface ground, peripheral wheel, 320 grit

Figure 3.3.7 Surface finish on a 95% alumina ceramic produced by various surface finishing methods, as demonstrated by scanning electron microscopy and 'Talysurf' traces.

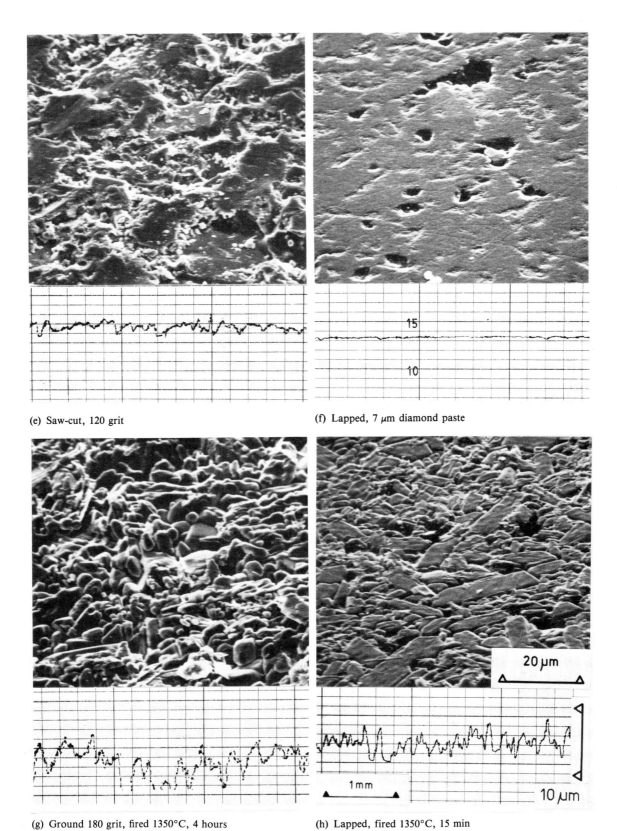

(e) Saw-cut, 120 grit

(f) Lapped, 7 μm diamond paste

(g) Ground 180 grit, fired 1350°C, 4 hours

(h) Lapped, fired 1350°C, 15 min

Section 3.3.2.3 suggested manufacturing tolerances on as-fired ceramic components of $\pm$ 2% or $\pm$ 0.2 mm whichever is the greater, perhaps larger for glasses. In practice, dependent on the material, component size, shape and manufacturing method, better reproducibility from one component to the next can be achieved. Manufacturing expertise, quality control, investment in tooling, choice of materials and manufacturing methods will often enable a component to be manufactured in large numbers to higher precision without expensive post-firing machining operations. The main factors influencing dimensional variation have been discussed earlier, but once a material and its manufacturing route have been decided upon, the final specification requires an engineering drawing with all relevant tolerances. In part, these should follow from detailed discussions with manufacturers, but some aspects may not. For completeness, we summarize in this Section aspects of tolerance as they affect engineering dimensions and give some examples of how tolerances should be considered. The Section discusses tolerances based on each step of the manufacturing process:

1. accuracy of tooling
2. accuracy of setting of manufacturing machinery
3. accuracy of secondary operations, e.g. green machining
4. wear and deterioration of tooling
5. variation in firing and in powder shrinkage
6. variation in firing distortion
7. accuracy of post-firing operations.

Each type of tolerance is considered separately using examples, and some idea is given of its magnitude. It should be remembered, however, that different manufacturers may suggest different levels for their respective products.

For moulded glassware, there are similarities to the above list, e.g. setting of machinery and post-firing operations, but other aspects are different. Broadly speaking, allowance has to be made for variable mould fill (especially with hand moulding), the thermal expansion of the mould and glass from room temperature to the normal mould and glass setting temperatures, and distortion after moulding. For drawn rod or tube, the principal factor is quality control to obtain consistent diameters, with modification of drawing conditions to achieve them. Such factors are not dealt with in detail in this Handbook since they tend to be individual to a particular glass type and component shape, and it is more difficult to generalize than with ceramics. See the Bibliography for other sources of information.

The sum of all the appropriate contributions to variation in dimensions will give the appropriate level of tolerance required for a particular product and manufacturing method. If this level creates difficulty in assembly or in actual use of the component, then consideration clearly has to be given to changing some aspect of the manufacturing process in order to reduce the required tolerance on the ceramic.

3.3.5.1. Tolerances based on tooling

This is of greatest importance in the die-pressing operation where the profile of the component in the section perpendicular to the pressing direction is fixed by the tooling and the accuracy of its manufacture.

Example 1:

A planar component with a series of holes (Figure 3.3.8). In the green state, the relative size of the holes and their distances from the periphery are fixed by the tool dimensions and the accuracy of its manufacture. They cannot be altered without expensive tooling alterations. The tooling accuracy is typically better than 0.02 mm. These dimensions should be regarded as a set, and provided the firing shrinkage is consistent, the whole family of dimensions moves together. If the linear shrinkage on firing increases by 1%, all dimensions decrease by 1%. This family of dimensions can usually be held to a high level of reproducibility from one component to another, sometimes as close as 0.25% as measured on the fired component.

Figure 3.3.8
Relative dimensions of a planar component with a series of holes in it.

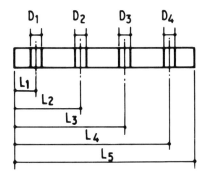

Example 2:

A stepped or multi-diameter hole in a component produced by compaction of ceramic powder onto a multi-diameter pin, such as in isostatic pressing (Figure 3.3.9). The three internal diameters, one of which could be threaded, would be concentric by virtue of the original toolmaking. The lengths of the three sections would also be related to one another in the same way. Again, these dimensions would move as a family during firing. The actual relative dimensions of the fired component might vary slightly from that calculated from the tooling as a function of taper or slight variations in shrinkage along the length. However, once the tooling has been made, there is almost absolute repeat from one green component to the next.

Figure 3.3.9
Relative dimensions in a cylindrical component made by isostatic-pressing onto a mandrel.

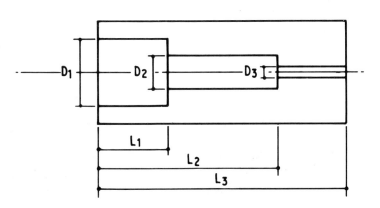

3.3.5.2 Tolerances based on setting manufacturing machinery

In automatic pressing or in extrusion some adjustment is always possible in the length or position of certain die components. The setting of these components, such as the punch throw in automatic die-pressing, controls the green dimensions of the ceramic part and also for a given mould fill, the green density of the component. Shrinkage will then vary according to the green density.

Example 3:

Automatic die pressing. The lengths L_1 and L_2 (Figure 3.3.10) are fixed by the distance the punch moves in pressing, whereas the length L'_2 is fixed by the step in the die body. The values of L_1 and L_2 are usually reproducible in the green shape, but can be varied by the setting of the punch throw. The shrinkage allowance, green to fired, used to estimate die dimensions may be in error by a small amount as a consequence of inaccurate setting of punch throw or by variations in mould fill, both of which affect the green density of the ceramic.

Figure 3.3.10
Variable dimensions in the machine setting for die-pressing.

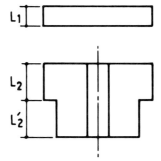

Example 4:

Extrusion. The positioning of holes (Figure 3.3.11) is controlled by the setting of the die components. The typical accuracy of this setting depends on the size of extrusion and the skill of the manufacturer, but is commonly of the order ± 0.02 mm on small pieces to ± 0.2 mm on larger tubes. More

Figure 3.3.11
Variable eccentricity due to machine setting in extrusion.

particularly in thin-walled sections, departures from concentricity can lead to variations in green density from one side of the section to the other, or to variations in the degree of alignment of platy particles in the extrudate. Both these factors can lead to distortion on subsequent firing, even in the absence of slumping.

3.3.5.3 Tolerances based on secondary operations

A green ceramic body shaped by one of the primary powder compaction or wet methods often requires further shaping before firing. Secondary operations in common use include grinding, turning, drilling, milling, even hand filing, and the green dimensions are then determined by the accuracy of these operations. The dimensions relative to a datum on the green shape are determined by the operator and the jigs involved. Green shapes are generally not especially hard or strong, and consequently cannot be clamped tightly. The resulting accuracy is then much worse than might be achieved on a metal, and typically ± 0.1 mm is obtained. The repeatability of firing shrinkage and distortion also contribute to the final tolerances achievable, so there is little point in specifying very high accuracy when machining in the green state.

Example 5:

A hollow cylindrical green shape requiring profiling of the exterior after pressing, e.g. by die- or isostatic-pressing of a plain cylinder. Concentricity of the outside to the bore is determined by the arrangement by which the bore can be aligned with the axis of the lathe for turning. Inaccuracies may be minimized by using a support mandrel based on the same dimension as that used in the primary shaping process, where this is possible. If the primary method was extrusion, distortion of the shape during handling or drying may preclude this.

3.3.5.4 Tolerances based on wear and deterioration of tooling

Most ceramic powders are extremely abrasive. It is important to consider the following points when as-pressed and fired shapes are being made in long runs:

1. The tool material. Hardened steel wears much faster than hardmetal tooling but may be more cost-effective for short runs where tool amortization is a significant factor in the cost equation.
2. The expected life of the tooling in terms of the number of components to be produced.
3. Which dimensions will alter or which other effects will appear when wear becomes significant, and to what extent these are significant in end use. Typical effects of wear include:
   (a) reduction of the diameter of pins in tooling
   (b) increased clearance between punches and dies or other moving parts in the tooling in contact with the abrasive powder
   (c) chipped edges on components due to break-away of moulding flash caused by increased clearance
   (d) loss of surface finish or definition of profiles on punches and other parts of tooling, particularly those subject to high-pressure contact with the abrasive powder.
4. The extent to which tools can be rectified by regrinding or replacement of parts, rather than complete replacement.
5. The commercial responsibility of the initial cost of the tooling, refurbishing the tooling, or its complete replacement during normal life.

From the design point of view, the effects of tool wear on dimensions and shape can be minimized by ensuring that, for example, hole sizes are generous, and that no sharp corners are required so that ragged edges can be satisfactorily removed by rumbling. The likely changes in dimensions should be discussed with manufacturers since each shape and material are likely to present different rates of wear.

3.3.5.5 Tolerances for variations in firing and in shrinkage

Ceramics produced by methods that do not involve reaction with furnace gases during high-temperature firing to the extent that the component weight is significantly affected (apart from burn-out of binders) can be assessed for quality by the density of the whole component or of parts. If the green shaping processes have been carried out correctly, then a fairly precise weight of powder for a given volume of component will have been used in die-pressing, or the appropriate compaction pressure will have been used in isostatic pressing. The weight of the component will then be fairly constant and any change in the shrinkage of the green shape due to batch variation or to differences in the heating schedule (e.g. under-fired or over-fired) will not affect the final weight of the component, only its final dimensions. This variation in shrinkage could result in differences in dimensions between components of equal weight. Thus the size and mass, or preferably the density, of fired components can be measured as a check that the material properties have reached a certain standard. (This may of course not be an adequate check on strength which is a function of microstructure and defect distribution. These features are generally not directly related to bulk density.) This also checks that all stages of the production have been satisfactorily carried out, right from the chemical reactivity of the starting batch of prepared raw materials. In addition, the normal shrinkage of a particular batch mix is used as a yardstick in estimating the green dimensions of a component, and hence the tooling dimensions. Unless a manufacturer's product is reproducible in its behaviour, the reproducibility of the final dimensions is in doubt. So a size check on the production line can be used directly to ensure that the batch behaviour is normal. In the majority of materials, fired density is usually consistent to better than $\pm 0.5\%$, representing $\pm 0.2\%$ in linear dimensions.

Density can vary from one point to another in a component made by shaping methods such as die-pressing, injection-moulding and extrusion, especially in hollow-section articles of varying wall thickness. This arises because the compaction pressure is not uniform at all points due to friction effects at die walls, for example. In firing, areas of low density tend to shrink more and lead to distortion as demonstrated earlier in Figure 3.3.2. The tolerances required in such circumstances are likely to vary with the particular shape, and each case needs to be considered separately. Typically, a variation in green density of $\pm 2\%$ is not unusual in a die-pressed shape of uneven section, and if the fired density is uniform, this can lead to an unrestricted linear shrinkage variation of 0.7%, perhaps more in some directions if shrinkage is restrained perpendicular to these directions.

Example 6:

A short cylinder with a recessed hole produced by die-pressing has a high level of compaction under the punch tip and a lower level in the thin-walled areas (Figure 3.3.12a). On firing (Figure 3.3.12b), the thin-walled areas shrink further and lead to inward tapering of the cylinder if the base is relatively thick, or to downward bowing of the base if this area is thin. To minimize these effects, the depth of the hole should be less than say one half of the length of the cylinder. Alternatively, the component could be designed with tapered wall thickness which would have the effect of improving compaction in the thin-walled areas.

Example 7:

A cylinder or rod with length somewhat larger than the diameter is subject to considerable die-wall drag in pressing, with the result that the green density in the mid-section is lower than at the punch faces. This causes waisting in firing, typically by up to 1% (Figures 3.3.12c and 3.3.12d). To minimize this, the ratio of length to diameter or wall thickness should be reduced. Alternatively, the component could be made by cutting extruded and fired material into short lengths, or by isostatic pressing.

Figure 3.3.12
Distortion induced on firing by non-uniformity of green density showing
(a) areas of high (H) and low (L) green density for a thin-bottomed and for a thick-bottomed shape;
(b) the distortion on firing;
(c) and (d), waisting distortion in tubes or rods pressed to length caused by large ratios of length to diameter or wall thickness.

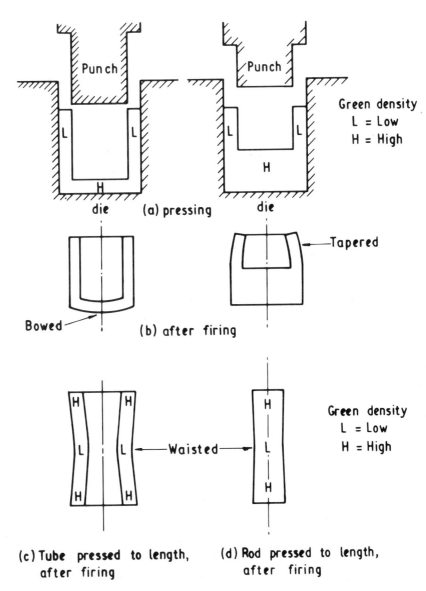

253

3.3.5.6 Tolerances based on distortion under own weight in firing

Many ceramics can deform under their own weight at the upper firing temperature because they are soft at this temperature, particularly if they contain a liquid phase. The softening of certain binders before burn-out can have the same result. These effects lead to unwanted distortion in firing, perhaps even to cracking or lowering of strength. A few points to note are as follows:

1. Small components are less likely to distort than large ones.
2. Substantially solid components are less likely to distort than hollow components.
3. Components having similar dimensions in all directions are less likely to distort than those with one or more dimensions substantially smaller.
4. Components with a substantial base section and small height are less likely to distort than those with no natural base to support their weight during firing.
5. Long thin components can be maintained fairly straight if it is possible to fire them standing up or hanging from one end. Bowing can be as low as 1 mm per metre.
6. There are limitations on dimensions for suspension firing; the weight of the component can cause necking and fracture.
7. Thin-walled tubing and other hollow components may develop ovality in firing, due either to sag if laid flat, or uneven heating and frictional drag if stood up.
8. There is a limit to the length to thickness ratio of rods or plates laid flat due to frictional drag developed at ends or edges. This may occur despite the use of ceramic powder between components and the kiln furniture, or the embedding of components in powder. The effect may be reduced by using a sacrificial tile of the same material as a support to shrink with the component.

It is difficult to give guidelines on typical tolerance allowances for firing distortion because each case has to treated individually. The manufacturer is probably in the best position to estimate what allowances should be made.

3.3.5.7 Tolerances based on post-firing machining and grinding

In general these follow the capability of the particular machining operation when used in a similar manner for hard metal parts. For example, tolerances as close as 0.02 to 0.002 mm in overall dimensions, and flatness of better than 0.001 mm can be achieved by diamond grinding. However, certain limitations must be borne in mind:

1. Ceramics and glasses have very limited elasticity and are generally non-magnetic. Clamping awkward shapes can pose problems. Thin sections can easily crack due to clamping and grinding loads, and even to thermal shock caused by the heat generated.
2. Ceramics and glasses are very prone to chipping during starting and finishing of the cutting operation, especially if cutting is interrupted.
3. Maintenance of gauging equipment can present problems if contact methods are used, due to the abrasive nature of the components. Carbide- or ceramic-tipped gauges are usually required.

4. Grinding quality should always be assessed by using a fluorescent crack detector.
5. Grinding lubricants should always be removed as soon as possible.
6. Ground components should generally be handled separately as they are prone to damage at critical edges. This may not be necessary with small components with chamfered edges.

3.3.5.8 Example specification for a ceramic tube

The points that need to be considered concerning dimensions and technical specification can be illustrated by the problem of how to define a simple tube having an external diameter, an internal diameter and a length. (In some circumstances the specification could be for a wall thickness and outside diameter rather than inside and outside diameters.) The points in this specification are purely technical and do not include any cosmetic ones such as colour shades, etc. The green shaping and firing methods for such a component could be quite diverse. Each method produces its own range of potential faults or variations in tolerance described earlier. Examples of these methods include:
1. die-press complete
2. isostatically-press, and machine outside diameter and end-faces
3. extrude, and machine end-faces
4. injection-mould complete
5. slip-cast complete
6. machine from solid on all four surfaces from a blank made by any one of the above methods, perhaps incorporating one or more faces produced during the primary shaping operation

with the added post-fabrication variables:
7. firing the component on its end
8. firing the component on its side
9. fired in a single or multiple layers

coupled with post-firing machining operations:
10. rumbling to smooth all surfaces
11. grinding or other machining of one or more surfaces.

The production sequence actually followed would usually be based on the dimensional requirements of the tube and the number required after discussions with a manufacturer.

Bearing in mind the tolerances that can be achieved by the various production methods, the allowable dimensions for the tube need to be specified as follows:
1. the three basic dimensions; length, inside diameter, outside diameter
2. tolerances on all three dimensions, expressed as plus and minus variation on the required size
3. ovality of the bore and outside diameter: expressed as maximum and minimum diameters, or permitted differences from the required size
4. concentricity of the bore to the outside diameter (or vice-versa)
5. maximum variation on outside diameter or bore due to taper or double taper (barrelling or waisting)

6. bow or bending out of straight
7. parallelism of the bore to the outside (or vice-versa), i.e. the wall thickness and its variation
8. squareness of the ends to the bore or to the outside diameter
9. parallelism of the two end surfaces
10. maximum or minimum chamfers or radii on the outside diameter or bore at one or both ends.

Other aspects include:
11. surface finish on bore, outside diameter and end faces
12. surfaces to be ground, lapped or polished, the area to be covered and the specification of the finish in terms of roughness, flatness and freedom from defects
13. alternatively to 12., rumbling to remove sharp corners
14. the requirements for glazing some or all surfaces, the dimensional and technical specification for the glaze, and areas which should not be glazed.

Note that particular tolerances on dimensions may vary from place to place, and close levels may be required only for a restricted part of the component, such as outside diameter for fitting metal end caps, or bore for the insertion of short metal rods.

In addition, quality-control procedures and other contractual aspects need to be specified at the same time:
15. specification on material, manufacturer's code, etc.
16. testing of components for dimensional acceptibility by the use of jigs or fixtures: e.g. should the tube accept a rod of given diameter and length in the bore, or should the tube pass through a second tube of given length and bore? Should these two tests be combined to give a concentricity test in a single jig?
17. special tests or observations in respect of the finishing operations: e.g. directionality of grinding, damage to surface by crushing, acceptability of edge chipping
18. acceptability standards for defects: localized edge chipping, scratching, cracking (not usually permitted), adhesions, inclusions, small holes or pits; parts of the component where these may be accepted or not accepted
19. surface condition with regard to cleanliness, freedom from oil, from dust, from metal marks, and from lapping debris; cleaning procedures to be adopted
20. quality assurance on the physical properties of the components: bulk density, open porosity, mechanical proof-testing (testing a sample or every component), thermal tests, electrical tests, chemical tests, fluorescent dye testing, ultrasonic inspection for holes, X-ray tests, etc.; define whether such tests are to be on prototypes only, or on routine production, whether every component is to be tested or whether a sampling procedure is to be used; isolate sampling and testing costs from manufacturing costs if required
22. define liability for defective components
23. define liabilities for initial tooling, ownership of tooling, liability for costs of replacing or refurbishing tooling
24. define labelling or marking procedures to be used, and the durability of the marking if on the component itself; if components are to be marked

by inscribing on the green product, define where this is to be done and note whether it is likely to affect later machining or inspection procedures
25. packaging requirements for transit and storage
26. any specifications on release procedures, e.g. government or other body
27. confidentiality of the component design.

Without these specifications, the commercial relations between the customer and the manufacturer can easily get into difficulties. Although the situation may seem rather complicated, many of the above points may not be important in a particular situation, but it is as well to raise them with the intended supplier(s). A little forethought can often eliminate the expense of large numbers of rejects and the inter-company wrangling that can ensue.

If the same problem is posed for a glass tube, the situation is very similar. It could either be moulded, or cut from a drawn tube. If the dimensions are critical it may need to be ground, but a precision bore can be achieved by shrinking onto a mandrel. However it is made, the tolerances need to be considered in the same way as for a ceramic tube, and the quality-control procedures might also be the same, except that visual examination can reveal more with a glass than with a ceramic.

3.3.6 Example engineering drawings

The following examples are engineering drawings of small to medium-sized components based on real designs. The purpose is to give the reader some worked examples of design which incorporate a range of pre- and post-firing shaping techniques and the tolerances levels that are required or can be achieved. In each case, the following tolerances are assumed unless otherwise stated on the drawings:

on dimensions: $\pm 2\%$ or ± 0.2 mm whichever is the greater
on camber (out of flat): 0.125 mm/25 mm (5 mm/m)
on angles: $\pm 1°$
all external corners broken
all internal corners may have a radius of 0.4 mm.

These represent typical manufacturer's tolerance levels which can usually be achieved on as-fired shapes, but better than this can be achieved, subject to negotiation on individual circumstances.

With each example are notes on the function of the component, the material that might be specified, the reasons for the tolerance levels and the shaping methods used to achieve them.

Example 1: Medium voltage stand-off insulator, Figure 3.3.13

This could be made from any suitable insulating ceramic, and would have brass inserts to take locating bolts. Such a component would be pressed as a blank cylinder, the holes would be drilled and the outside would be turned in the green state. The edges of the holes would be broken to accommodate an unspecified internal radius on the brass insert flange. Overall tolerances are unstated, implying that the as-fired dimensions are adequate. The drilled holes are of greater diameter than the insert to allow for glueing in. The outside is glazed all over with a low-tension glaze except for one end, on which it is stood for glaze firing.

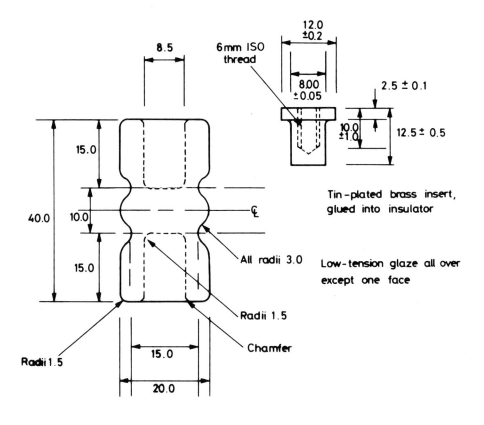

Figure 3.3.13
A simple stand-off insulator.

12.0
±0.2

8.5

6mm ISO
thread

8.00
±0.05

2.5 ± 0.1

15.0

10.0
±1.0

12.5± 0.5

40.0

10.0

Ȼ

Tin-plated brass insert,
glued into insulator

15.0

All radii 3.0

Low-tension glaze all over
except one face

Radii 1.5

15.0

Chamfer

Radii 1.5

20.0

Example 2: Pin base for electronic components, Figure 3.3.14

This pin base is designed to be soft-soldered into metal tubes. The series of holes in the disc would be made in an initial die-pressing with a straight outside profile. The holes need to be positioned more accurately than the standard tolerances would allow, but in the material chosen this can be achieved. The locating recess would probably be machined in the green state. The close tolerance on the outside diameters and the need for concentricity dictate grinding before low-temperature metallizing. Since the brass pins are to be 'clinched' (their tops peened over like a rivet) into the holes, a fairly strong material is required, in this case an alumina ceramic. Inspection tests would check that all pins are tight and that no cracks develop as a result of the clinching process.

Example 3: Small shaft seal, Figure 3.3.15

This component is typical of a wide variety of ceramic seal rings and could be made in a hardmetal, an alumina ceramic or a silicon carbide. In each case, a blank ring might be pressed, and then machined oversize in the green state. For a small ring, the internal corner undercuts would also be made in the green state. These would aid final diamond grinding to allow clean corners to be obtained. After firing, all external faces are ground to achieve flatness and cylindrical symmetry rather than very close tolerances, and all external corners are broken. The working face is then lapped flat and smooth to better than 2 light bands (about 1μm). On a large ring (e.g. 150 mm

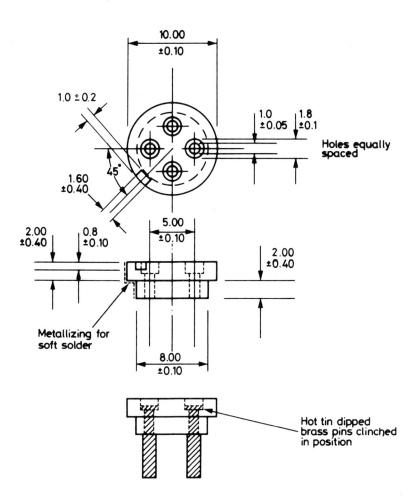

Figure 3.3.14
An electronic pin base.

10.00
±0.10

1.0 ± 0.2

1.0
±0.05

1.8
±0.1

Holes equally
spaced

45°

1.60
±0.40

2.00
±0.40

0.8
±0.10

5.00
±0.10

2.00
±0.40

Metallizing for
soft solder

8.00
±0.10

Hot tin dipped
brass pins clinched
in position

diameter or greater) the same principles would apply except that the undercuts would probably have to be ground after firing because in the green state they could be ineffective within as-fired tolerances.

Example 4: Mechanically clamped insulating leadthrough, Figure 3.3.16

A high-strength alumina ceramic is required in order to withstand the clamping stresses on the flange. The critical tolerance areas are the outside diameters of the flange and the opposite end section, and there is a note that these should be accurately concentric. The mating face of the flange also has to be accurately parallel to the opposite end. Such a component would be isostatically pressed on a cylindrical mandrel and then the outside would be turned oversize in the green state to give the stated as-fired dimensions. The holes in the end would also be drilled in the green state. After firing, the grinding would be done, probably in multiple operations without removing from the chuck or collet to preserve the concentricity and parallelism. These would be checked on each component during and after grinding. Glazing with a high-tension glaze would be done either before or after grinding.

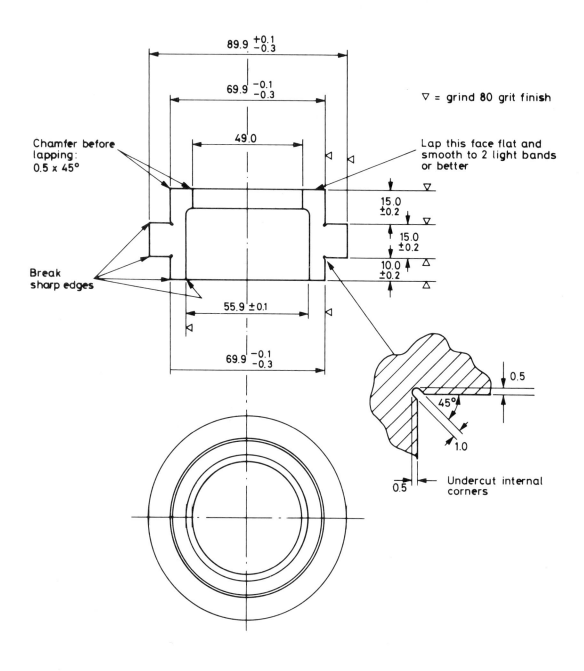

$89.9 \begin{smallmatrix} +0.1 \\ -0.3 \end{smallmatrix}$

$69.9 \begin{smallmatrix} -0.1 \\ -0.3 \end{smallmatrix}$

49.0

∇ = grind 80 grit finish

Chamfer before lapping: 0.5 x 45°

Lap this face flat and smooth to 2 light bands or better

15.0 ± 0.2

15.0 ± 0.2

10.0 ± 0.2

Break sharp edges

55.9 ± 0.1

$69.9 \begin{smallmatrix} -0.1 \\ -0.3 \end{smallmatrix}$

0.5

45°

1.0

0.5

Undercut internal corners

Figure 3.3.15 A small ceramic shaft seal.

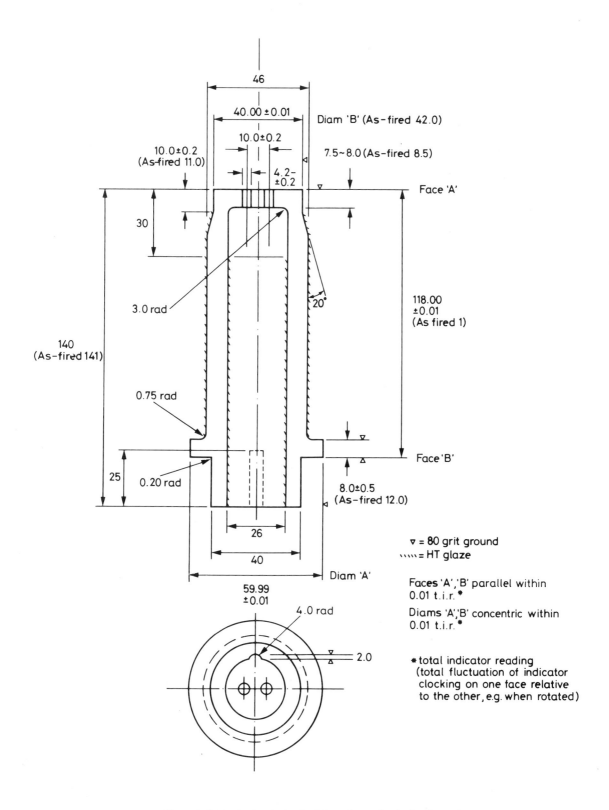

Figure 3.3.16 An insulating leadthrough, mechanically-clamped.

Example 5: Precision coil former, Figure 3.3.17

The precise sequence of operations would depend on the fineness of the thread, and on the tolerance levels required on the thread pitch and diameter. Diamond grinding after firing would be required for accurate pitches and diameters, and also for thin sections of thread. In the case illustrated, the dimensions are not critical, and the entire article could be machined in the green state. The blank would be isostatically pressed on a mandrel and the outside would be turned appropriately. The longitudinal grooves would be form-ground with a white alumina wheel with the component appropriately

Figure 3.3.17
Precision coil former.

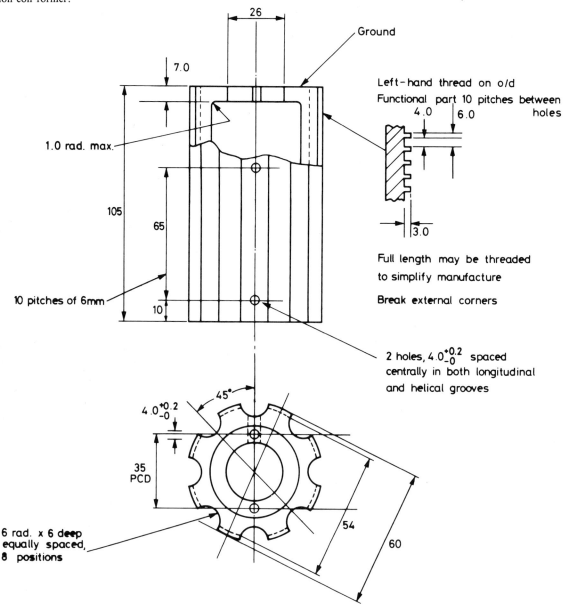

Ground

Left-hand thread on o/d
Functional part 10 pitches between holes
4.0   6.0

Full length may be threaded to simplify manufacture

Break external corners

2 holes, $4.0^{+0.2}_{-0}$ spaced centrally in both longitudinal and helical grooves

1.0 rad. max.

10 pitches of 6mm

$4.0^{+0.2}_{-0}$

35 PCD

6 rad. x 6 deep equally spaced, 8 positions

indexed. Holes would be drilled in the appropriate positions probably by setting the component on suitable jigs. Corners would be broken during the various machining stages.

Example 6: Klystron valve spacer, Fig 3.3.18

This complex component is used in the gun body of a Klystron tube microwave generator as an insulator. Its complex form is dictated by electrical requirements. It requires very accurate diamond grinding of a high-alumina ceramic with low loss at GHz frequencies. A die- or isostatically-pressed

Figure 3.3.18
Klystron valve spacer.

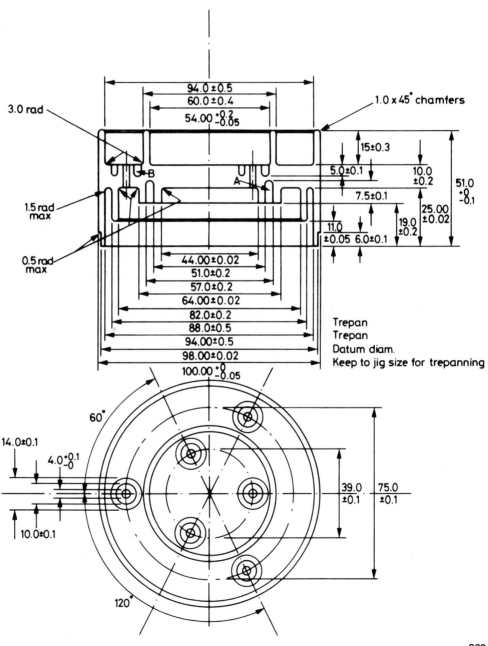

blank would first be green-machined to rough shape, for which an additional drawing would be made. Only those features leaving substantial wall thickness would be introduced at this stage. After firing, the outside diameters would be diamond-ground relative to the reference diameter. The narrow annular groove 'A' would be produced by trepanning, as would also the grooves 'B'. Diamond trepan tools would be made specially for the task. Accurate positioning of the grooves would be achieved by use of a special jig. In this example, the holes would be directly drilled whilst the component is jigged. External surfaces to be exposed to air in use would be glazed for ease of cleaning, and surfaces for joining to metal parts then metallized. It may seem unusual to glaze ground surfaces, but the grinding operations are necessary to ensure accurate jigging for grinding all other surfaces. This example is a demonstration of the complexity and accuracy that it is possible to achieve in an engineering ceramic, but the unit cost is clearly very high.

3.3.7 Summary of points on specification of simple shapes

Material choice. Ensure that the properties of the material are adequate for the task in hand, both in installation and use. Ensure that the shape required can be readily manufactured. Consider cost in relation to performance.

Design of shape. Discuss ideas on dimensions, geometry and tolerances with manufacturers. Try to use as-fired dimensions where possible, and allow appropriate tolerances on mating metal parts. Try to eliminate areas prone to damage, such as sharp edges or corners. Try to design for reliable manufacture and do not insist on unnecessarily close tolerances.

Joining to other materials. Be cautious in using mechanical clamping methods; avoid bending or high localized stresses. Consider the component tolerances and the ability of the joining method to accommodate them.

Trial pieces. A small quantity of trial pieces may be made in a different way to larger-scale production. Ensure that properties and tolerances are maintained in production when appropriate. Ensure that tests done on trial pieces are realistic, in particular with regard to mechanical loading. Bear in mind that mechanical properties, particularly strength, quoted in brochures may sometimes bear little resemblance to the actual performance in use.

Component specification. Ensure that critical parts of the specification are realistic, are agreed previously with the manufacturer, and are testable to an agreed procedure. The component cost will obviously rise with increasing demands on specification and testing. Size and geometry checks should be designed appropriately. Mechanical proof-testing needs to be clearly specified.

3.4

Complex design problems

The preceding Section dealt with factors affecting the design of simple components with emphasis on ease of production and cost minimization. However, design is often a question not merely of geometry, but also of performance in use. This is particularly true when high mechanical loading, or temperature gradients or transients are involved, and when brittle materials are rigidly joined to other materials. Essentially the problem is one of estimating stress and likelihood of failure.

This whole subject area is a difficult one with ceramics because the lack of ductility means that locally, stresses are not relieved by plastic deformation, and this can lead to modelling difficulties. Secondly, the scatter of fracture strength of ceramics means that estimating the probability of fracture in the long term can be fraught with error. Progress is being made in understanding how this should be done, and although the principles are well established, in practice, materials are not necessarily sufficiently reproducible and their long-term properties are not sufficiently well characterized for the results to be reliable. Consultation with experts in the field of lifetime or reliability prediction should be sought where appropriate. See the Bibliography to this Section for source books on the subject, and also Section 6 for advisory organizations.

3.4.1 Designing for loaded applications

Calculation of stresses, particularly those due to ill-defined loading or heat transfer, is always difficult and prone to error. It cannot usually be done analytically, and recourse has to be made to techniques such as finite element analysis (FEA) to obtain a stress distribution. The stress levels can then be compared with typical mechanical property test data and the liability of failure estimated.

Techniques such as FEA are complex and, as with all such methods, the accuracy of the input data and the numerical calculation method determine the accuracy of the output. They are best entrusted to the specialist who understands their limitations.

Perhaps the easiest and most convenient route, in general terms, to solving a design question is a combination of trial and analysis. An initial design might be drawn up incorporating necessary features and avoiding such common pitfalls as stress concentration at points of clamping, holes, notches and sharp external and internal corners. A few components might then be ordered for practical trials which include an element of overload. If the trials are successful, well and good, and if a problem of reliability arises, the solution may be obvious by inspection; some area may require thickening, a hole may have to be eliminated or repositioned, a thermally insulating barrier may be needed, etc. If the solution is not obvious, then an FEA might be used to seek further guidance. For example, the effect on stress distribution of small changes in geometry or materials properties might be investigated. In the case of joints, thermal expansion mismatch problems can be investigated. In taking such a route, the designer also gains first-hand experience of dealing with manufacturers and of handling the material.

3.4.2 Designing for resistance to thermal shock

FEA is considered to be not particularly reliable for modelling thermal shock because of the very rapid change of stress levels both temporally and spatially. Tests on simplified shapes are not reliable indicators because geometry is important. There is no real substitute for the practical trial, especially if the shock can be made more severe than in use.

A number of points should be watched in designing to minimize the risk of thermal failure:

1. Choose a material which has the best potential performance based on thermal shock parameters relevant to the conditions of use. Such materials are generally those of lowest thermal expansion coefficient and/or highest thermal conductivity. High resistance to loss of strength in severe thermal shocks is shown by materials with weak or microcracked microstructures (see Section 2.6.2.3), but these may not be strong enough to bear mechanical loads in addition to thermal ones. Note that the choice may be limited by cost.

2. Consider the areas of the component likely to suffer most from the effects of temperature changes. Remove sharp corners from these areas because they suffer more rapid changes than flat or smoothly rounded surfaces. Try to ensure that the ceramic component sees nearly uniform conditions of heat transfer over its surface.

3. Minimize the thickness of the component commensurate with retaining sufficient mechanical strength. This reduces temperature differentials.

4. Try to reduce the severity of thermal gradients or thermal shock in the component by shielding it from direct heating.

5. Avoid direct joints to metal components suffering the same thermal conditions. The relatively high thermal conductivity of most metallic materials means that they will change their bulk temperature more rapidly and thereby may impose unacceptably high thermal mismatch strains on the ceramic component. If a strong or vacuum-tight joint to a metal component is essential, the metal component should be made as thin-walled and compliant as possible. If rigid joints are not necessary, a thermal barrier between the ceramic and the metal may reduce the risk of thermal failure.

6. Remember that ceramics are liable to thermal fatigue, so that performance in repeated cycling may be much worse than that in a single cycle.

3.5

Joining to other components

Many failures of ceramics and glasses occur because of faults in joining rigidly to other components. With as-fired components of uncertain dimensions or flatness, care has to be taken that loads in use, or even in the joining operation, are not concentrated in small regions with increased risk of fracturing.

The following types of joint may be employed with as-fired dimensions:
1. bolting
2. threaded parts
3. crimping
4. clamping
5. glueing/cementing
6. glaze and glass joints.

Other methods need more accurate dimensional control, i.e. ground surfaces:
7. shrink-fitting
8. metallizing/soldering/brazing
9. vacuum-tight clamp sealing
10. diffusion-bonding.

3.5.1 Bolting

Direct bolting to rigid substrates is to be avoided if possible because of the risk of local fracture around the bolt head. If bolting is required, then soft washers (e.g. lead, aluminium) are recommended to absorb local loads. Wherever possible, bolts with large heads or with hard washers under the heads should be used to spread the load over a second, soft washer in contact with the ceramic (Figure 3.5.1). Direct contact between the various types of spring and shake-proof washers and the ceramic surface is to be avoided.

Since as-fired surfaces are seldom perfectly flat, mating surfaces will be in contact at only a few points. The load can be spread by using a soft gasket, but non-spreading materials such as asbestos, soft metals, nylon mesh reinforced rubbers and plastics are preferred. If no gasket is used, the design should minimize the risk of bending the ceramic when it is loaded by the bolt. Furthermore, for the same reason a minimum number of bolts should be used, never more than three. Two bolts, or even one plus a locator, is ideal. Limiting the area of possible contact with the substrate can reduce the tendency to rock, provided bolting is through the contact areas and not between them, which might result in bending. If necessary the feet can be

Figure 3.5.1
Techniques of bolting ceramics
to other components.

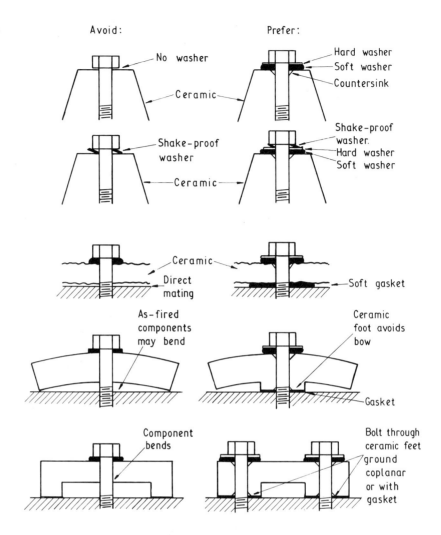

ground coplanar to improve mounting. The area of the feet should be sufficient to support bolt loads plus loads in use. If more than one bolt is used, allow adequate clearance on the holes for dimensional tolerance on hole separation. Act cautiously if sideways forces on the ceramic component are to be borne by the bolt. One possible precaution is to line the hole with a lead or polymer sleeve to spread the load, but it may be better to redesign with attachments in the direction of the imposed load.

A useful design principle in clamping a ceramic with a bolt is to take the compressive load on the ceramic as far away from the edges of the bolt-hole as possible. This may be done by chamfering the edge of the bore, or by using a large load-spreading washer, or by profiling the clamping surface of metal or ceramic.

Always tighten bolts to a safe specified torque to give sufficient clamping pressure but do not over-tighten. If loosening of bolts becomes a problem, then one of the temporary adhesives designed for this function should be used.

Rivetting should be avoided because of the unknown forces involved. If rivetting is essential, radial serrations in the ceramic around the rivet holes help to prevent the rivet turning relative to the ceramic and reduce the risk of breakage in assembly. 'Pop-rivetting' can sometimes be used, as in this case the mating surface is with soft aluminium. However, extensive trials should be carried out because cracks developed around the hole in the ceramic are difficult to detect and could be a source of service failure.

Even more care has to be taken with relatively weak glasses. Bolting is to be avoided unless loads are well spread. Bolt holes should be lined with rubber or soft metal grommets and the bolts should not be tight. Mating surfaces should be ground flat and a soft gasket used if possible. Clamping offers a better solution in general.

3.5.2 Threaded lugs or holes

Threads in or on ceramic materials should not be used as a means of rigidly fastening a ceramic component into an assembly. The reason is that the accuracy of an as-fired thread, either internal or external is in doubt as a consequence of as-fired tolerances. The load is not borne uniformly by the thread but by a small locality because there is no deformation mechanism in the thread to allow redistribution of the load. Internal threads may shatter as a bolt is tightened, and external ones may crack off due to bending. Threads should be used only as locators and should not be tight. In addition, to allow for tolerances they should have a generous degree of slackness on diameter.

An alternative approach is to fix a metal stud or nut into a ceramic component with a suitable adhesive or cement. For example, a hexagonal-head bolt may be retained by gap-filling solder or an organic adhesive which acts as a soft load-spreader, cushioning bolt-head rotation. The internal shape of the hole should provide a suitable key for the adhesive. If a threaded metal or plastic insert is used, the insert should project above the ceramic surface so that when the bolt is tightened the insert takes the load and is not pulled out of the ceramic by the tension in the thread (as in Figure 3.3.13).

Threads introduced after firing by form grinding can clearly be more accurate, but they are expensive and the same points about unsuitability for load bearing apply.

Coarse internal threads can be successfully moulded into the bore of a ceramic component in the green state, and this offers a cheap method of producing loose-fitting caps or nozzles, for example for electrical insulation or for welding. This is suitable where loads are light and are applied by hand rather than with tools.

Coarse external threads can be moulded on to glassware, as on a screw-cap bottle, or on a length of piping to be joined by a nut to a metal tube or to another glass tube. Such a situation should not stress the joint, and precautions should be taken to prevent the glass tube from coming into contact with other hard materials by the use of soft sealing gaskets. See Creyke et al. (in Bibliography) for some examples of threads in glass.

3.5.3 Crimping

Thin metal edges can be crimped or rolled onto ceramic components but only with caution. It is normally done only on high-strength ceramics such as alumina, and requires careful process control. It is best avoided if there are uncertainties. An example is the rolled lip which fixes the insulator into the metal housing of an automotive spark plug.

If crimping is contemplated, the local loads should be taken well away from the edge of the ceramic and there should be a limiting safety feature on the load such as a restriction on the thickness of the metal to be crimped, or the use of a softmetal interlayer such as copper.

3.5.4 Clamping

Clamping requires many of the safeguards described above for bolting; consideration of load spreading and avoidance of bending loads. Clamping is the preferred method for glass components, using soft gasket materials. Mating surfaces should be ground flat, or to the same profile (e.g. cone joints). Applications for this technique include pressure windows, flange-jointed piping and chemical plant. Clamping for vacuum or gas tightness is described in Section 3.5.9.

3.5.5 Adhesives

Glueing or cementing offers an attractive means of making an essentially stress-free joint for use when high temperatures and vacuum tightness are not involved. Cold-cure resins and glues adhere well to ceramics because of the relative surface roughness, which can be improved by grit-blasting if necessary. Adhesion to glasses is also good. Hot-cure resins, particularly the more brittle varieties, should be used with caution because of the effects of thermal expansion mismatch between the resin, the ceramic and other material on cooling to ambient. For example, if a cure at 150°C is required, the joint is stress-free at that temperature, but the high coefficient of thermal expansion of the resin causes it to go into tension on cooling. The joint may crack, or may cause unacceptable distortion in thin-section components, such as thin ceramic tiles glued to metal sheet.

For optimum performance glue-line thickness may need control according to manufacturers' recommendations, but in any event, moderate out-of-flatness of the ceramic component face may be compensated for by variations in glue thickness.

Care must be taken that the adhesive chosen is suitable under the condition of use. For example, some organic adhesives may swell in oil or water, and care must be taken with design to avoid a hydraulic bursting effect in confined spaces.

Inorganic cements, such as Portland cement, find uses in joining ceramics, usually with the cement always in compression. High-tension porcelain insulators may be made by joining individual sections together with cement. These are usually for use in axial compression as post insulators. Suspension insulators, on the other hand, are usually made in one piece or may be assembled in the green state using ceramic slip between the individual sections to avoid the relative weakness of cement joints in tension. However, metal end components are usually attached by cement. Figure 3.5.2 shows examples of both types of cement joint. Keying on both surfaces is important to

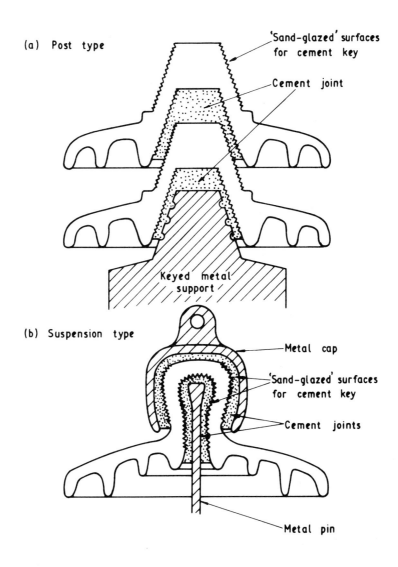

Figure 3.5.2
Portland cement joints in
(a) a stacked ceramic post
insulator, and
(b) a single disc suspension
insulator.

(a) Post type

'Sand-glazed' surfaces
for cement key

Cement joint

Keyed metal
support

(b) Suspension type

Metal cap

'Sand-glazed' surfaces
for cement key

Cement joints

Metal pin

ensure a mechanical bond. A very rough so-called "sand glaze" is used on joint surfaces of the ceramic. Accelerated curing of the cement is necessary to avoid long-term changes in service which may crack the porcelain.

3.5.6 Glaze or glass joints

Glazing is a technique appropriate for joining most types of ceramic and some of the more refractory glasses. For small pieces with reasonably flat mating faces, it is necessary simply to coat each face with a suitable glaze slip, place the surfaces in contact and fire to fuse the glaze and bond the two pieces together. It is most often used with dissimilar ceramic materials, or in assembling large complex pieces, such as stacked insulators. For small, less complex pieces better structural integrity is obtained if the component is made in one piece. However, much depends on the geometry and whether this can be made readily by existing techniques.

Mating surfaces can be ground to ensure an even glaze layer thickness.

The geometry and jigging arrangements should be such that positioning is maintained on firing the glaze and that the glaze, when fluid, fills the gap to be sealed with perhaps a little extruded at the periphery. A small applied load is desirable to assist glaze flow with small components. Pore-free joints are more easily made by bringing pre-glazed surfaces into contact and firing again.

Some glazes remain essentially glassy, some react with the materials being joined and crystallize at the interface and some are deliberately formulated to crystallize. Materials in this latter category are usually termed 'devitrifying glazes', and are designed for use where subsequent processing or application involves higher temperatures than those allowable at the joining stage. For example, colour TV tube face-plates are joined to the cone part with a devitrifying fritted glaze at a low temperature to protect the phosphors. Having devitrified, the glaze allows subsequent baking out at a higher temperature during tube evacuation.

Glazed joints are best used in compression to avoid static fatigue effects. In any event the glaze is weaker than the ceramics being joined. The thermal expansion coefficient of the glaze should be lower than that of the materials being joined so that the glaze goes into biaxial compression in the plane of the joint, but not so low that the joint fails because of shear stresses at the interface. Glaze mismatch can be determined most readily by the sandwich method whereby the strain birefringence in the glass component of a ceramic (or metal)/glass/ceramic sandwich is measured.

Most oxide ceramics can be joined by silicate glasses or glazes since a glass, when fluid, tends to react well with the surface of the ceramic and provide a good bond. Joints can also be made with borate- and phosphate-based glasses. Non-oxide ceramics are more difficult to join. They tend to react with glasses to release gas bubbles which weaken the bond.

A joint between two similar glasses can be made most simply by fusing them together, provided they are not prone to devitrification and do not have grossly different softening points. A joint between different glasses can be made only if the expansion coefficients are similar. If they differ by more than $0.5 \times 10^{-6} \mathrm{K}^{-1}$ there is a strong risk of cracking when cold. The risk depends greatly on geometry. The same is true when glasses are joined to other materials.

Fusion joints between glasses and some metals or ceramics can be made provided care is taken in matching of expansion coefficients. Consultation with specialists is recommended, because size and geometry of both glass and metal (or ceramic) may be limited for a given combination of materials. For accurate positioning of metal components, jigging will be required, but, in general, close tolerances on the glass will not be possible. In some cases where gap-filling is required, a blowing agent is added to increase the volume of the glass when fused.

'Solder glasses' are used for low-temperature hermetic sealing of ceramic-based electronic packages and other electrical devices.

Glass-to-metal joints can be made by the use of glass preforms, as in assembling metal pins into ceramic or metal plates. Common types of fusion joint are tungsten/'Pyrex', 'Kovar' (and other iron-nickel alloys of similar type)/'Pyrex', platinum/soda-lime or lead glass, copper/copper-sealing glasses. The seal is often not direct, but through intermediate glasses which bond well to the metal, either directly or through a suitable oxide layer. The choice of seal materials and geometry will depend on the use to which the complete unit is put. Seals to soft metals are not appropriate to vacuum use. For a treatise on the subject see J H Partridge, *Glass-to-Metal Seals*, or W H Kohl, *Materials and Techniques for Electron Tubes*.

3.5.7 Shrink-fitting

Shrink-fitting metal components on to ceramic rods or tubes is feasible because of the high compressive strength of most ceramics, but care needs to be exercised from two points of view:
1. the shrink-fitting process should not involve excessive thermal shock on the ceramic
2. the pressure under the contact area generates axial tensile stresses in the ceramic which are greatest at the ends of the contact area.

These tensile stresses will lower the effective remaining strength of the ceramic, and if excessive can fracture the material immediately. The stresses are lowest for short axial contact lengths, but higher shrink pressures are required to obtain the same grip on the component. The stresses can be reduced by tapering the metal component thickness towards the ends of the contact area.

Shrink-fitting is therefore best considered as a means of locating a ceramic component rigidly, but is not necessarily the most suitable joining method where there are significant additional mechanical loads. The stronger the ceramic, the more effective the shrink-fit joint will be. Tungsten carbide hardmetals are commonly fitted in this way into metal components for use as dies and forming tools.

3.5.8 Metallized and brazed joints

The types of joint discussed so far are not vacuum-tight except the direct glass-to-metal or glass-to-ceramic joints. However, completely hermetic seals are often required for use as lead-throughs and vacuum devices for use under arduous conditions. The temperature and strength limitations of glasses sealed to metals have led to the development since the mid-1930s of various ways of producing a soldered or brazed joint between a ceramic insulator and a metal component.

The subject is a complex one, and successful products are made generally by proprietary techniques. It is therefore not possible to be very specific about current commercial joining procedures, and in this Section, discussion is restricted to general points about the principles of the various techniques, and about geometry and thermal expansion matching.

To join a ceramic and a metal, the joining medium has to wet both materials well. In general, metals do not adhere well to ceramics or glasses and an interlayer is required. In the glass- or glass-ceramic-to-metal joint, a suitable oxide coating on the metal is partially dissolved in the glass, i.e. a chemical bond is achieved. This type of joint cannot be made with ceramics, since it would be undesirable to attempt fusion of the ceramic even if it were possible.

The usual way of approaching the problem is to place a metal coating on to the ceramic by powder painting, spraying or printing, firing to give a strongly adherent layer, and then using a solder or braze to join the metal component to the coating. Before dealing with specific types of coating the following general points should be made:

1. Success in producing a good brazed joint depends on:
   (a) the braze and its compatibility with the metallized surface and the metal component
   (b) the stresses produced in a joint by its geometry and the thermal expansion mismatch between component parts
   (c) the adherence of the metal coating to the ceramic
   (d) the quality of the joint.

2. The choice of metallizing and brazing materials is determined essentially by the requirements of the end use, in particular the temperature and the corrosive nature of the environment. Combinations of materials may be limited because of wetting or compatibility problems. For example, it may be necessary to electroplate the metallized layer and the mating surface of the metal component to prevent the braze dissolving the metallizing or failing to wet the metal.

3. The stresses produced in a joint depend on:
   (a) the thermal expansion mismatch between ceramic, braze and metal
   (b) the relative thickness of ceramic and metal, and the geometry of the joint
   (c) the mechanical properties of both metal and braze, in particular, their ability to relax stresses by deformation in thin sections of soft metal.
   (d) the brazing temperature.

4. The strength of the joint depends on:
   (a) the pre-existing joint stresses
   (b) the properties of ceramic, braze and metal
   (c) the integrity of interfaces.

5. The adherence of the metallized layer on the ceramic depends on a large number of practical variables:
   (a) the type of ceramic and its surface finish
   (b) the type of metallizing
   (c) the type of chemical bond
   (d) the particle size of the metal powder and its composition (it may contain a number of components, including metals, reducible metal oxides, glasses, carbides and hydrides)
   (e) the thickness of the coating
   (f) the heating cycle and the atmosphere used to make the bond.

From these points it is clear that considerable development work has to be done to make a successful novel ceramic-to-metal joint. Even changes in geometry can ruin a successful design, for example, increasing the dimensions of the joint. The inexperienced user would therefore be well advised to seek specialist advice on particular requirements because it is not always the strongest joint that makes the best vacuum seal.

3.5.8.1 Summary of methods

Table 3.5.1 summarizes the materials and manufacturing methods of various types of metallized joints. This Table is based on general information available on the various basic combinations of materials that can be used. Proprietary techniques may differ appreciably from what is shown, in

Table 3.5.1 Summary of metallizing and brazing methods

No.	Metallized layer type	Suitable ceramics	Metallizing materials in finely-divided form	Metallizing temperature, atmosphere	Additional layers required	Suitable solders or brazes
1.	Silver, silver/ platinum	Hard glasses Most ceramics	Mixtures of $PtCl_4$, Ag_2O, Ag and Pt	500–900°C in air	none	Sn, Pb or Pb solders[1]
2.	Silver, silver/ platinum + fluxing glass	Hard glasses Most ceramics	Mixtures of $PtCl_4$, Ag_2O, Ag and Pt. + <20% soft glass or flux, e.g. lead borate	500–900°C in air	Ag, Ag/Pt	Sn, Pb or Pb solders[1]
3.	Silver + copper oxide	Most ceramics	Ag_2O + <10%CuO, Cu_2O	>940°C in air	Ag, Ag/Pt	Sn, Pb or Pb solders[1]
4.	Molybdenum + silver	Most ceramics	Mo + ~10% Ag_2O	1300°C in dry H_2	Ni[2]	Cu, Cu/Ag, Ag
5.	Molybdenum + glass	Most ceramics	Mo + 10–20%glass	1200–1300°C in dry H_2	Ni[2]	Cu, Cu/Ag, Ag
6.	Nickel + glass	Most ceramics	NiO + ~10% glass	1300°C in dry H_2	Metallized layer needs buffing	Solders, Cu/ Ag
7.	Copper, copper alloys	Most ceramics	CuO (+ alloying oxides)	1100°C in air + 900°C in H_2	none	Solders
8.	Tungsten or molybdenum (+ manganese or iron)	Oxide ceramics BeO, Al_2O_3 (debased type)	W or Mo (+ Mn or Fe compounds, e.g. 80% Mo, 20% Mn)	1450–1650°C in wet H_2	Ni[2]	Cu/Ag, Au/Cu
9.	Titanium or zirconium[3] (active metal joints)	Oxide and some non- oxide ceramics	Ti and Zr, or more commonly TiH_4, ZrH_4 or other compounds	>1000°C in inert atm.	none	Zr, Ti eutectic brazes
10.	Molybdenum + titanium	Pure alumina	Mo + TiN or TiC	1450–1900°C in wet H_2	Ni[2]	Cu/Ag, etc.

[1] Excessive reaction between solder and metallized layer can be prevented by an additional electroplated layer of copper on the metallizing, or by using a solder with a high silver content, e.g. Cu/Ag.

[2] Nickel coating can be achieved by electroplating, or by a second coating as in 6. above but without glass.

[3] This process can be done by direct brazing in vacuum with an 'active metal' braze, using optionally TiH_4 or ZrH_4 as fluxes to wet the ceramic, i.e. a one-stage process.

particular with regard to minor components in the metallizing material, to firing schedules, and to brazes and the techniques for brazing.

The so-called 'molybdenum-manganese' process (No. 8 in Table 3.5.1) is one of the most commonly used for joining alumina components to metals despite the high firing temperature. It is considered that the presence of some mobile glassy phase in the ceramic at the firing temperature is essential to the production of a strong bond, although the actual mechanism is uncertain. Migration of the glass from the ceramic into the metallizing layer of molybdenum (possibly with manganese or iron or their compounds added) seems to be a condition for obtaining a strong joint. Thus a 95% alumina containing perhaps 10–15% by volume of a glassy phase will produce a strong bond with molybdenum powder alone, but a 99.5% alumina will not, and it is necessary to add a glass or glass-forming material such as manganese silicate to effect a bond to glass-free materials. The grain size of the ceramic also appears to be important. Most commercial aluminas designed for metallizing have mean grain sizes in excess of 10 μm, usually 15–20 μm, providing wide channels for the ready flow of glass to the surface. The large grain size is disadvantageous from the point of view of strength of the ceramic, but advantageous in reducing the tendency to creep during the high-temperature firing. Since faces to be metallized are often accurately ground, distortion during firing is undesirable.

The temperature capability and resistance to corrosion of the seal depend more upon the properties of the braze than on those of the metallized layer. Clearly, joints made using lead- or tin-based solders are not refractory, and do not require a high-temperature metallized layer on the ceramic. One of the lower-temperature types (e.g. 1 to 7 in the Table) should suffice. As the use-temperature requirement is raised, more-refractory brazes are needed, and the metallized layer, including any electroplating, must withstand alloying solution by the braze. At the same time, since the more refractory brazes tend to be mechanically hard and offer less opportunity to relax stresses due to thermal expansion mismatch on cooling, greater care has to be taken to ensure matching of thermal expansion coefficient between the ceramic and metal components. This tends to restrict greatly the combinations of materials that can be used to form satisfactory joints. Many oxide ceramics have expansion coefficients in the range $6–10 \times 10^{-6} K^{-1}$, and the matching metallic materials tend to fall into the nickel-iron alloys group (e.g. 'Nilo-K'). Tungsten or molybdenum are suitable for lower expansion coefficient ceramics.

Increasing use is being made of 'active metal' joints, (e.g. 9, 10 in the Table). In this technique an 'active metal', usually titanium or zirconium, is used to make a direct bond with the ceramic. The chemical reactivity of metallic titanium or zirconium, especially if produced by decomposition of a compound such as the hydride, nitride or carbide in contact with a ceramic, is such that a direct reaction-bond can be readily produced. The ceramic surface can be metallized by coating with a suspension of metal or compound and then firing in inert conditions. The joint is made by subsequent brazing using a titanium- or zirconium-based braze. Alternatively the joint can be made directly by vacuum brazing with a braze cored with active metal, perhaps using a hydride as a flux. In a similar process a titanium compound may be mixed with molybdenum and fired in wet hydrogen, as in the molybdenum/manganese process. This however requires a further electroplated nickel layer for conventional brazing.

Some braze metals can effect a direct bond with some non-oxide materials, such as silicon-containing silicon carbide. The silicon content of such materials is an important factor in promoting wetting, but excessive reaction between braze and silicon should be avoided because of the brittleness of silicides. Silicon nitride in various forms can be directly brazed with difficulty. Advice should be sought from manufacturers and specialists.

3.5.8.2 Geometrical considerations

Most engineering metal alloys have coefficients of thermal expansion rather greater than those of most ceramics. Rigid joints between ceramics and metals are therefore stressed on cooling from the brazing temperature to a degree depending on the geometry, on the relative thickness of ceramic and metal, and on the ability of the metal and braze to relax stresses.

Consideration of thermal expansion mismatch is often not necessary when using soft solders or soft metal components, but as the temperature capability of the joint is raised by using more refractory metals and higher brazing temperatures, not only is there a greater mismatch on cooling to ambient temperature but there is also a lesser ability to relax stresses. It is therefore desirable to try to match the thermal expansions of ceramic and metal over the temperature range from ambient to the brazing temperature, and to ensure that the ceramic components are thick-walled compared with the metal attached (as in Figure 3.5.3a).

It is desirable to place the ceramic in slight compression by allowing the metal to clamp down on it by relative thermal contraction from the brazing temperature, as in a disc seal (Figure 3.5.3e). If the metal component is made too stout, the clamping stress produces excessive axial tension in the ceramic, and weakens the product.

In the tube seal (Figure 3.5.3b), the stresses are predominantly in shear at the interface between ceramic and braze, and a successful joint requires a strong metallized layer and a strong braze not subject to embrittlement. A balancing ring of ceramic may be required.

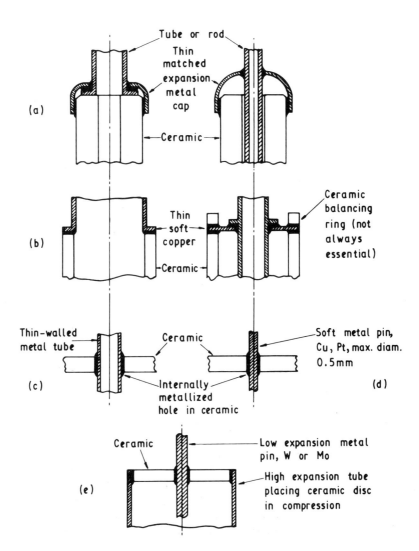

Figure 3.5.3
Various types of seal (braze shown dark in exaggerated thicknesses):
(a) leadthrough joints for heavy section conductors;
(b) large bore tube and disc joints;
(c) tube through a disc;
(d) soft pin in a disc;
(e) hard pin in disc seal.

With internal seals involving, for example, tubes or rods (Figures 3.5.3c and 3.5.3d), the metal ideally should be closely matched to the ceramic in thermal expansion coefficient. Thin-walled tubes of soft metal can be sealed without difficulty since the metal yields on cooling. With solid rods, the stresses developed are rather higher. Soft pins of copper or platinum can be brazed into metallized holes in a ceramic disc such as alumina provided they do not exceed about 0.5 mm diameter, otherwise the metallized layer splits. For larger pins, a low-expansion metal such as tungsten or molybdenum can be used. These contract less than most ceramics on cooling from the brazing temperature, and place the interface in compression. However they also put the ceramic into hoop tension which has to be balanced by an outer compression seal on the ceramic disc. This presents no great difficulty since the outer seal can be used to fix the component to a structure.

When heavy sections of metal are to be joined to ceramics to form a vacuum-tight seal and there is a significant thermal expansion mismatch, as with heavy-section copper to carry a high electrical current or thermal flux, it is necessary to employ a thin-walled convoluted or curved section of matched thermal expansion material (e.g. 'Nilo-K' for alumina) between the metal and the ceramic as for example in Figure 3.5.3a. This will accommodate the mismatch by bending without unduly stressing the ceramic.

3.5.8.3 Brazing operations

Since ceramics are prone to thermal stress fracture, temperature gradients in the ceramic component should be minimized both in the manufacture of the seal and in connecting the seal to another component.

In making the seal itself, *flame heating is to be avoided*. In general, a uniform temperature is desirable, such as is achieved by slow electrical heating in a vacuum or protective atmosphere furnace. The seal parts are assembled with rings of brazing wire in appropriate places. When the braze melts, it runs into the gaps between ceramic and metal components to make the seal. Parts may be pre-'tinned' and pre-fluxed as appropriate to the braze material.

The metal parts of the seal generally have to be joined to other components under conditions that preclude slow heating. Flame brazing can be used *provided the ceramic seal is protected from direct flame impingement* (e.g. by insulation) and is kept thermally remote from the brazing area. Preferably, a joint should be made by a *rapid* method, such as induction heating, or suitable welding techniques.

3.5.9 Vacuum-tight clamp joints

The principles of clamping ceramic or glass components are similar to those of bolting, i.e. minimizing of local stresses. A vacuum- or gas-tight joint between a ceramic or glass component and a metal component, or between ceramic or glass components, generally requires close control of tolerances in order to provide a flat or conical mating surface. In pressure windows, for example, a gasket material is always used between the glass plate and the mating metal components to avoid local stress concentration and to provide the seal medium. The clamping ring is bolted down by tightening the nuts in a sequence such that compression is uniform, e.g. for six bolts on a ring flange the tightening sequence might be 1–4–2–5–3–6. Joints between glass tubes may be clamped in the same way if the tubes have flat ground flanges on mating ends, again using a sealing gasket. If there are no flanges, then joints usually require some form of compression seal using a soft O-ring. Due allowance has to be made to cushion the joint against bending forces which might bring the tube ends into local contact with the clamping rings or with each other inside the union.

Surface finish for clamp sealing depends on the type of joint, but generally a fine ground or lapped finish is needed to minimize leakage past the gasket.

3.5.10 Diffusion-bonding

Whereas metallizing and brazing require high temperatures and the infiltration of a liquid braze into the joint region, diffusion-bonding between a ceramic and a metal is essentially a single-step, solid-state process. In this method the bond is produced by diffusing an interposed metal foil into both components while the joint is under pressure at a temperature near but not exceeding the melting point of the foil.

One such technique for joining debased alumina ceramics to metal alloys of similar expansion coefficient employs aluminium metal as the bonding material. Thin aluminium foil is placed between ceramic and metal alloy, a load is appled to ensure good contact, and the assembly is heated to a temperature near the melting point of aluminium. Aluminium diffuses into the surface of the metal alloy and also bonds to the alumina ceramic with some reaction with glassy phases. On cooling a strong bond is produced.

Other combinations include silicon carbide to some metals using platinum or nickel foil, and tungsten carbide to mild steel using nickel or cobalt foil. The principal requirement is that the finish of the mating surfaces must be flat (or of uniform curvature) to a few fringes, but not highly polished. Some element of surface roughness is thought to be needed to enhance the local diffusion processes. The precise mechanisms of joint formation are not well understood. Reduction of the ceramic species by the atmosphere and the close proximity of metal, as well as thermodynamic effects of solution of the reacting species may be important factors.

3.6

Inspection and testing

As mentioned in Section 3.3.5, specifications should incorporate some element of inspection and testing. Responsibility for this may rest solely with the manufacturer, or partly with the manufacturer and partly with the purchaser, depending on the capability of the manufacturer and his willingness to undertake the required test. The purchaser may have to inspect products himself if specialized equipment or conditions are required, or if the ceramic component is built into a device before testing is relevant.

Inspection takes several forms depending on the criticality of various types of manufacturing defect that can affect end use. In this Section, various inspection and testing techniques are described, together with their limitations.

3.6.1 Sizing

Sizing jigs, rather than gauges, are often the best way of ensuring that the components are within the band of tolerance specified. Some examples are shown in Table 3.6.1. If the requirements in terms of combined tolerances

Table 3.6.1 Methods of sizing using jigs

Dimension	Test for oversize	Test for undersize
Length	Fails to pass an opening of maximum acceptable size.	Passes an opening of minimum acceptable size.
Outside diameter	Fails to pass through a ring of maximum acceptable diameter.	Passes through a ring of minimum acceptable diameter.
Inside diameter	Probe of maximum acceptable diameter passes through bore.	Probe of minimum acceptable diameter fails to pass through bore.
Bow	Acceptable components pass through between plates set apart by the maximum thickness plus bow allowed. Rods or tubes can be rolled through such a gap. Alternatively, internal and external bow tests can be performed by using a straight test tube or rod respectively of suitable diameter and of greater length than the component, or these can be combined into a single test (c.f. Figure 3.4).	
Combined dimensions	Special jigging is usually required combining the above techniques, e.g. for coaxiality of inside and outside diameters of tubes, relative positioning of sets of holes in plates, etc.	
Complex form	Optical methods can be used, e.g. projection of the component shape onto a standard template.	

on several dimensions are complex, the design of a jig to simulate the requirements of the final assembly into which the component is to be placed is probably the easiest way of sizing. Measurement of dimensions is adequate if these are straightforward, such as the length of a short rod, but this process tends to be slower than simple sizing.

Wear should be allowed for on all contacting devices including jigs and gauges because ceramic materials are very abrasive.

3.6.2 Visual inspection

Surface defects such as scratches, pits, small holes, inclusions, iron spots, metal marks, chips on edges or corners and unground patches on a ground component due to depressions failing to clean up, can all be inspected visually. This process can clearly be somewhat subjective and the customer needs to consider carefully whether inspection is feasible and that the agreed specification for maximum defect sizes is clear and checkable. For example, edge chips may be acceptable to some degree on certain critical edges. To define the pass/fail limits, the following levels of acceptance have to be considered:

1. maximum size of chip in terms of length along the edge and into each surface
2. total length of chips or number of chips per edge, and the number of edges that must be chip-free
3. maximum size of corner chips
4. presence of edge cracks in chipped areas.

Correct lighting is important in visual inspection, particularly on white or light-coloured materials. A magnifier is usually required to avoid eye fatigue. Inspection inside holes requires some form of periscope. Surface porosity, grinding damage and cracks may require enhancement by a coloured or fluorescent dye (the latter is especially required on dark materials) in order to be readily visible.

Defects within a material cannot be inspected optically unless the material is sufficiently translucent.

3.6.3 Internal defect detection

3.6.3.1 Ultrasonic testing

The use of ultrasonic testing for the detection of internal defects relies on the ability to distinguish holes or cracks from normal microstructure. The limit of resolution depends on the wavelength of the sound used and the extent to which the grain boundaries in the material and the free surface cause scattering of the signal which may mask the defect. The best resolution is typically 100 μm, which is adequate for many purposes, but not for detection of strength-determining cracks, flaws or large grains in advanced ceramics.

Acoustic microscopy is a developing technology which may in the future offer the potential for internal inspection of thin components and studying the integrity of coatings or joints. Resolution is claimed to be rather better, about 3 μm.

3.6.3.2 X-ray methods

X-ray shadowgraphs can provide information on the presence of defects down to a minimum size which is defined by the X-ray source size and the differences in absorption characteristics between the defect and the matrix material through the thickness under test. In many types of ceramic containing low atomic number species, the contrast obtained between the matrix and a defect is lower than in most metals, so that detection limits parallel to the X-ray beam tend to be rather worse than in metals. If the minimum change in absorption that can be resolved with certainty is 5%, then the minimum defect size detectable is about one twentieth of the component thickness, i.e. 0.5 mm for a 10 mm thickness.

3.6.3.3 Thermal methods

The presence of large-scale internal porosity or other types of large defect can sometimes be detected by changes in thermal properties. If a component containing such a defect is heated, small variations in surface temperature may result. These can be detected by the use of a temperature-sensitive paint or by IR imaging techniques.

3.6.3.4 Density

The density of a ceramic is often specified to be greater than a minimum or to lie within a band. This is to ensure that the material achieves certain levels of as-fired tolerance on the shaped component. It also indicates that it has been correctly formulated and fired, and should therefore possess acceptable levels of mechanical properties corresponding to the density. Density can be measured by the traditional Archimedes method, provided due account is taken of open porosity levels (see Section 2.3.2), either on complete small components or on fragments of large ones. Mean densities of large, regularly-shaped pieces can be obtained fairly accurately by weighing and measuring dimensions.

Variations in density between components can be detected by variations in elastic moduli as determined by time-of-flight or resonance methods. Such techniques are used routinely for quality control in the vitreous-bonded grinding wheel industry.

3.6.4 Mechanical testing

None of the above-mentioned techniques will guarantee detection of the single strength-controlling defect in a component to be subjected to load in use. Furthermore the strength of any individual component is indeterminate until it is actually tested. Overload proof-testing has therefore been developed to guarantee a certain level of strength, or conversely the absence of particularly weak or flawed components (see Section 2.5.3.5 for a physical explanation and mathematical derivation). In this technique, the component is subjected to loading, usually in the manner it will see in use, but to a rather higher level and only for a very short time. If the loading and unloading are done quickly and smoothly, then the strength-controlling defects are momentarily stressed but do not have time to grow to any significant extent unless the failure stress is exceeded. If a component survives the proof test, it is guaranteed to survive for a longer period of time at a lower load. The appropriate overload factor can be determined approximately from the strength characteristics of the material and its susceptibility to slow crack growth in the working environment. Alternatively, one can use an overload factor which breaks say 10% of the components in preliminary trials, thus removing the weak end of the distribution of fracture strengths (or lifetimes under load). One then has some guarantee that those components with bad flaws have been eliminated.

Proof-testing has its advocates and its critics. There may be objections because of the damage the test itself can do if it is not performed correctly. Sometimes an assembly cannot be subjected to the required overload factor because joints or other regions start to fail at stresses not encountered in normal use, e.g. cement joints in high-voltage insulators. Nonetheless, proof-testing will eliminate those components that are abnormally weak before they cause breakdown or damage in use.

Proof-testing will not take into account physical changes to the material during use, such as high-temperature annealing, abrasive damage or chemical corrosion. These need to be accounted for in different ways.

Simple proof-testing may be a part of routine inspection in manufacture, but is usually subject to special arrangements. Complex components, or devices into which a ceramic component is incorporated will normally have to be tested by the purchaser.

3.6.5 Other acceptance tests

Gas-tightness of joints, seals or whole components (e.g. closed end tubes) may be guaranteed by manufacturers, but the purchaser is advised to check on the basis for the claim. Gas-tightness may mean no bubbling when immersed in water and subjected to internal air pressure at 2 psi. If there are specific requirements for leak-tightness, helium leak testing is to be preferred. For use at high temperatures, diffusion of gaseous species in ceramics may be significant and limit any type of gas-tightness.

Thermal shock testing may be appropriate in some circumstances, but this needs to be specified very carefully to define shock conditions representative of end use and also suitable procedures to detect any cracking so that the pass/fail criterion can be determined.

3.7

Bibliography for Section 3

The references cited below offer general reading in the subject areas covered by this Section.

Section 3.2 Manufacturing methods

Kingery, W D. *Ceramic fabrication processes*, Technical Press of MIT and John Wiley and Sons Ltd., Mass./New York, 1958.

Tooley, F V. *Handbook of glass manufacture* (2 vols.), Ogden Publishing Co., New York, 1953.

Vincenzini, P (editor). *Advances in ceramic processing, Proceedings of CIMTEC III*, Rimini, Italy, May 27–31, 1977, National Research Council, Research Laboratory for Ceramics Technologies, Faenza, Italy, 1978.

Section 3.3 Dimensional tolerances and surface finish

Creyke, W E C, Sainsbury, I E J, Morrell, R. *Design with non-ductile materials*, Applied Science Publishers, London 1982.

Shand, E B. *Glass engineering handbook*, 2nd edition, McGraw Hill, New York, 1958.

Tompkinson, J C. *Design engineering series—ceramics*, edited by Beadle, J. D., Morgan Grampian/Design Engineering, London/West Wickham, 1969.

Section 3.4. Complex design problems

Boley, B A, Weiner, J A. *Theory of thermal stresses*, John Wiley, London and New York, 1960.

Braiden, P M. Techniques for stress analysis of ceramics. *Proc. Brit. Ceram. Soc.*, 1982, **32**, 315–32.

Creyke, W E C, Sainsbury, I E J, Morrell, R. *Design with non-ductile materials*, Applied Science Publishers, London, 1982.

Hasselman, D P H. Thermal stress resistance parameters for brittle refractory ceramics, a compendium. *Bull. Am. Ceram. Soc*, 1970, **49**(12), 1033–7.

Hasselman, D P H. Elastic energy at fracture and surface energy as design criteria for thermal shock resistance. *J. Amer. Ceram. Soc.*, 1963, **46**(11), 535–40.

Roark, R J, Young, W C. *Formulas for stress and strain*, 5th. edition McGraw Hill, New York, 1975.

Segerlind, L J. *Applied finite element analysis*, John Wiley and Sons Ltd., New York, 1976.

Zienkiewicz, O C. *The finite element method*, 3rd. edition, McGraw Hill, London, 1977.

Section 3.5 Joining to other components

Creyke, W E C, Sainsbury, I E J, Morrell, R. *Design with non-ductile materials*, Applied Science Publishers, London, 1982.

Partridge, J H. *Glass-to-metal seals*, Society of Glass Technology, Sheffield, 1949.

Burke, J J, Gorum, A E, Tarpinian, A. (editors). *Advances in joining technology*, Brook Hill Publishing Co., Chestnut Hill, Mass., USA, 1976.

Section 3.6 Inspection and testing

McGonnagle, W J. *Non-destructive testing*, 2nd. revised edition, Gordon and Breach, New York and London, 1971.

Sharpe, R S, Cole, H A, Heselwood, W C (editors). *Quality technology handbook*, 3rd. edition, IPC Science and Technology Press, London, 1977.

SECTION 4

Applications of technical ceramics

4.1

Introduction

This Section gives a list of applications of technical and engineering ceramics that are mostly covered by this Handbook. The applications include not only those which are well established, but also those which are under development, such as in internal combustion engines. Applications are split into the following areas:

Electrical
Mechanical
Thermomechanical (including metal processing)
Machinable materials
Optical
Chemical
Experimental engine technologies.

Clearly in some instances applications might be placed in more than one of the above categories, so some entries are duplicated where appropriate. Under each application suitable materials are given, with an indication of cost as 'L' (low), 'M' (medium), or 'H' (high). The cost of components is to a large extent dictated by complexity of shape, tolerances, tooling costs and the number purchased (see Section 3). As a guide, clay-based products are in the 'L' category, oxides such as alumina and magnesia, and non-oxides such as silicon carbide and carbon are in the 'M' category unless of exceptionally high purity, and the more exotic materials such as beryllia, boron carbide, hot-pressed silicon nitride etc., are in the 'H' category. Finally, the particular properties or combinations of properties that make the listed materials suitable for the application are noted. Very often cost is a major factor, rather than performance. The absence of entries under this heading is intended to imply that most materials would be acceptable, those listed being in common use because of availability.

This Section cannot be considered as complete because many applications of ceramics are highly specific to particular devices. The intention is that the list should highlight materials that might usefully be considered by the engineer for his application based on what is commonly used by others. The listing does not include applications of ceramic coatings.

4.2

Applications list

Note: The following abbreviations are used to distinguish various types of material:

RBSN — Reaction-bonded silicon nitride (porous)
HPSN — Hot-pressed silicon nitride (dense)
SSN — Sintered silicon nitride (sintered at low pressure with additives)
RBSC — Reaction-bonded silicon carbide (dense, silicon infiltrated)
HPSC — Hot-pressed silicon carbide (dense)
SSC — Sintered silicon carbide (sintered to dense form with additives)
SZ   — Cubic stabilized zirconia
PSZ — Partially-stabilized zirconia
PSTZ — Partially-stabilized transformation-toughened zirconia
TZP — Tetragonal zirconia polycrystals (all-tetragonal type)

The term tungsten carbide is intended to cover the wide range of tungsten carbide based hardmetals that is available. It is possible to choose materials with properties suited to particular applications. No subdivision of hardmetals is made in the following Table.

Application	Materials	Cost	Advantageous properties and comments
Electrical insulation			
Structural power insulators	Siliceous, aluminous, and cristobalite porcelains, usually glazed	L	Size availability, expansion matched to steel.
Small low-tension insulators, external	Siliceous, aluminous, and cristobalite porcelains, usually glazed	L	Cheap, usually plastic-processed.
Small low-tension insulators, internal	As for external use but can be open porous	L	Cheap, can be pressed to shape rather than turned.
Spark and glow plug insulators	Alumina	L–M	High strength, thermal stress resistance.
Eyelets, cable cleats, cable racks, bus bar supports, terminal blocks, staywires	Aluminous porcelain Alumina	L M	High strength. High strength.
Bushes, sleeves, beads bobbins, up to 200°C	Porcelains, all types	L	
Bushes, etc., above 200°C	Refractory porcelains, mullites, aluminas	L–M	Thermal shock resistance, high electrical resistivity for the highest operating temperatures.

Application	Materials	Cost	Advantageous properties and comments
Electrical insulation (*contd*)			
Aerial insulators	Aluminous porcelain	L	} High strength, low loss.
	Alumina	M	
Coil formers:			
Small to medium, low-power	Porcelains, steatites	L	
High-power	Cordierite	L	Thermal shock resistance for high power resistors.
Precision	Alumina	M	Low dielectric loss, high strength.
For high frequencies	Low-loss steatite	L–M	Low loss.
High-temperature	Electrical refractories	L	Refractoriness, thermal shock resistance.
Fuse bodies:			
Medium to large	Porcelain	L	
Small, high-power	Alumina	M	High strength, high thermal conductivity.
Medium to large, high-power	Cordierite	L	Thermal shock resistance.
Vacuum envelopes and leadthroughs, vacuum interrupters	Glasses	L	Matched expansion to specific metals.
	Porcelains, forsterites	L–M	Higher strength, high expansion.
	Alumina, beryllia	M–H	High strength, refractory for metallizing and brazing.
	Glass-ceramics	M–H	Directly made seals matched to metals.
Vacuum device insulating components	Alumina	M	Good high-temperature properties.
	Boron Nitride	H	Best high-temperature electrical insulation.
	Porous alumina	M	For easy degassing.
Electronic packaging:			
Substrates	Alumina	M	High strength, flat, resistant to glaze attack. High thermal conductivity. Brown varieties for light shielding.
	Beryllia	H	Very high thermal conductivity.
Chip carriers, heat sinks	Alumina	M	Strong, good dielectric characteristics.
	Beryllia	H	High thermal conductivity.
	Aluminium nitride	H	High thermal conductivity.
Power semiconductor housings	Alumina	M	} High strength, metallizable to give hermetic seals.
	Beryllia	H	
Radomes, missile nose-cones	Alumina	M	Strong, ablation-resistant, good dielectric properties.
	Alumina/titanate composites	H	Controlled temperature variation of dielectric properties.
	Beryllia	H	Good thermal properties.
	Glass-ceramics	M–H	Low permittivity.
Microwave components	Alumina	M–H	} Low loss at $> 10^{10}$ Hz.
	Beryllia	H	
	Glass-ceramics	M–H	
Magnetic tape cutters	Zirconia PSTZ, TZP	H	Non-magnetic.

Application	Materials	Cost	Advantageous properties and comments
Electrical conduction			
Heating elements	Silicon carbide	M	Good resistivity/temperature relation. Max. 1600°C.
	Molybdenum disilicide	M–H	Max. 1700°C.
	Lanthanum chromite	M–H	Max. 1800°C vertical.
	Carbon	L–M	Max. 2800°C, inert conditions only.
	Zirconia SZ	H	Max. 2400°C, needs hot ends.
	Titanium diboride/BN composites	H	Aluminium evaporator boats.
R.F. susceptors	Carbon, graphite	L–M	Easily machined to shape.
	Silicon carbide	M–H	Can be used in air to 1600°C, but needs to be moulded and fired to shape.
Electrodes	Tin oxide	M	Limited in temperature to 1400°C, limited solubility in glasses.
	Carbon, graphite	L	Inert but limited to 400°C in air.
Medium resistivity materials	Titania (reduced)	M	Used for electrostatic discharge in thread guides.
	Special oxides	H	Specialist materials only.
Ionic conductors:			
Oxygen	Zirconia SZ	M–H	From 500 to 1000°C.
Sodium	Beta-alumina	H	From 300 to 500°C.
Others	Specialist materials	H	Mostly developmental.
Mechanical strength and wear resistance			
Mill linings	Porcelains (mainly aluminous types)	L	Cheap, small mills can be made monolithic.
	Alumina	M	Less alkali contamination than porcelain, also less wear.
	Zircon	L	Harder than porcelain, cheaper than alumina.
	Tungsten carbide	H	Hard, tough but very expensive and gives metallic contamination.
Milling media (choice depends to a large extent on scale of operation and type and level of contamination that are acceptable)	Agate (SiO$_2$)	M–H	
	Porcelain	L	Where contamination not important.
	Steatite	L	Used for mixing rather than grinding.
	Alumina	L–M	Hard and wear resistant. Low alkali contamination.
	Zirconia SZ	M–H	Wear resistant and dense.
	Tungsten carbide	M	Very dense, but gives metallic contamination.
Pestles, mortars:			
For soft to medium hard materials	Soda-lime or boro-silicate glasses	L	
	Porcelain (chemical)	L–M	
	Agate	M	Low alkali contamination.
For hard materials	Alumina	M	⎫
	Boron carbide	H	⎬ Hardness, strength.
	Tungsten carbide	H	⎭

Application	Materials	Cost	Advantageous properties and comments

Mechanical strength and wear resistance (*contd*)

Application	Materials	Cost	Advantageous properties and comments
Chute linings for ore and abrasive materials handling	Cast fused basalt	L	Cheap and moderately wear resistant.
	Alumina	M	Stronger, harder, can be used in thinner section.
Agricultural implements (e.g. spring tine tips)	Alumina	M	Developing area, needs good toughness and wear resistance.
Shot blast nozzles	Alumina	M	Wear resistance and strength.
	Boron carbide	H	Harder, greater life.
Abrasive powder and slurry handling and mixing, nozzles, jets, scrapers, etc.	Alumina	M	Hardness, wear resistance.
	Silicon carbide	M	
	Boron carbide	H	Very hard.
Food processing, mixing and extrusion, etc.	Alumina	M	Hard and non-toxic.
Grinding wheel mould liners	Alumina	M	Hard, wear resistant.
	Silicon carbide	M	
	Boron carbide	H	Very hard.
Ceramic tooling dies	Tungsten carbide	H	Hardness, wear resistance, toughness.
	Boron carbide	H	Hardness, wear resistance.
	Silicon carbide SSC	H	
Crushing rolls	Alumina	M	Hardness, strength.
	Tungsten carbide	H	Hardness, strength, toughness.
Ballistic tiles	Alumina	M	Hard, strong.
	Boron carbide	H	Less dense than alumina.
Material cutting; tool tips, drill tips:			
General purpose	Tungsten carbide	H	Hardness, toughness, (generally more versatile than ceramics).
Indexable inserts for hard alloys (usually at high speed)	Alumina (usually hot-pressed)	H	Hardness, strength, limited toughness.
	Alumina/TiC	H	Hardness, strength.
	Alumina/zirconia	H	Enhanced toughness.
	Sintered sialons	H	Hardness, strength, wear resistance.
	Cubic boron nitride	H	Very hard, compatible with ferrous metals.
For nonferrous metals only	Diamond (polycrystalline)	H	Very hard, fairly tough.
For rock drilling and cutting	Diamond	H	Hardest and most wear resistant.
	Tungsten carbide	H	Hardness and toughness.
Tool dressing materials	Porcelains	L	For alumina and silicon carbide.
	Boron carbide	H	For diamond tools.
Cold die parts:			
Extrusion and drawing dies for tubes and wires	Zirconia PSTZ	H	Low friction, strong.
	Tungsten carbide	H	General purpose.
Wire drawing cones	Diamond	H	For fine wires.
	Alumina	M	Good friction, wear resistance.
	Zirconia PSTZ	H	Low friction, good finish to wire.
Stamping dies, roller dies	Tungsten carbide	H	Tougher than most ceramics.
	Silicon nitride HPSN	H	Strength and hardness, low coefficient of friction.

Application	Materials	Cost	Advantageous properties and comments
Mechanical strength and wear resistance (*contd*)			
Pump parts and liquid handling:			
Vanes, impellers	Coated metal alloys	M–H	Hardness of surface.
	Alumina	M	Hardness, strength, corrosion resistance.
Seal rings for shafts	Alumina	M	Acid resisting varieties available, limited in thermal shock.
	Silicon carbide	M-H	Very hard, acid resisting.
	Tungsten carbide	H	Tough, wear resisting but not especially corrosion resistant.
Hydraulic plungers	Tungsten carbide	H	Wear and liquid erosion resistance, strength.
	Silicon nitride HPSN	H	
	Silicon carbide HPSC, SSC	H	
	Alumina/sapphire	M-H	Wear and corrosion resisting.
Valve facings	Alumina	M	Hard, non-corroding.
Guides, runners in paper handling, etc.	Alumina	M	Good all-round properties.
	Silicon carbide SSC	M-H	Very hard, acid resisting.
Slideways, wear-resisting pads	Alumina	M	Hardness.
	Silicon nitride HPSN	H	Low coefficient of friction.
Thread-spinning nozzles	Silicon carbide	M	⎫
	Boron carbide	H	⎬ Low wear.
	Tungsten carbide	H	⎭
Thread-guides (pins, eyelets, rollers, etc.) for textiles	Titania (reduced form for electrostatic discharge).	M	Low friction, fine-grained.
	Alumina	M	Hard and wear resistant. Can be coloured for thread visibility.
Tape reading heads and guides	Alumina	M	Hard, wear resisting.
Magnetic disc reading heads	Alumina	M	Hard, wear resisting.
	Glass-ceramics	M	High level of polish for air cushion effect.
Precision bearings	Alumina	M	Hard, strong.
	Sapphire	H	Very hard.
	Silicon nitride HPSN	H	Hard, low friction, very fine grained.
	Silicon carbide	H	Hard, low friction.
	Boron carbide	H	Very hard, good finish.
Precision tool parts, sizing rings, jigs	Silicon carbide	M	Hard, good surface finish.
	Boron carbide	H	Very hard.
	Tungsten carbide	H	Hard, readily brazed.
Bone replacement, e.g. hip joints, dental prostheses	Alumina	M-H	Hard, wear and corrosion resistant.
	Sapphire	H	Hard and exceptionally corrosion resistant, good polishability.
Thermomechanical applications			
Thermocouple insulators and sheaths	Electrical refractories	L	Fine-textured types based on sillimanite or mullite.
	Alumina	M	⎫ High purity needed for precious metal couples.
	Beryllia	H	⎬
	Thoria	H	⎭

Application	Materials	Cost	Advantageous properties and comments
Thermomechanical applications (*contd*)			
Heating element supports:			
Coiled wire elements	Sillimanite, mullite refractories	L	Thermal shock resistant, but porous.
	Vitreous silica	L–M	Thermal shock resistant, infra-red transmitting.
Support tubes for rod heating elements	Sillimanite refractories	L	Thermal shock resistant.
Insulators for lamp elements	Steatite	L	
	Alumina	M	Strong, refractory.
Hot plates with integral elements	Alumina	M	Metallizable, high thermal conductivity.
Hot plates for separate elements	Glass-ceramics	M	Low thermal expansion, good thermal shock resistance.
Resistance thermometer element bases	Alumina	M	Strong, good finish, dimensionally stable.
Lamp holders	Porcelain	L	
Hot-metal probes	Silicon carbide	M	Refractory grades, thermal shock resistant.
	Silicon nitride	M	Not wetted by many metals.
Larger bore tubing for furnaces, etc.	Sillimanite refractories	L	Permeable, coarse-textured.
	Vitreous silica	M	Can be glass-worked, shock resistant.
	Mullite	M	Impervious, thermal shock resistant.
	Alumina	M	Impervious, refractory, high-purity grades resist reducing atmospheres.
	Silicon carbide (recrystallized type)	H	High purity for semi-conductor processing.
Saggars for material processing	Vitreous silica	L–M	Good thermal shock resistance.
	Silicon carbide	M	Thermal shock resistance, good high temperature strength.
	Aluminosilicate refractories	L	General purpose.
	Alumina (recrystallized)	M	High purity, refractory.
Kiln furniture	Aluminosilicate refractories	L	Thermal shock resistant, creep resistant.
	Silicon carbide refractories	M	Thermal shock resistant, creep resistant plus higher temperature capability.
Pins for refractory insulations	Alumina (various high-strength varieties)	M	Strong, refractory.
Furnace rollers, runners and guides	Alumina	M	Refractory grades usually chosen.
	Silicon carbide	M	Abrasion resistant.
	Refractory concretes	L–M	For large pre-cast items.
Burner parts, e.g. burner matrices, jets	Mullite	L	Thermal shock resistant, corrosion resistant.
	Silicon nitride RBSN	M	Thermal shock resistant, corrosion resistant.
	Silicon carbide RBSC	M	Thermal shock resistant, corrosion resistant.
	Zirconia PSZ	M–H	With controlled thermal expansion characteristics.

Application	Materials	Cost	Advantageous properties and comments
Thermo-mechanical applications (*contd*)			
Gas burner radiants	Aluminosilicate refractories	L	Thermal shock resistant.
	Mullite	L	For tubular radiants.
Regenerator and recuperator cores	Cordierite	L	Thermal shock resistance.
	Silicon nitride	M	
	Lithium aluminosilicate	H	Excellent thermal shock resistance.
	Aluminous keatite	H	For gas turbines, sulphate resisting.
High temperature gas valve parts, fans, etc.	Silicon nitride	H	Thermal shock resistance, strength, corrosion resistance.
	Silicon carbide, RBSC, SSC	M–H	
	Sialons, SSNs	M–H	
Metal welding applications:			
Weld pool rings	Mullite ceramics	L	Thermal shock resistance.
	Cordierite ceramics	L	Thermal shock resistance.
	Alumina	M	Strong, fair thermal shock resistance.
	Silicon nitride RBSN	M	Thermal shock resistant, resistant to wetting.
Welding nozzles	Alumina	M	Refractory, reusable.
	Silicon nitride RBSN	M	Refractory, reusable.
Welding jigs	Silicon nitride HPSN	H	Thermal shock resistant, precision dimensions.
	Silicon nitride RBSN	M	
	Sialons	H	
	Alumina	M	Less good in thermal shock.
	Pyrophyllite	L	Useful for prototypes.
	Graphite	M	
Liquid metal handling:			
Casting tubes, probes, etc.	Alumina	M	Refractory, strong, but poor in thermal shock.
	Vitreous silica	M	Affected by strongly reducing conditions.
	Graphite	M	Forms carbides with some metals.
	Silicon nitride RBSN	M	Useful for liquid aluminium. Good in thermal shock.
Casting cores	Aluminosilicate refractories	L	Thermal shock resistant, creep resistant.
	Vitreous silica	M	High precision, removed by leaching.
	Sintered vitreous silica	M	
Hot-pressing dies	Graphite	M	Easily machined, but not very strong.
	Silicon nitride HPSN	H	Strong, but not easily machined, needs a susceptor.
	Alumina	M–H	Strong refractory, but needs a separate susceptor, can be used in air.
Rocket nozzles	Graphite	M	Refractory, but not very ablation-resistant.
	Carbon/carbon composites	H	Strong and refractory.
	Silicon carbide RBSC	M	Strong and ablation-resistant.

Application	Materials	Cost	Advantageous properties and comments
Thermomechanical applications (*contd*)			
Catalyst supports	Alumina	M	Usually porous types.
	Cordierite	M	Thermal shock resistant.
	Aluminosilicate	L–M	Refractory, thermal shock resistant.
	Zirconia PSZ	M–H	Refractory.
Laboratory test equipment for high-temperature use under stress	Silicon nitride HPSN	H	} Strong, refractory.
	Silicon carbide HPSC	H	
	Alumina	M	Strong, refractory, easily machined.
Domestic cooker tops, hot-plates, bench tops cooking ware	Glass-ceramics	M	Low expansion coefficient, retains flatness, good thermal shock resistance. Easily cleaned.
Nuclear reactors:			
Element separators	Alumina	M–H	Low neutron capture cross-section.
Moderators	Beryllia	H	} Low atomic mass.
	Boron carbide	H	
Machinable materials for jigs, prototypes, etc.			
Insulators	Pyrophyllite (unfired)	L	Fine textured, anisotropic in as-quarried blocks, firing shrinkage small, hard when fired.
	Block talc	L	Hardened by firing, becomes porous, anisotropic.
	Machinable refractories	L	Usually castable or mouldable, porous.
	Machinable glass-ceramics	M	Hard, vacuum-tight, can be machined by WC-tipped tools, no firing required.
	Boron nitride	H	Good insulator but expensive, anisotropic.
Conductors	Carbon, graphite	L–M	Some grades contain hard slag-like inclusions and require diamond tools for long tool life.
Optical applications			
Telescope mirrors	Specialist glasses	M	Good polish.
	Silica glass	H	Low expansion coefficient.
	Glass-ceramics	H	Can have zero expansion coefficient.
Construction materials for lasers	Silica glass	M–H	Good thermal shock resistance.
	Glass-ceramics	H	Can have zero expansion coefficient.
	Beryllia	H	High thermal conductivity for heat dissipation.
	Sapphire	H	Windows for IR transmission.
Optical benches	Glass-ceramics	H	Can have zero expansion coefficient.
Synchrotron mirrors	Silica	H	Tends to distort and crack, but good finish.
	Silicon carbide	H	Stiff, strong, dimensionally stable. Good finish if SiC coated, e.g. by chemical vapour deposition.

Application	Materials	Cost	Advantageous properties and comments
Optical applications (*contd*)			
High temperature windows	Sapphire	H	Low IR absorption.
IR windows	MgF_2, CaF_2, calcium aluminate glasses	M-H	Low IR absorption.
Lamp envelopes:			
High power	Silica glass	M-H	Thermal shock resistant.
High pressure sodium vapour lamps	Alumina, translucent	H	Resistant to sodium vapour.
Chemical components			
Large scale chemical plant, tower packing, vessels, pipes	Borosilicate glass	L	Good resistance to acids and solvents.
	Chemical stoneware	L	Resistant to acids.
	Chemical porcelain	L	High strength, acid resistant.
Laboratory ware:			
Crucibles, boats	Chemical porcelain	L	Thermal shock resistant.
	Vitreous silica	M	Thermal shock resistant.
	Alumina, beryllia	M	Pure, refractory.
	Beryllia, thoria, zirconia SZ, vitreous carbon, boron nitride	H	Specialist materials for particular melts. See Section 2.9.
Funnels	Chemical porcelain	L	Resists acids to 100°C.
Filter media	Porous glasses	L	Controlled pore size.
	Porous ceramics	L-M	For particular uses and chemical reactivities.
Components in chemical plant:			
Floats, tubes	Alumina	M	Acid-resisting types.
Ball valves, nozzles	Alumina	M	Hard, corrosion resistant,
	Glass-ceramics	M	capable of being precision machined.
Pump bodies	Chemical porcelain	L	Complex shapes can be made.
Pump seals, bearings, shafts, impellers	Alumina	M	⎫
	Silicon carbide	H	⎬ Hard, corrosion resistant.
	Tungsten carbide	H	⎭
High pressure liquid chromatography pumps	Sapphire	H	Best acid resistance.
Rubber-dipping formers	Aluminious porcelain (glazed)	L	High strength, accurate shapes, may be large.
Catalyst supports (usually in porous form)	Aluminia	M	
	Cordierite	L-M	Thermal shock resistant.
	Zirconia SZ, PSZ	M	Refractory.
Experimental engine technologies			
Reciprocating internal combustion engines:			
Cylinder blocks (monolithic)	Silicon nitride RBSN	M	Low expansion, good dimension control.
Pistons	Silicon nitride RBSN, SSN	M-H	Thermal shock resistance, strength.
	Silicon carbide RBSC	H	Thermal shock resistance.

Application	Materials	Cost	Advantageous properties and comments
Experimental engine technologies (*contd*)			
Reciprocating internal combustion engines: (*contd*)			
Piston crowns	Silicon nitride RBSN, SSN	M–H	Thermal shock resistance.
	Aluminium titanate	M	
Injector nozzles	Silicon nitride SSN, sialons	H	Strength, thermal shock resistance.
Cylinder liners	Zirconia PSTZ	H	Matched thermal expansion to cast iron, low friction.
	Silicon carbide RBSC	H	Refractory, thermal shock resistant.
Exhaust pipe liners	Silicon nitride RBSN	M	Thermal shock resistance.
	Aluminium titanate	M	
	Alumina fibre composites	M	Insulating, thermal shock resistance.
Bearing surfaces	Zirconia PSTZ, TZP	H	Low wear, low friction.
	Silicon nitride HPSN	H	Very hard, strong.
Exhaust ports	Zirconia PSTZ	H	Low wear, matched expansion to cast iron.
Turbochargers:			
Rotors	Silicon nitride RBSN, SSN	M–H	Thermal shock resistance, strength.
Stators	Silicon nitride RBSN	M–H	Thermal shock resistance.
Bearings	Silicon nitride HPSN	H	Hardness, refractoriness.
Gas turbines:			
Rotors	Silicon nitride RBSN, HPSN, SSN, sialons and composite structures	M–H	Thermal shock and creep resistance, high strength.
Stators	Silicon nitride RBSN	M–H	Thermal shock resistance.
Volutes	Silicon nitride RBSN	M	
	Silicon carbide RBSC	M	
Fuel injectors and burners	Silicon carbide RBSC	M	
	Silicon nitride RBSN	M–H	
Regenerators	Aluminous keatite	M–H	Very low thermal expansion, acid resistance.

SECTION 5

Manufacturers and suppliers

5.1

Introduction

For ease of reference, Section 5.2 gives a list of types of material, with reference numbers to manufacturers and suppliers in the following Sections where company names and addresses, together with their product types and applications are given. The manufacturers of the various types of material covered by this Handbook are listed separately, and are divided as follows:

Section 5.3   Suppliers of technical ceramic materials and components.

Section 5.4   Suppliers of technical glasses and glass-ceramics.

Section 5.5   Suppliers of carbon and graphite.

Section 5.6   Suppliers of bonded tungsten carbide hardmetals (primary manufacturers).

This division is made so that manufacturers' names for the four product types can be scanned. This is very little duplication between the lists. The lists are not intended to be complete, but should give readers in the Western world, particularly those in the UK, adequate information for making enquiries about most types of product. Attention is drawn to the fact that some manufacturers specialize in certain types of applications or length of production runs, and thus may have limited manufacturing capability or expertise. In addition, for the more advanced types of material, developments are occuring rapidly, and many companies are embarking on production in new areas, often while cutting back in more traditional ones. The reader is warned that this directory is likely to date quickly.

5.2

Index to materials

Note: This summarizes available information from the listed firms in October 1984. Blank entries do not imply no supplier.

Material type	Reference numbers to manufacturers	
	UK	Overseas

Technical ceramics

Material type	UK	Overseas
Quartzitic and aluminous porcelains	5, 6, 18, 24, 26, 27, 35, 37, 46, 48.	109, 113, 120, 124, 129, 132, 133, 136, 138, 139, 140, 143, 145, 147, 149, 152, 153, 155, 157, 160.
Siliceous chemical stoneware	25, 33.	123, 141, 142, 147.
Porous aluminosilicate refractories (e.g. for electrical purposes)	5, 6, 24, 26, 27, 32, 33, 36, 40, 46, 49.	102, 109, 126, 127, 131, 142, 145, 147, 152.
Other porcelains (cordierite, celsian, zircon)	5, 6, 24, 37.	109, 124, 132, 136, 145, 147, 153, 154.
Steatite, forsterite	6, 37, 40.	109, 110, 130, 132, 136, 143, 145, 146, 147, 154.
Mullite ceramics	32, 37, 42.	127, 131, 132, 135, 136, 141, 145, 147, 152.

Oxides:

Material type	UK	Overseas
High-alumina	8, 17, 21, 22, 23, 24, 28, 32, 34, 37, 38, 39, 40, 42, 43, 44, 45, 46, 47.	101, 102, 109, 110, 114, 115, 117, 118, 121, 122, 123, 125, 127, 131, 132, 134, 135, 136, 139, 141, 142, 145, 147, 148, 151, 152, 153, 154, 155, 157, 159.
Beryllia	16, 17.	107, 110, 132, 137, 148, 154.
Magnesia	—	114, 123, 131, 141.
Spinel (MgO.Al$_2$O$_3$)	—	123, 131.
Zirconia	7.	114, 121, 123, 131, 132, 140, 141, 156, 157, 161.
Thoria	—	114, 131.
Tin oxide	19.	—
Chromic oxide	19.	—
Titanium dioxide	40, 45.	110, 114, 154.
Lanthanum chromite	—	141, 144.

Material type	Reference numbers to manufacturers	
	UK	Overseas

Technical ceramics (contd)

Non-oxides:

Silicon carbide	10, 12, 23, 29, 32, 33, 36.	102, 104, 111, 112, 116, 125, 128, 129, 132, 142, 148, 156.
Silicon nitride, silicon aluminium oxy-nitrides (sialons)	2, 8, 12, 31, 33.	102, 105, 111, 112, 125, 126, 132, 142, 147, 156, 157.
Aluminium nitride	—	157.
Boron nitride	9, 12, 20.	148, 158.
Boron carbide	7, 12.	105, 107, 111, 112, 148, 158.
Titanium diboride	9, 33.	111, 112, 119, 142, 158.
Zirconium diboride	33.	111, 112, 142.
Titanium carbide and composites with TiC	—	111, 112, 121.
Molybdenum disilicide	—	108, 116.
Fluorides	—	114.

Machinable ceramics:

Pyrophyllite	13, 15.	118.
Steatite/talc	—	—
Glass-ceramics	see under Glasses	
Refractories	41.	104.
Porous fused silica	18, 19, 46.	157.

Others

Glass-bonded mica	3.	—
Single-crystal sapphire	30.	132.
Single-crystal quartz	11, 14.	—
Kiln furniture products	1, 6, 26, 32, 33.	103, 142.
Electronic (dielectric) ceramics	28, 34, 42, 45.	132, 139, 147.
Speciality hot-pressing	—	105, 111, 112, 134.

Technical glasses and glass-ceramics

Technical glasses:

Soda-lime	206, 211, 212, 216, 217.	250, 252, 256.
Borosilicate	202, 204, 205, 210, 211, 213, 216.	250, 251.
Special compositions	201, 203, 208, 209, 211, 214, 216.	250, 251.
Silica glasses	209, 215.	250, 253, 255, 258.
Sintered fused silica	see under Machinable ceramics	
Glass-ceramics	207.	250, 254, 257.
in machinable form	—	250, 259.

Material type	Reference numbers to manufacturers	
	UK	Overseas

Carbon and graphite

Material type	UK	Overseas
Carbon and graphite	301–303.	351, 352, 354, 355, 356, 357, 358, 359, 360, 361.
Vitreous carbon	—	351, 353, 357, 361.
Pyrolytic graphite	—	351, 359, 361.
Siliconized graphite	303.	352, 357, 358, 359, 360, 361.

Hardmetals

Material type	UK	Overseas
Hardmetal materials	401–424.	See Brookes' directory referenced in 5.6 below.

5.3

Manufacturers – ceramics

In this and subsequent lists, UK manufacturers are listed first, together with foreign companies that have a UK manufacturing base and a direct selling agency for all types of product irrespective of where they are made. Foreign manufacturers, together with UK or West European offices or sales agencies are listed second.

The lists cannot be considered complete. In compiling them, only information to hand has been included, and that available for foreign companies is sparse. The addresses are believed to be correct at the time of compilation, but no responsibility is taken for the information displayed. A number of other companies also supply ceramics, e.g. as wear-resistant tiling, but do not manufacture them. Only primary UK manufacturers are listed.

5.3.1 UK manufacturers and foreign manufacturers with UK plant

No.	Manufacturer	Product range
1	Acme Marls Ltd Clough Street Hanley Stoke-on-Trent Staffs, UK	Kiln furniture, refractory products.
2	Advanced Materials Engineering Ltd Vauxhall Industrial Estate Ruabon Wrexham Clywd, LL14 6HY, UK	Reaction-bonded and hot-pressed silicon nitride.
3	Allen-Bradley Mouldings Ltd Love Lane Circencester Gloucestershire, GL7 1QY, UK	Injection mouldings in glass-bonded mica.
4	Allen-Bradley Electronics Ltd Bede Road Jarrow Tyne and Wear, NE22 3EN, UK	Resistor cores and formers.
5	Allied Insulators Ltd High Tension Products PO Box 17 Milton Stoke-on-Trent Staffs, ST2 7EE, UK	Porcelains and other clay-based products, kiln furniture, electrical refractories.

5.3.1 (contd)

No.	Manufacturer	Product range
6	Allied Insulators Ltd Low Tension Products Albion Works Uttoxeter Road Longton Stoke-on-Trent Staffs, ST3 1PH, UK	Smaller-sized porcelain and other clay-based products, particularly pressed items.
7	Anderman and Ryder Ltd* Central Avenue East Molesey Surrey, KT8 0QZ, UK	High alumina ceramics for electrical and engineering purposes. Zirconia for oxygen sensors.
8	Associated Engineering Developments Ltd Cawston House Cawston Rugby Warwickshire, CV22 7SA, UK	Reaction-bonded silicon nitride.
9	Borax Consolidated (Borides) Ltd Leeway Newport Industrial Estate Newport Gwent, UK	Boron nitride, titanium diboride.
10	British Nuclear Fuels Ltd REFEL Business Centre Risley Warrington Cheshire, UK	Reaction-bonded silicon carbide.
11	Brookes Crystals (1961) Ltd Cornhill Ilminster Devon, TA19 0AH, UK	Quartz crystals.
12	The Carborundum Co. Ltd Refractories and Electronics Div Rainford St Helens Lancs, UK (*Agents for Carborundum Co., PO Box 1054, Niagara Falls, NY 14302, USA) (European office for products of the Advanced Materials Division is at Hans-Voelber-Weg 7, D7120 Bietigheim, FR Germany. Silicon carbide products are also available from Daneite Hard Metals Ltd, PO Box 9, Carr Hill, Balby, Doncaster, DN4 8DJ, UK)*	Special refractories, silicon carbide, boron nitride, boron carbide.
13	Carters (Merchants) Ltd UCM House 3/5 Swallow House Princes Street London, W1A 1BB, UK	Pyrophyllite.

* Now Morgan Matroc, Anderman Division (November 1984)

No.	Manufacturer	Product range
14	Cathodeon Crystals Ltd Linton Cambridge Cambs., CB1 6JU, UK	Quartz crystals.
15	Ceramic Substrates and Components Ltd Stag Works Farnham Common Bucks, UK	Pyrophyllite and components machined from it.
16	Consolidated Beryllium Ltd PO Box 5 Milford Haven Dyfed, SA73 2PP, UK	Beryllia.
17	Coors Porcelain (UK) Ltd 35, Cavendish Way Southfield Industrial Estate Glenrothes, Fife, Scotland, UK. (*Agents for Coors Porcelain Inc., 600, Ninth Street, Golden, Ohio 80401, USA*)	All types of porcelain, all types of alumina ceramic, substrates for electronics, chemical porcelain, zirconia and silicon carbide.
18	Doulton Industrial Products Ltd Filleybrooks Stone Staffs, UK (Also Doulton Insulators Ltd, Two Gates, Tamworth, Staffs, UK)	Porcelains and other silicate ceramics, insulators and technical items. Fused silica cores for casting.
19	Dyson Refractories Ltd Griff Works Stannington Sheffield UK	Special refractories, tin oxide, chrome, zirconia, slip-cast fused silica.
20	Fulmer Components Ltd Stoke Poges Slough Bucks, SL2 4QD, UK	Pyrolytic boron nitride.
21	GEC Ceramics Ltd PO Box 29 Lichfield Road Stafford Staffs, UK	High alumina ceramics, including metallized components, and glass-ceramics.
22	GEC Engineering Research Centre Glass/Ceramics Group Materials Division Stafford Laboratory PO Box 30 Lichfield Road Stafford Staffs, ST17 4LN, UK	Ceramic and glass-ceramic developments.
23	G R Stein Ltd Genefax House Tapton Park Road Sheffield, S10 3FJ, UK	Alumina milling media, heavy refractories, special refractories, including silicon carbide.

No.	Manufacturer	Product range
24	A G Hackney Ltd Westport Road Burslem Stoke-on-Trent Staffs, UK	Porcelains and other aluminosilicate ceramics, insulators and other technical products.
25	Hathernware Ltd Hathern Loughborough Leicestershire, UK	Chemical stoneware, tower packings.
26	Hewitt and Sons Ltd Victoria Road Fenton Stoke-on-Trent Staffs, UK	Kiln furniture, special refractories, electrical refractories, low-tension porcelain.
27	International Ceramics Ltd Denby Derbyshire, DE5 8NX, UK	Cores for casting, refractory components, rods, tubes, etc.
28	ITT Components Ltd South Denes Great Yarmouth Norfolk, UK	Dielectric and electronic ceramics, high-alumina components for electronics.
29	Kanthal Electroheat Ltd Inveralmond Perth Scotland, UK	Silicon carbide heating elements, silicon carbide components.
30	A and D Lee Ltd Unit 19 Marlissa Drive Midland Oak Trading Estate Lythalls Lane Coventry, UK	Sapphire machined to requirements.
31	Lucas-Cookson-Syalon Ltd Cranmore Boulevard Shirley Solihull Warwickshire, UK	Sialon ceramics, development work.
32	Morgan Refractories Ltd Neston Wirral Cheshire, L64 3RE, UK	Refractory tubing and components, special refractories.
33	Norton Refractories Ltd King Street Fenton Stoke-on-Trent Staffs., ST4 3LY, UK *(UK agents for Norton Refractories Inc. One New Bond St., Worcester, Mass 01606, USA, and Norton SA, BP 8, Rue de l'Ambassadeur, F–78702 Conflans-Ste Honorine, France. Norton also have an international office at Cartwright House, 39/43 Monument Hill, Weybridge, Surrey, KT13 8RN, UK)*	Kiln furniture, silicon carbide and silicon nitride of all types, alumina refractories, special refractories.

5.3.1 (*contd*)

No.	Manufacturer	Product range
34	Oxley Electronics Ltd Priory Park House Ulverston Cumbria, UK	Electronic ceramics.
35	Park Royal Porcelain Ltd* Cox Hill Sandy Beds, SG19 1QQ, UK	Porcelains and related ceramics, insulators and large components.
36	Refractory Mouldings and Castings Ltd Market Place Kegworth Derby, DE7 2EF, UK	Special moulded refractories of all types.
37	Rosenthal Technical Components Ltd 3 Abercorn Trading Estate Bridgwater Road Alperton Wembley Middx, UK. (*Sales agency for Rosenthal Technical Components, Colyton, Devon, and UK agency for Rosenthal Technik AG (FR Germany) – see Section 5.3.2 for details.*)	Ceramics and components of all types.
38	Royal Worcester Industrial Ceramics Ltd Tonyrefail Mid-Glamorgan CF39 8YW, Wales, UK	Alumina ceramics for electrical and engineering usage, thread guides.
39	Smiths Industries Ceramics and Ignition Co. Ltd** St. Peters Road Rugby Warwickshire, CV21 3QR, UK	Alumina ceramics for electrical and engineering use, thread guides and spark plug insulators.
40	Steatite and Porcelain Products Ltd*** Bewdley Road Stourport-on-Severn Worcs, UK	Alumina ceramics for electrical and general use, thread-guides steatite and cordierite, electronic ceramics.
41	Super Refractories Ltd Unit C Lewis Road East Moors Cardiff, UK	Special refractories, machinable refractories.
42	Thermal Syndicate PLC PO Box 6 Wallsend Tyne and Wear, NE28 6DG, UK	Refractory tubing and components in high alumina and mullite. Also various types of fused silica and quartz.
43	Thorn Lighting Ltd Melton Road Leicester Leics, UK	Translucent alumina ceramics.

* Now Morgan Matroc, Park Royal Division (November 1984)
** Now Lodge Ceramics Ltd (November 1984)
*** Now Morgan Matroc Ltd (November 1984)

5.3.1 (*contd*)

No.	Manufacturer	Product range
44	Unilator Technical Ceramics Ltd Vauxhall Industrial Estate Ruabon Wrexham Clywd, LL14 6HY, UK	Alumina ceramics for electrical and general use, thread-guides, dielectric ceramics.
45*	Geo. Wade Ltd Greenhead Street Burslem Stoke-on-Trent Staffs, UK	Porcelain and other aluminosilicate ceramics, high-alumina ceramics.
46*	Wade (Ireland) Ltd Watson St Portadown Northern Ireland, UK	High-alumina ceramics, including large pressings. Sintered fused silica.
47	The Worcester Royal Porcelain Co. Ltd The Royal Porcelain Works Severn Street Worcester Worcs, WR1 2NE, UK	Chemical and analytical porcelain.
48	Zirconal Processes Ltd Cosmos House Bromley Common Bromley Kent, BR2 9TL, UK	Special refractories of all types.

*High-alumina ceramics from Nos. 45 and 46 are marketed by Wade (Advanced Ceramics) Ltd, 67 Regent Street, Leicester, LE1 6YF, UK.

5.3.2 Foreign manufacturers and agencies

No.	Head Office	Agency	Product range
101	Alberox Corp Industrial Park New Bedford Mass 02745, USA	Teknis Ltd Teknis House Meadrow Godalming Surrey, GU7 3HQ, UK	High alumina ceramics and metallized parts.
102	Annawerk Keramische Betriebe GmbH Postfach 1144 D–8633 Rödental 1 FR Germany	—	Wide range of technical ceramics, including honeycomb materials, advanced ceramics.
103	Aremco Products Inc PO Box 429 Ossining NY 10562, USA	The Meclec Co 5/6 Tower Close Shoeburyness Essex, SS3 9QP, UK	Coatings and ceramic potting compounds.
104	Asahi Glass Co. Ltd Ceramics and Refractories Div 1–2 Marunouchi 2-chome Chiyode-ku Tokyo 100 Japan	—	Silicon carbide, silicon nitride, cordierite, zirconia, aluminium titanate.
105	Avco Systems Division Systems Div Lowell St Wilmington Mass 01887, USA	—	Hot-pressed materials.
106	Boride Products Inc 2879 Aero Park Drive Traverse City Michigan, 49684, USA	—	Boron carbide.
107	Brush-Wellman Inc Ceramic Div Van Syckels Rd Hampton NJ 08827, USA	Brush-Wellman Inc 1, rue Traversiere 77174–Villeneuve Le Comte France	Beryllia.
108	Bulten-Kanthal* S–3401 Hallstahammar Sweden (see also Kanthal Electroheat Ltd, Perth, Scotland, UK)	Bulten-Kanthal Stephen Newall Ltd* 14B, Shepcote Way Tinsley Industrial Estate Sheffield, UK	Molybdenum disilicide.
109	C.E.C. (Refractaires) 99 av. Aristide Briand F–92120 Montrouge Cedex France	—	Ceramics of all types.
110	Centerflex Ceramics Corp 188, Eighth Avenue Hawthorne NJ 07507, USA	Prestbourne Process Engineering Ltd Newbrooke House Lodge Lane Dutton Warrington Cheshire, UK	Alumina, beryllia, forsterite, steatite, titania.

* Now Kanthal A B, agency Kanthal Ltd.

No.	Head Office	Agency	Product range
111	Cerac Inc Box 1178 Milwaukee Wis 53201, USA	Testbourne Ltd 9, Sheppard Road Basingstoke Hants, RG21 3HT, UK	Custom hot-pressed products.
112	Ceradyne Inc 3030–A Red Hill Ave Santa Ana California 92705, USA	Englass Ltd Scudamore Road Leicester, UK	Advanced ceramics and custom hot-pressing.
113	Ceramica Industriale FER, SPA Via Pacini 49 Seregno 20028 Italy	—	Porcelain ceramics for electrical insulators.
114	Céramiques Techniques Désmarquest Zone Industrielle No. 1 27025 Evreux – Cedex France	—	Refractory tubing, crucibles. Sintered fluorides.
115	Ceraver 53, rue de la boetie 75008 Paris France	—	Technical ceramics of all types, metallized components.
116	Cesiwid Electrowärme GmbH D8520–Erlangen Neumühle 4 FR Germany (*A division of Sigri* *Electrographit GmbH.*)	Southern Engineering Sales Ltd 98, Ashley Road Walton-on-Thames Surrey, KT12 1HP, UK	Silicon carbide, esp. heating elements, molybdenum disilicide.
117	Diamonite Products Manufacturing Inc 453, West McConkey St Shreve Ohio, 44676, USA	—	High-alumina ceramics.
118	Duramic Products Inc 426 Commercial Ave Palisades Park New Jersey NJ 07650, USA	Prestbourne Process Engineering Ltd Newbrooke House Lodge Lane Dutton Warrington Cheshire, UK	Machined components, esp. pyrophyllite.
119	Elektroschmelzwerk Kempten GmbH 8000 München Postfach 609 FR Germany	New Metals and Materials Ltd Chancery House Chancery Lane London, WC2, UK	Boron carbide.
120	Fabrica Isolat. Porcellana Romagnano Sesia 20100 Italy	—	Porcelain insulators of all types.
121	Feldmühle AG Postfach 1149 7310 Plochingen FR Germany	—	High-alumina and other oxide ceramics for electrical and engineering uses.

No.	Head Office	Agency	Product range
122	Frenchtown American Corp Eighth and Harrison Sts Frenchtown NJ 08825, USA	—	Alumina ceramics and metallized assemblies.
123	Friedrichsfeld GmbH Postfach 7 D–6800 Mannheim 71 FR Germany	Degussa Ltd Paul Ungerer House Earl Road Stanley Green Handforth Wilmslow Cheshire, SK9 3RL, UK	Refractory tubing, crucibles, etc. in MgO, Al_2O_3, ZrO_2. Standard thread guides, shaft seals, special components in alumina.
124	Fusi SPA Via Ortiles 80 Milano 20159 Italy	—	Fuse bodies, electrical ceramics.
125	General Electric Co 159, Madison Ave New York NY 10016, USA (*'Lucalox' alumina, fused quartz and speciality glasses are available from GE Co Lamp Components and Technical Products, 21800 Tungsten Rd, Cleveland, Oh 44117, USA*)	International General Electric Co. of NY Ltd Park Lorne 111 Park Road London NW8 7JL, UK	Specialist ceramics and components.
126	G T E Sylvania Chemical and Metals Div Hawes Street Towanda Pa 18848, USA	G T E Sylvania Precision Materials Group Edison Road Elms Industrial Estate Bedford, MK41 0HU, UK	Silicon nitride, ceramic recuperators.
127	Haldenwanger 1 Berlin 20–Spandau Pichelswerder Str. 12 FR Germany	Anderman and Co 145 London Road Kingston-upon-Thames Surrey, UK	Refractory tubing and crucibles.
128	Hitachi (Research Lab.) 3-1-1, Sawai-cho Hitachi-shi Ibaraki-ken 317 Japan	—	Sialons, sintered silicon carbide.
129	Ibiden Co. Ltd 1 Kandamachi 2-chome Ogaki 503 Japan	—	Silicon carbide, graphite.
130	Ifö AB 29500 Bromölla Sweden	—	Porcelain and steatite.
131	H Koppers GmbH 4000 Düsseldorf-Herdt Wiesenstrasse 61 FR Germany	Anderman and Co 145, London Road Kingston-upon-Thames Surrey, UK	Refractory tubing and crucibles.

No.	Head Office	Agency	Product range
132	Kyocera Corp 52–11 Inoue-cho Higashino Yamashina-ku Kyoto 607 Japan	Feldmühle Kyocera Europa Postfach 1143 D7310 Plochingen FR Germany	Technical and engineering ceramics of all types.
133	Manifattura Ceramica Pozzi SPA Via Ugo Bassi 8/a Milano 20159 Italy	—	Electrical insulators in porcelain.
134	Materials Research Corp Route 303 Orangeburg NY 10962, USA	Materials Research Corp Ballards Lane Finchley London N12	Alumina ceramic substrates.
135	McDanel Refractory Co. Box 560 Beaver Falls Pa 15010, USA	—	Refractory tubing, etc.
136	Narumi China Corp Narumi-cho Midori-ku Nagoya 458 Japan	Narumi China Ltd Mercer House 780a Hagley Road West Oldbury Warley West Midlands B68 0PJ, UK	Technical ceramics of all types.
137	National Beryllia Corp Haskell NJ 07420, USA	—	Beryllia.
138	Nederlandse Keram. Bedr. BV Postbus 396 5900 A J Venlo Netherlands	—	Porcelains.
139	NGK Insulators Ltd 2–56 Suda-cho Mizuho-ku Nagoya Japan	NGK (Europe) SA 36, av des Arts 1040 Brussels Belgium	Technical ceramics of all types.
		Prestbourne Process Engineering Ltd Newbrooke House Lodge Lane Dutton Warrington Cheshire, UK	Electronic substrates.
	also NGK Spark Plug Co. Ltd NTK Technical Ceramics Division 14–18 Takatsuji-cho Mizuho-ku Nagoya Japan	NGK Spark Plugs (UK) Ltd Units 7 and 8 Garrick Industrial Centre Garrick Road Hendon, London NW9 6AQ, UK	High alumina ceramics for all applications, zircon, mullite, aluminium titanate, cordierite, silicon nitride and silicon carbide.

No.	Head Office	Agency	Product range
140	Nilcra Ceramics Pty. Ltd 239, Separation St Northcote, 3070 Victoria Australia	—	Zirconia drawing dies.
141	Nippon Kagaku Togyo Co Woko Shoken Bldg 8th Floor, No 3 Katahame 3-chome Higashi-ku Osaka 541 Japan	—	Chemical porcelain of all types, crucibles, refractory tubes and components, lanthanum chromite heating elements.
142	Norton Industrial Ceramics Div One New Bond Street Worcester Mass 01606, USA	Norton Industrial Ceramics Ltd King Street Fenton Stoke-on-Trent Staffs, ST4 3LY, UK	All types of refractory, engineering ceramics in silicon carbide and silicon nitride.
143	Porzellanfabrik Langenthal AG 4900 Langenthal Switzerland	—	Porcelain and steatite.
144	Pyrox SARL 36–bis, Rue G Lenotre 78120 Rambouillet France	The Carbolite Company Bamford Mill Bamford Sheffield, S30 2AU, UK	Lanthanum chromite heating elements.
145	Richard Ginori Soc. Ceramica It. SPA Via Goldoni 10 Milano 20129 Italy	—	All types of porcelain insulators.
146	Ernst Roederstein GmbH 8300 Landshut Ludmillastrasse 23–25 FR Germany	Steatite Insulations Ltd Hagley House Hagley Road Birmingham B16 8QW, UK	Steatite components, other electronic ceramics.
147	Rosenthal Teknik AG Division I 8672 Selb Wilhelmstr. 14 FR Germany	Rosenthal Technical Components Ltd 3 Abercorn Trading Est Bridgwater Road Alperton Middx, UK	Porcelain insulators grinding media, etc.
	Division II D8590 Marktredwitz Postfach 109 FR Germany		Refractory tubes, smaller insulators in all types of oxide ceramics.
	Division III D–8560 Lauf Postfach 46 FR Germany		Steatite, piezoelectric ceramics, high-alumina ceramics for engineering.

No.	Head Office	Agency	Product range
148	Showa Denko KK 13–9 Shiba Daimon 1 chome Minato-ku Tokyo Japan	Showa Denko Europe GmbH D–4000 Düsseldorf Charlottenstr. 51 FR Germany	Alumina, beryllia, silicon carbide, boron nitride, boron carbide.
149	Siemens AG Wittlesbacherplatz 2 Postfach 103 D–8000 München FR Germany	Siemens Ltd Siemens House Windmill Road Sundbury-on-Thames Middx, TW16 7HS, UK	Ceramic insulators for power engineering.
150	Societa Ceramiche Ind. Li SPA Milano 20159 Italy	—	Steatite and porcelain.
151	Speceram Les Fabriques d'Assortiments Reunies SA Les Paquerettes SA CH–2416 Les Brenets Switzerland	—	Precision alumina.
152	Staatliche Porzellan Manufaktur Berlin D–1000 Berlin 12 Wegelystrasse 1 FR Germany	Anderman and Co 145, London Road Kingston-upon-Thames Surrey, UK	Refractory tubing, crucibles, etc.
153	Stettner u. Co Hersbruckerstrasse 22 Postfach 7 8650 Lauf FR Germany	—	Technical ceramics of all types, electronic ceramics.
154	3M Corp Technical Ceramic Products Division 3M Center St Paul Minn 55101, USA	3M (UK) Ltd PO Box 38 Yeoman House 57/63, Croydon Road Penge London, SE20 7TR, UK	Oxide ceramics of all types, steatites, thread guides, substrates.
155	Tinlot SA (Ceramics Isolantes) Nessonvaux 4640 Belgium	—	Porcelain insulators
156	Toray Industries Inc 2–2 Nihonbashi Muromachi Chuo-ku Tokyo 103 Japan	Toray Europe Ltd 7th Floor 35/8, Portman Sq London, W1H 0BS, UK	Zirconia oxygen sensors, silicon nitrides.
157	Toshiba Corp Metal Products Division 26–5 Toranomon 1 chome Minato-ku Tokyo 105 Japan	—	Alumina, silicon nitride aluminium nitride, zirconia, silicon carbide.
	also Toshiba Ceramics Co. (see no. 258 under Glasses)	—	All types of technical ceramics.

No.	Head Office	Agency	Product range
158	Union Carbide Corp Carbon Products Div 120 South Riverside Rd Ill 60606, USA	Union Carbide (UK) Ltd 8 Grafton Street London, W1A 2LR	Boron carbide, boron nitride, carbon and graphite, TiB_2.
159	Wesgo Division GTE Products Corp 477, Harbor Road Belmont Calif 94002, USA	—	Alumina ceramics.
160	Westinghouse Electric Corp Switchgear Division Industrial Ceramics Dept 333 W. Third St Porcelain Park Derry Penn 15627, USA	Westinghouse Electric Group Regal House London Rd Twickenham Middx, TW1 3QT, UK	Porcelains and insulators.
161	Zircoa Products 31501 Solon Road Solon Ohio 44139, USA	Corning Glass GmbH 6200 Wiesbaden Hagenauer Str. 47 FR Germany	All types of zirconia.

For further details on ceramic companies in the US, see the Company Directory Issues of the American Ceramic Society Bulletin (January Issues), published by the American Ceramic Society, Columbus, Ohio, USA.

5.4

Manufacturers – glasses and glass-ceramics

5.4.1 UK manufacturers and foreign manufacturers with UK plant

No.	Manufacturer	Product range
201	Abrahams and Co (B'ham) Ltd Brama Teams Glass Works Gateshead Tyne and Wear NE8 2RA, UK	Special glasses.
202	Chance Brothers Ltd Pickersleigh Avenue Malvern Link Worcs, UK	Glass tubing, scientific glassware.
203	Chance Pilkington Ltd Glascoed Road St Asaph Clwyd, North Wales, UK	Optical glasses, special scientific glasses.
204	Corning Ltd Wear Glass Works Sunderland Tyne and Wear, UK	'Pyrex' and other technical glasses.
205	Corning Ltd Process Plant Division Newstead Industrial Estate Trentham Stoke-on-Trent Staffs ST4 8JG, UK	Process plant in glass.
206	Doulton Laminated Glass Ltd Saffron Way Sittingbourne Kent, UK	Thermally strengthened glass.
207	GEC Ceramics Ltd PO Box 29 Lichfield Road Stafford Staffs, UK *(Development work undertaken by GEC Engineering Research Centre, Glass/Ceramics Group, Materials Division, PO Box 30, Lichfield Road, Stafford, Staffs, ST17 4LN, UK)*	Glass-ceramics.

No.	Manufacturer	Product range
208	General Electric Company PLC Hirst Research Centre East Lane Wembley Middx, UK	Special glasses for seals and electrical purposes, glass-to-metal seals.
209	Glass Bulbs Ltd Harworth Doncaster S Yorks, UK *also at:* Sheffield Rd Chesterfield S41 8LD, UK	Special glasses of all types including tubing.
210	John Montcrieff Ltd North British Glassworks, PO Box 10 St Catharine's Road Perth, Scotland, UK	Borosilicate glass for technical purposes, gauge glasses, chemical glassware.
211	Nazeing Glassworks Ltd Nazeing New Road Broxbourne Herts, EN10 6SU, UK	Industrial glassware of all types.
212	Pilkington Brothers PLC Head Office Prescot Road St Helens Lancs, UK	Sheet glass.
213	Pilkington PE Ltd Glascoed Road St Asaph Clwyd, N Wales, UK	Special glass equipment.
214	Plowden and Thompson Ltd Dial Glass Works Stourbridge West Midlands, DY8 4YW, UK	Glass rod, tubing, and cullet.
215	Thermal Syndicate PLC PO Box 6 Wallsend Tyne and Wear NE28 6DG, UK	All types of fused silica products.
216	J and B Treasure and Co. Ltd 12–24 Vauxhall Road Liverpool, L3 6DN, UK	Industrial glassware, boiler gauge glasses, borosilicate pressings.
217	Triplex Safety Glass Co Ltd Eckersall Road Kings Norton Birmingham, UK	Thermally strengthened glass.

5.4.2 Foreign manufacturers and agencies

The range of companies listed below are primarily those making fused quartz and glass-ceramics, i.e. speciality products. Also shown are principal flat glass manufacturers importing into the UK. For details of other foreign companies, see the directories listed at the end of the section.

No.	Manufacturer	Agency	Product range
250	Corning Glass Works Houghton Park Corning NY 14830, USA	Corning Ltd Technical Products Division Castle Chambers 3 Sheet Street Windsor Berks, UK	Special glasses and glass-ceramics.
		McGeogh and Co Ltd 124, Witton Avenue Witton Birmingham, B6 7DZ, UK	Corning's machinable glass-ceramic.
251	Corning France 44 Ave de Valvins Box 61 77211 Avon Cedex France	Corning Ltd Technical Products Division Castle Chambers 3 Sheet Street Windsor Berks, UK	Technical glasses of all types.
252	Glaverbel SA Ch. de la Hulpe 166 Bruxelles 1170 Belgium	—	Flat glass.
253	Heraeus Quarzschmelze GmbH D-6450 Hanau Postfach 463 FR Germany	Heraeus Silica and Metals Ltd Unit 3 120 Oyster Lane Byfleet Woking Surrey, KT14 7LE, UK	Fused quartz and silica.
254	Nippon Electric Glass Export Division 16 Tagaguki-cho Kita-ku Osaka Japan	Semitek Agents (B'ham) Mercer House 780A Hagley Rd West Warley West Midlands, B68 0PJ, UK	Technical glasses of all types, transparent glass-ceramics.
255	Quartz et Silice 8, Rue d'Anjou F-75008 Paris France	Nuclear and Silica Products Ltd 44, The Green Woburn Green High Wycombe Bucks, UK	Fused quartz and silica.
256	Saint Gobain Industries 62 bd. v. hugo 92209 Neuilly France	—	Flat glass of all types.

5.4.2 (*contd*)

No.	Manufacturer	Product range	
257	Jenaer Glasswerk Schott u. Gen. D-6500 Mainz 1 Postfach 2480 Hattenbergerstrasse 10 FR Germany	—	All types of technical glass, low expansion glass-ceramics.
258	Toshiba Corp Shinjuku Namura Bldg Shinjuku-ku Tokyo 160 Japan	—	Silica glass, sintered fused silica.
259	Carl Zeiss Jena Jena German Democratic Republic	C Z Scientific Instruments, Ltd PO Box 43 2, Elstree Way Borehamwood Herts, WD6 1NH, UK	Machinable glass-ceramic.

For further details of primary and secondary glass manufacturers, see the current editions of:

1. *European Glass Directory and Buyers Guide,* Publ. Fuel and Metallurgical Journals Ltd, Queensway House, 2 Queensway, Redhill, Surrey.
2. *American Glass Review,* Factory Directory Issues (e.g. **100,** (8A), Feb. 1980).
3. *The Glass Industry,* Directory Issues (e.g. **60,** 10, 1980).
4. *Bulletin Amer. Ceram. Soc.,* January editions, publ. Amer. Ceram. Soc. (Company Directory).
5. National Glass and Glazing Societies and Federations.

5.5

Manufacturers – carbon and graphite

5.5.1 UK manufacturers

No.	Manufacturer	Product range
301	Anglo Great Lakes Ltd Newburn Haugh Newcastle-upon-Tyne Tyne and Wear, UK	All types.
302	British Acheson Electrodes Ltd Grange Mill Lane Sheffield S9 1HS, UK	All types.
303	Morgan Carbon Ltd Battersea Church Road London, SW11, UK	All types, also siliconized products.

5.5.2 Foreign manufacturers and agencies

No.	Manufacturer	Agency	Product range
351	Le Carbone Lorraine 45, Rue des Acacias F-75821 Paris France	Le Carbone (GB) Ltd South Street Portslade Brighton Sussex, UK	All types, including vitreous carbon.
352	Duramic Products Inc 426, Commercial Ave Palisades Park NJ 07650, USA	Prestbourne Process Engineering Ltd Newbrooke House Lodge Lane Dutton Warrington Cheshire, UK	Graphite machined to requirements, siliconized graphite.
353	Fluorocarbon Process Systems Div PO Box 3640, 1432 South Allec St Anaheim Calif 92803, USA	Hi-Temp Materials 3, Cedars Ave Mitcham Surrey, CR4 1HN, UK	Vitreous carbon.

No.	Manufacturer	Agency	Product range
354	Great Lakes Carbon Corp Graphite Products Div 6200 Pine Avenue Niagara Falls NY 14303, USA	Anglo Great Lakes Ltd Newburn Haugh Newcastle-upon-Tyne Tyne and Wear, UK	All types.
355	Ibiden Co Ltd 1-Kandu-machi 2-chome Ogaki 503 Japan	—	All types.
356	Poco Graphite Inc Box 2121 Decatur Texas 76234, USA	—	All types.
357	Sigri Electrographit D-8901 Meitingen bei Augsburg FR Germany	—	All types.
358	Syntax Corp Box 791 Bay City Mich 48706, USA	—	Graphite, siliconized graphite.
359	Toshiba Ceramics Co Ltd PO Box 3012 Shinjuka Namura Bldg Shinjku-Ku Tokyo 160 Japan	—	Carbons, graphites, siliconized graphite.
360	Ultra Carbon Corp Box X-747 Bay City Mich 48707, USA	—	Graphite, siliconized graphite.
361	Union Carbide Corp Carbon Products Div 120 Sth Riverside Plaza Chicago Illinois 60606, USA	Union Carbide (UK) Ltd 8, Grafton Street London, W1A 2LR, UK	All types, including vitreous carbon.

5.6

Manufacturers – hardmetals

5.6.1 UK manufacturers

No.	Manufacturer	No.	Manufacturer
401	Albe (England) Ltd Newton Works 51, Bideford Avenue Perivale Middx, UK	409	Dymet Alloys Ltd Frimley Road Camberley Surrey, GU15 2QG, UK
402	Edgar Allen Tools Ltd PO Box 78 Shepcote Lane Sheffield S9 1QT, UK	410	Firth Brown Tools Ltd Speedicut Works Carlisle Street East Sheffield, S4 7QP, UK
403	F C Annett and Co. Ltd Albion House Lind Road Sutton Surrey, UK	411	Hall and Pickles Ltd PO Box 161 Hydra Steel Works Ecclesfield Sheffield, UK
404	Artisan Sintered Products Ltd Shepley Industrial Estate Audenshawe Manchester M34 5DW, UK	412	Higher Speed Metals Ltd Brocco St Sheffield, S3 7GN, UK
405	Beever Tools Ltd Wellthorne Works Stone Lane Woodhouse Sheffield, S13 7PT, UK	413	Hillcliff Hard Metals Ltd Coleford Road Sheffield S9 5PF, UK
406	Thomas Bolton and Sons Ltd PO Box 1 Froghall Stoke-on-Trent Staffs, ST10 2HF, UK	414	Hoy Carbides Ltd PO Box 1 Princes Risborough Aylesbury Bucks, UK
407	Cintride Ltd Grange Lane Works Ecclesfield Road Sheffield, S5 0DR, UK	415	Kennametal Ltd PO Box 29 Pensnett Trading Estate Brierley Hill West Midlands DY6 7NP, UK
408	Daneite Hard Metals Ltd PO Box 9 Carr Hill Balby Doncaster, DN4 8DJ, UK	416	Marwin Hard Metals Ltd Golf Course Lane Braunstone Leicester, UK

5.6.1 (*contd*)

No.	Manufacturer	No.	Manufacturer
417	Maxicarb Hardmetals Ltd Burrell Road Haywards Heath West Sussex RH16 1TR, UK	420	Sandvik (UK) Ltd Manor Way Halesowen Worcs, B62 8QZ, UK *and* PO Box 63 Torrington Avenue Coventry, CV4 9AD, UK
418	Nuloy Ltd Hulley Road Hurdsfield Industrial Estate Macclesfield Cheshire, SK10 2NF, UK	421	Tungsten Electric Co. Ltd Beraston House Tenbury Wells Worcs, WR15 8LF, UK
419	Penistone Hardmetals Co. Ltd 61, Manchester Road Sheffield, S10 5DY, UK		

All the above manufacturers are UK-based. For further details of hardmetal manufacturers, both primary and secondary, see *World Directory and Handbook of Hardmetals* by K J A Brookes, publ. Engineers Digest, 3rd. edition, 1983.

SECTION 6

Materials and design expertise in ceramics and brittle materials

6.1

Expertise in UK

In the following list of sources of advice in the UK, various facets of services are indicated as follows:

1. Materials and product development.
2. Materials testing and evaluation.
3. General advice and consultation.
4. Engineering design expertise, including design analysis.

Organisation	Abilities
British Industrial Ceramic Manufacturers Association Federation House Station Road Stoke-on-Trent Staffs, UK	3.
British Ceramic Research Association Ltd Queens Road Penkhull Stoke-on-Trent Staffs, ST4 7LQ, UK	1, 2, 3, 4.
British Glass Industry Research Association Northumberland Avenue Sheffield S10 2UA, UK	1, 2, 3.
Brunel Industrial Services Bureau Brunel University Uxbridge Middlesex, UB8 3PH, UK	2, 3, 4.
Cambridge Consultants Science Park Melton Road Cambridge CB4 4DW, UK	3, 4.
Ceramic Centre UKAEA Harwell Didcot Oxon, OX11 0RA, UK	1, 2, 3, 4.
Cranfield Product Engineering Centre Cranfield Institute of Technology Cranfield Beds, UK	2, 3, 4.

Organisation	Abilities
ERA Technology Ltd Cleeve Road Leatherhead Surrey, UK	2, 3, 4.
Fulmer Research Institute Ltd Stoke Poges Slough Bucks, SL1 4QD, UK	1, 2, 3, 4.
Glass Advisory Council 6, Mount Row London W1, UK	3.
Glass and Glazing Manufacturers Federation 19, Portland Place London W1, UK	3.
GEC Engineering Research Centre Mechanical Engineering Laboratory Whetstone Leicester, UK	1, 2, 3, 4.
GEC Engineering Research Centre Glass Ceramics Group Materials Division PO Box 30 Lichfield Road Stafford Staffs, ST17 4LN, UK	1, 2, 3.
Imperial College of Science and Technology Department of Metallurgy and Materials Science Prince Consort Road London, SW7 2BP	1, 2, 3.
National Centre for Tribology UKAEA Risley Warrington Cheshire, UK	2, 3.
National Physical Laboratory Queens Road Teddington Middlesex, TW11 0LW, UK	1, 2, 3, 4.
Pafec Ltd Thane Road Lenton Industrial Estate Nottingham, NG7 2GT, UK	4.
Pilkington Brothers PLC Technical Advisory Service Prescot Road St Helens Lancs, UK	1, 2, 3, 4.
University of Leeds Department of Ceramics The University Leeds, LS2 9JT, UK	1, 2, 3.

Organisation	Abilities
University of Newcastle Wolfson Research Group for High Strength Materials The University Newcastle-upon-Tyne, UK	1, 2, 3.
University of Sheffield Department of Ceramics Glasses and Polymers Northumberland Road Sheffield 10, UK	1, 2, 3.
University of Warwick Department of Physics Coventry CV4 7AL, UK	1, 2, 3.

6.2

Expertise overseas

Listed below are some of the major organisations that can offer advice and design expertise in the field of brittle materials. For countries not included below, the reader is recommended to refer to national societies and trade federations.

Australasia
CSIRO, PO Box 225, Dickson, ACT 2602, Australia.
New Zealand Pottery and Ceramic Research Association, Lower Hutt, New Zealand.

France
CNRS Glass Lab., University of Montpelier II, Place Eugène-Bataillon, 34060 Montpellier.
École des Mines de Paris, Centre des Matériaux, BP 87, 91003 Evreux Cedex.
École Nationale Superieure de Céramique Industrielle, 6 Grand Rue, 92430 Sèvres.
Institut de Céramique Francaise, 44 rue Copernic, 75016 Paris.
Institut du Verre, 34 Rue Michel-Ange, F-75016, Paris.
Societé Francaise de Céramique, 23 Rue de Cronstadt, 75015 Paris.

Federal Republic of Germany
Battelle-Institut eV, Römerhof 35, Postfach 900160, D-6000 Frankfurt-am-Main 90.
University of Clausthal, Institut für Nichtmetallische Werkstoffe, Zehntnerstrasse, D-3392 Clausthal-Zellerfeld.
Deutsche Keramische Gesellschaft, Menzenberger Strasse 47, D-534 Bad Honnef.
Max-Planck-Institut, Seestr. 92, D-7000 Stuttgart 1.
Max-Planck-Institut, Pulvermetallurgische Laboratorium, Heisenbergerstr. 5, D-7000 Stuttgart 80.

Italy
Stazione Sperimentale del Vetro, 30121 Venezia-Murano, Via Briati 10.
Centro di Ricerca e Sperimentale per l'Industria Ceramica, Via Martelli 26, Bologna.

Sweden
The Glass Research Institute, Box 3093, S-350 03, Växjö.

Switzerland
Battelle – Centre de Recherche de Genève, 7 Route de Drize, CH-1227 Carouge – Geneva.

USA
Alfred University, NY State College of Ceramics, Alfred, NY 14802.
Battelle Memorial Institute, 505 King Avenue, Columbus, Ohio 43201.
Massachusetts Institute of Technology, 77 Massachusetts Ave, Cambridge, Mass 02139.
National Bureau of Standards, Washington, DC.
Pennsylvania State University, Ceramic Sci. and Eng. Section, 201 Steidle Bldg, University Park, Pa 16802.
Rutgers, The State University, Dept. of Ceramics, New Brunswick, NJ 08903.
University of Illinois, 204 Ceramics, Urbana, Ill 61803.
University of Missouri-Rolla, Ceramic Eng. Dept, Fulton Hall, Rolla, Mo 65401.
Virginia Polytechnic Institute and State University, College of Engineering, Blacksburg, Va 24061.

SECTION 7

Standards related to ceramics, glasses, graphite, cemented carbides and components made from them

7.1

Introductory note

This list of standard test methods, recommended practices and specifications is included because reference is frequently made to them in technical literature. Some may appear to have limited applicability, but sometimes are used as the basis for determining properties on other types of material; i.e. they are the nearest equivalent to what should be used. Included are not only British Standards, but also standards of the American Society for Testing and Materials (ASTM), American National Standards Institute (ANSI) standards, publications of the International Electrotechnical Commission (IEC), International Standards Organisation (ISO) standards, and some Federal Republic of Germany (DIN) and European (EN) standards. The listing is as complete as possible, but developments in the standards organizations mean that designations and titles are frequently changed and added to, so the list should not be considered as definitive. The reader is advised to check the current position with the relevant authorities when appropriate, and to keep an eye open for new developments. As ISO and EN standards are developed, national standards organizations are tending to adopt them as national standards, often without substantial modification, and they are frequently given a national standard number, or occasionally, as in the DIN case, the ISO or EN designation is retained.

7.2

British Standards

7.2.1 Glasses

BS 572:1960	Interchangeable conical ground glass joints.
BS 857:1967	Safety glass for land transport.
BS 952:—	Glass for glazing. (Two parts)
BS 1207:1961	Hollow glass blocks.
BS 1540:1949	Moulded electrical insulating materials for use at radio frequencies. (Includes vitreous silica and other glasses.)
BS 1751:1952	General purpose glass stopcocks.
BS 2598:—	Glass plant, pipeline and fittings. (Four parts)
BS 2649:—	Methods for the analysis of glass. (Four parts)
BS 2761:1963	Spherical ground glass joints.
BS 3193:1967	Glass components for domestic appliances.
BS 3275:1960	Glass for signs and recommendations on glazing for signs.
BS 3447:1962	Glossary of terms used in the glass industry.
BS 3473:1962	Methods for testing the chemical resistance of glass used in the production of laboratory glassware.
BS 3517:1962	Methods for thermal shock tests on laboratory glassware.
BS 4031:1966	X-ray protective lead glasses.
BS 5051:—	Security glazing. (Two parts)
BS 5103:—	Permissible limits of metal release from glassware and glass ceramic ware. (Two parts)
BS 5357:1976	Code of practice for the installation of security glazing.
BS 5516:1977	Code of practice for patent glazing.
BS 5544:1978	Specification for anti-bandit glazing (glazing resistant to manual attack).
BS 5713:1979	Specification for hermetically-sealed flat double glazing units.
BS 5895:1980	Specification for borosilicate glass tubing for laboratory apparatus.
BS CP122:—	Walls and partitions of blocks and slabs, part 1.
BS CP152:1972	Glazing and fixing of glass for buildings.

7.2.2 Ceramics

BS 16:1974	Telegraph material (insulators, pole fittings, etc.)
BS 137:—	Insulators of ceramic material or glass for overhead lines with a nominal voltage greater than 1000V. (Two parts)
BS 784:1973	Methods of test for chemical stoneware.
BS 1539:1949	Moulded electrical insulating materials for use at high temperatures. (Covers glass-bonded mica, under review.)
BS 1540:1949	Moulded electrical insulating materials for use at radio frequencies. (Covers dielectrics, under review.)
BS 1598:1964	Ceramic insulating materials for general electrical purposes. (Probably being replaced by BS 6045:1981 (three parts) based on IEC 672:1980.)
BS 1634:1973	Dimensions of stoneware pipes and pipe fittings for chemical purposes.
BS 3288:—	Insulator and conductor fittings for overhead power lines. (Two parts)
BS 3297:—	High voltage post insulators.
BS 3679:1963	Acid-resisting bricks and tiles.
BS 4034:1966	The requirements for resistance to water absorption and crazing of vitrified hotelware.

BS 4145:1967 (1979)	Glass mica boards for electrical purposes.
BS 4495:1969	Recommendations for the flame spraying of ceramic and cermet coatings.
BS 4789:1972	Ceramic components for use in envelopes for electronic tubes.
BS 4860:1972	Permissible limits of metal release from glazed ceramic ware. (Two parts)
BS 4963:1973	Tests for hollow insulators for use in high voltage electrical equipment.
BS 5612:1978	Specification for dental porcelains for jacket crowns.
BS 6045:1981	Ceramic and glass electrical insulating materials. (Three parts, Part 1 confirmed, Parts 2 and 3 to be confirmed; replacing BS 1598:1964, developed from IEC 672:1980.)

7.2.3 Carbon and graphite

| BS 96:1954 (1977) | Carbon brushes (parallel-sided) for use on commutator and slip ring machines. |

7.2.4 Cemented carbides

BS 3821:1974	Hardmetal dies and associated hardmetal tools. (Three parts)
BS 4193:1980	Hardmetal insert tooling. (Four parts)
BS 4276:1968	Hard metal for wire, bar and tube drawing dies.

7.3

ASTM (American Society for Testing and Materials) Standards

7.3.1 Glasses

C147–76	Internal pressure test on glass containers.
C148–77	Polariscopic examination of glass containers.
C149–77	Thermal shock test on glass containers.
C158–72	Flexure testing of glass (determination of modulus of rupture).
C162–71	Glass and glass products, definition of terms relating to.
C169–75	Soda-lime and borosilicate glass, chemical analysis of.
C224–78	Glass containers, sampling.
C336–71(1977)	Annealing point and strain point of glass by fiber elongation, test for.
C338–73	Softening point of glass, test for.
C598–72(1977)	Annealing point and strain point of glass by beam bending, test for.
C599–70(1977)	Process glass pipe and fittings, specification for.
C600–70(1977)	Thermal shock test on glass pipe.
C601–70(1977)	Pressure test on glass pipe.
C623–71(1977)	Young's modulus, shear modulus, and Poisson's ratio for glass and glass-ceramics by resonance, test for.
C657–78	D–C volume resistivity of glass, test for.
C676–74	Detergent resistance of ceramic decorations on glass tableware, test for.
C693–74	Density of glass by buoyancy, test for.
C724–76	Acid resistance of ceramic decorations on architectural type glass, tests for.
C729–75	Density of glass by the sink-float comparator, test for.
C730–75	Knoop indentation hardness of glass, test for.
C770–77	Glass stress optical coefficient, recommended practices for measurement of.
C777–78	Sulfide resistance of ceramic decorations on glass, test for.
C812–75	Hydrophobic contamination on glass by water condensation, test for.
C813–75	Hydrophobic contamination on glass by contact angle measurement, test for.
D879–62(1976)	Communication and signal pin-type lime-glass insulators, specification for.
D3556–79	Deposition on glassware during mechanical dishwashing, test for.
E228–71(1979)	Linear thermal expansion of rigid solids with a vitreous silica dilatometer, test for.
E438–71(1976)	Glasses in laboratory apparatus, specification for.
E546–75	Frost point of sealed insulating glass units, test for.
E576–79	Dew/frost point of sealed insulating glass units in vertical position, test for.
F218–68(1978)	Stress in glass, analyzing.
F428–77	Intensity of scratches on aerospace glass enclosures, test for.

7.3.2 Glass-to-metal seals

F14–68(1978)	Reference glass-metal bead-seal, recommended practice for making and testing.
F15–78	Iron-nickel-cobalt sealing alloy, specification for.
F18–64(1977)	Glass-to-metal headers used in electron devices, specification and method for evaluation of.
F29–78	Dumet wire for glass-to-metal seal applications, specification for.
F30–77	Iron-nickel sealing alloys, specification for.
F31–68(1978)	42% nickel – 6% chromium – iron sealing alloy, specification for.
F79–69(1973)	Type 101 sealing glass, specification for.
F105–72(1978)	Type 58 borosilicate sealing glass, specification for.
F140–73	Reference glass-metal butt seals and testing for expansion characteristics by polarimetric methods, recommended practice for making.

F144–73	Reference glass-metal sandwich seal and testing for expansion characteristics by polarimetric methods, recommended practice for making.
F204–76	Surface flaws in tungsten seal rod and wire, test for.
F218–68(1978)	Stress in glass, analyzing.

7.3.3 Technical ceramics and ceramic whitewares

(*Note*: tests on ceramic whitewares, although designed for tableware types of material, are often used on technical ceramics of all types; hence some of the more appropriate ones are listed here.)

C12–77	Practice for installing vitrified clay pipelines, recommended practice for.
C242–77	Ceramic whitewares and related products, definition of terms relating to.
C301–78	Vitrified clay pipe, testing.
C327–56(1970)	Linear thermal expansion of fired ceramic whiteware materials by the interferometric method, test for.
C329–75	Specific gravity of fired ceramic whiteware materials, test for.
C346–76	45-degree specular gloss of ceramic materials, test for.
C368–77	Impact resistance of ceramic tableware, test for.
C370–56(1975)	Moisture expansion of fired whiteware products, test for.
C372–76	Linear thermal expansion of porcelain enamel and glaze frits and fired ceramic whiteware products by the dilatometer method, test for.
C373–72(1977)	Water absorption, bulk density, apparent porosity, and apparent specific gravity of fired whiteware products, test for.
C408–76	Thermal conductivity of whiteware ceramics, test for.
C424–60(1975)	Crazing resistance of fired glazed whitewares by autoclave treatment, test for.
C425–77	Compression joints for vitrified clay pipe and fittings, specification for.
C483–66(1975)	Electrical resistance of conductive ceramic tile, test for.
C484–66(1975)	Thermal shock resistance of glazed ceramic tile, test for.
C485–73(1978)	Warpage of ceramic tile, measuring.
C501–66(1976)	Relative resistance to wear of unglazed ceramic tile by the Taber Abraser, test for.
C648–78	Breaking strength of ceramic tile, test for.
C650–71(1978)	Resistance of ceramic tile to chemical substances, test for.
C674–77	Flexural properties of ceramic whiteware materials, tests for.
C700–78a	Vitrified clay pipe, extra strength, standard strength and perforated, specification for.
C738–78	Lead and cadmium extracted from glazed ceramic surfaces, test for.
C773–74	Compressive (crushing) strength of fired whiteware materials, test for.
C798–75	Color permanency of glazed ceramic tile, test for.
C848–78	Young's modulus, shear modulus, and Poisson's ratio for ceramic whitewares by resonance, test for.
C849–76	Knoop indentation hardness of ceramic whitewares, test for.
D116–76	Vitrified ceramic materials for electrical applications, testing.
D495–73	High-voltage, low-current dry arc resistance of solid electrical insulation, test for.
D651–75	Tensile strength of molded electrical insulating materials, test for.
D1039–65(1976)	Glass-bonded mica used as electrical insulation, testing.
D1711–79	Electrical insulation, definition of terms relating to.
D1829–66(1976)	Electrical resistance of ceramic materials at elevated temperatures, test for.
D2149–68(1975)	Dielectric constant (permittivity) and dissipation factor of solid ceramic dielectrics at frequencies to 10MHz and temperatures to 500°C, test for.
D2442–75	Alumina ceramics for electrical and electronic applications, specification for.
D2757–70(1976)	Impervious steatite ceramics for electrical and electronic applications, specification for.
D2865–71(1976)	Calibrations of standards and equipment for electrical insulating materials testing, recommended practice for.
D3386–74	Coefficient of linear thermal expansion of electrical insulating materials, test for.
F77–69(1979)	Apparent density of ceramics for electron device and semi-conductor application, test for.
F109–73(1979)	Surface imperfections on ceramics, definition of terms relating to.
F356–75	Beryllia ceramics for electronic and electrical applications, specification for.
F394–78	Biaxial flexure strength (modulus of rupture) of ceramic substrates, test for.
F417–78	Flexural strength (modulus of rupture) of electronic-grade ceramics, test for.
G65–81	Conducting dry sand/rubber wheel abrasion tests.

7.3.4 Ceramic-to-metal seals

F19–64(1977)   Tension and vacuum testing metalized ceramic seals.
F44–68(1968)   Metallized surfaces on ceramic, specification for.

7.3.5 Cemented carbides

B276–79   Apparent porosity in cemented carbides, test for.
B294–76   Hardness testing of cemented carbides.
B311–58(1979)   Density of cemented carbides, test for.
B390–64(1976)   Apparent grain size and distribution of cemented tungsten carbides, recommended practice for evaluating.
B406–76   Transverse rupture strength of cemented carbides, test for.
B421–76   Electrical resistivity of cemented tungsten carbide, test for.
B437–67(1973)   Tension testing of cemented carbides.
B485–76   Diametral compression testing of cemented carbides.
B611–76   Abrasive wear resistance of cemented carbides, test for.

7.3.6 Carbon and graphite

C559–77   Bulk density in air of manufactured carbon and graphite articles by physical measurements, test for.
C560–77   Graphite, chemical analysis of.
C561–69   Ash in graphite, test for.
C562–69   Moisture in graphite, test for.
C565–78   Methods of tension testing of carbon and graphite mechanical materials.
C611–67(1976)   Electrical resistivity of manufactured carbon and graphite articles at room temperature, test for.
C651–70(1977)   Flexural strength of manufactured carbon and graphite articles using four-point loading at room temperature, test for.
C662–70(1976)   Impervious graphite pipe and threading, specification for.
C695–75   Compressive (crushing) strength of graphite, test for.
C709–77   Manufactured carbon and graphite, definition of terms relating to.
C714–72   Thermal diffusivity of carbon and graphite by a thermal pulse method, test for.
C747–74   Moduli of elasticity and fundamental frequencies of carbon and graphite materials by sonic resonance, test for.
C748–73   Rockwell hardness of fine-grained graphite materials, test for.
C749–73   Tensile stress-strain of carbon and graphite, test for.
C808–75   Reporting friction and wear test results of manufactured carbon and graphite bearing and seal materials, recommended guideline for.

7.3.7 Porcelain enamels

Note: there are numerous test methods for determining the properties and performance of this class of material applied to metal substrates. For further information see the current Index volume to the Annual Book of ASTM Standards.

7.4

ANSI (American National Standards Institute) Standards

Note: many of the ANSI standards are direct duplications of ASTM Standards. Where such duplication exists in the following list, only the cross-reference to the ASTM number is given.

7.4.1 Glasses

C131.30–1974	See ASTM F218–68.
Z26.1–1966 (R1973)	Safety glazing materials for glazing motor vehicles operating on land highways, safety code for.
Z80.1–1972	First-quality prescription opthalmic lenses, requirements for.
Z80.2–1972	First-quality contact lenses, prescription requirements for.
Z97.1–1972	Safety glazing material used in buildings, performance specifications and methods of test for.

7.4.2 Glass-to-metal seals

C131.4–1974	See ASTM F140–73.
C131.5–1974	See ASTM F144–73.
C131.30–1974	See ASTM F218–68.
Z173.5–1969	See ASTM F14–68.

7.4.3 Ceramics

A101.2–1975	See ASTM C798–75.
A106.2–1972	See ASTM C12–72.
A106.5–1972	See ASTM C301–72.
A106.6–1973	See ASTM C425–72a.
A106.7–1973	See ASTM C594–73.
A106.8–1975	See ASTM C700–74.

A108.1–1967 (R1972)	
A108.2–1967 (R1972)	
A108.3–1967 (R1972)	Specifications for wall and floor
A108.4–1968 (R1972)	tile installations with various
A108.5–1967 (R1972)	adhesives.
A108.6–1969	
A108.7–1969 (R1972)	

A173.1–1971	See ASTM C648–70.
A174.1–1971	See ASTM C650–70.
A174.2–1975	See ASTM C738–72.
A175.1–1971	See ASTM C627–70.
C83.24–1962 (R1972)	Piezoelectric ceramics, method of measurement of.
C131.28–1974	See ASTM F109–73.
Z173.32–1971	See ASTM D2442–70.
Z173.44–1971	See ASTM F77–69.

7.4.4 Ceramic-to-metal seals

Z173.12–1969   See ASTM F44–68.

7.4.5 Cemented carbides

B94.12–1968	Carbide-tipped masonry drills and blanks for carbide-tipped masonry drills.
B94.13–1968	Blanks for carbide burs.
B94.20–1968	Carbide blanks for twist drills, reamers, end mills and random rod, specification for.
B94.24–1969	Heavy-duty carbide inserts for cutting tools.
B94.36–1956(R1971)	Life tests for single-point tools of sintered carbide.
B94.37–1972	Carbide blanks and cutting tools, single-point, carbide-tipped, roller turner type.
B94.42–1972	Carbide blanks for tipping circular saws.
B94.46–1973	Carbide seats used with indexable inserts for clamp-type holders.
B94.47–1973	Carbide chip breakers used with indexable inserts for clamp-type holders.

7.5

American Military Specifications

MIL–I–10B   Insulating compound, electrical, ceramic, class L. (1966, amendment 1 1967, amendment 2 1976.)

7.6

IEC (International Electrotechnical Commission) publications

Note: many of the specifications and test methods listed below are the bases for British Standards, DIN Standards, and ISO standards.

IEC 168:1979 Tests on indoor and outdoor post insulators of ceramic or glass for systems with nominal voltages greater than 1000V.

IEC 233:1974 Tests on hollow insulators for use in electrical equipment.

IEC 273:1979 Dimensions of indoor and outdoor post insulators and post insulator units for systems with nominal voltages greater than 1000V.

IEC 383:1976 Tests on insulators of ceramic material or glass for overhead lines with a nominal voltage greater than 1000V.

IEC 483:1976 Guide to dynamic measurements of piezoelectric ceramics with high mechanical coupling.

IEC 642:1979 Piezoelectric ceramic resonators and resonator units for frequency control and selection.

IEC 672:1980 Specification for ceramic and glass insulating materials. (Three parts—probably being adopted as BS 6045:1981.)

7.7

ISO (International Standards Organization) Standards

7.7.1 Glasses

ISO	383–1976	Laboratory glassware—interchangeable conical ground joints.
ISO	384–1978	Laboratory glassware—principles of design and construction of volumetric glassware.
ISO	614–1976	Shipbuilding—toughened safety glass panes for ships' side scuttles and ships' rectangular windows—punch method of non-destructive strength testing.
ISO	641–1975	Laboratory glassware—interchangeable spherical ground joints.
ISO	695–1975	Glass—determination of resistance to attack by a boiling aqueous solution of mixed alkali.
ISO/R	718–1968	Methods for thermal shock tests on laboratory glassware.
ISO/R	719–1968	Determination of the hydrolytic resistance of glass grains at 98°C.
ISO/R	720–1968	Determination of the hydrolytic resistance of glass grains at 121°C.
ISO	1042–1975	Laboratory glassware—one-mark volumetric flasks.
ISO	1095–1976	Shipbuilding—toughened safety glass panes for ships' side scuttles.
ISO	1769–1975	Laboratory glassware—pipettes—colour coding.
ISO/R	1776–1970	Determination of the resistance of glass to attack by 6N hydrochloric acid at 100°C.
ISO	3254–1975	Shipbuilding—toughened safety glass panes for ships' rectangular windows.
ISO	3434–1975	Shipbuilding—heated glass panes for ships' windows.
ISO	3536/1–1975	Road vehicles—safety glasses—vocabulary (part 1).
ISO	3537–1975	Road vehicles—safety glasses—test methods for mechanical properties.
ISO	3538–1978	Road vehicles—safety glasses—test methods for optical properties.
ISO	3585–1976	Glass plant, pipeline and fittings—properties of borosilicate glass 3.3.
ISO	3586–1976	Glass plant, pipeline and fittings—general rules for testing, handling and use.
ISO	3587–1976	Glass plant, pipeline and fittings—pipeline and fittings of nominal bore 15 to 150 mm—compatibility and interchangeability.
ISO	3917–1976	Road vehicles—safety glasses—methods of test for resistance to radiation, high temperature, humidity and fire.
ISO	4793–1980	Laboratory sintered (fritted) filters—porosity, grading, classification and designation.
ISO	4803–1978	Laboratory glassware—borosilicate glass tubing.

7.7.2 Ceramics

ISO	1772–1975	Laboratory crucibles in porcelain and silica.
ISO	1775–1975	Porcelain laboratory apparatus—requirements and methods of test.
ISO	6474–1981	Implants for surgery—ceramic materials based on alumina.

7.7.3 Cemented carbides

ISO	883–1976	Indexable (throwaway) carbide inserts without fixation hole—dimensions. (See also BS 4193:1980 Part 2.)
ISO	1684–1975	Wire, bar and tube drawing dies—specifications.

ISO	1832-1977	Indexable (throwaway) inserts for cutting tools—designation, code of symbolization. (See also BS 4193:1980 Part 1.)
ISO	3252-1975	Powder metallurgy—vocabulary.
ISO	3312-1975	Sintered metal materials and hardmetals—determination of Young's modulus.
ISO	3326-1975	Hardmetals—determination of (the magnetization) coercivity.
ISO	3327-1975	Hardmetals—determination of transverse rupture strength.
ISO	3364-1977	Indexable (throwaway) carbide inserts with cylindrical fixing hole—dimensions. (See also BS 4193:1980 Part 3.)
ISO	3365/1-1977	Indexable (throwaway) carbide inserts for milling cutters—dimensions—Part 1, square inserts.
ISO	3365/2-1980	Part 2 triangular inserts.
ISO	3369-1975	Impermeable sintered metal materials and hardmetals—determination of density.
ISO	3878-1976	Hardmetals—Vickers hardness test.
ISO	3907-1977	Hardmetals—determination of total carbon—gravimetric method.
ISO	3908-1976	Hardmetals—determination of insoluble (free) carbon—gravimetric method.
ISO	3909-1976	Hardmetals—determination of cobalt—potentiometric method.
ISO	4489-1978	Sintered hardmetals—sampling and testing.
ISO	4499-1978	Hardmetals—metallographic determination of microstructure.
ISO	4501-1978	Hardmetals—determination of titanium—photometric peroxide method.
ISO	4503-1978	Hardmetals—determination of contents of metallic elements by X-ray fluorescence—fusion method.
ISO	4505-1978	Hardmetals—metallographic determination of porosity and uncombined carbon.
ISO	4506-1979	Hardmetals—compression test.
ISO	4883-1978	Hardmetals—determination of contents of metallic elements by X-ray fluorescence-solution method.
ISO	4884-1978	Hardmetals—sampling and testing of powders using sintered test-pieces.

7.8

DIN (Deutsche Institut für Normen) Standards

Coverage by DIN standards is extensive, and it is inappropriate to list all those related to ceramic, glass, hardmetals and articles made from these materials. For a full listing, the reader is referred to the latest annual catalogue of DIN Standards (in German and English) and for a list of those available in English translation, there is another annual catalogue, although coverage is much less complete. In the list below we give some of the more important standards related to materials performance and classification, but exclude those which are primarily specifications for articles manufactured from brittle materials. Key: E = available in English translation.

7.8.1 Glasses

DIN	1249 Part 1 1973	Sheet glass: thickness, types, sizes, tests.
	Part 2 1973	Sheet glass: terms for defects.
	Part 3 1978	Flat glass in building: plate glass, concepts, dimensions.
DIN	1259 Part 1 1971	Glass: terms and definitions for glass types.
	Part 2 1971	Glass: terms and definitions for glass products.
DIN 12111 1976		Testing of glass: grain method for the determination of hydrolytic resistance of glass as a material at 98°C and classification of glass into hydrolytic classes.
DIN 12116 1976		Testing of glass: determination of the acid resistance (gravimetric method) and classification of glass into acid classes.
DIN 28817 1976		Testing of glass: grain method for determination of the hydrolytic resistance of glass as a material at 121°C.
DIN 52303 1976		Testing of glass: bending test.(E)
DIN 52306 1973		Ball drop test on safety glass for vehicle glazing. (E)
DIN 52307 1976		Falling dart test on safety glass for vehicle glazing.
DIN 52308 1973		Boil test on laminated safety glass.
DIN 52313 1978		Testing of glass: determination of the resistance of glass products to thermal shock.
DIN 52314 1977		Testing of glass: tensile test for the determination of stress optical coefficient.
DIN 52320 Part 1 1978		Testing of glass: internal pressure test on hollow glass containers, especially glass containers, testing by attributes.
	Part 2 1978	As Part 1 but testing by variables. (Draft)
DIN 52321 1976		Testing of glass: thermal shock test on hollow glassware, especially containers, temperature difference less than 100°C.
DIN 52322 1976		Testing of glass: determination of the resistance to attack by alkali and classification of glass into alkali classes.
DIN 52323 1976		Testing of glass: thermal shock test on hollow glassware, especially laboratory glassware, temperature difference 100°C or more.
DIN 52327 Part 1 1977		Testing of glass: determination of stresses in glass-to-glass seals.
DIN 52328 1967		Testing of glass: determination of coefficient of linear thermal expansion.
DIN 52329 1967		Testing of glass: autoclave method for testing the water resistance of the interior surfaces of glass containers.
DIN 52333 1978		Testing of glass: Knoop hardness test.

DIN 52337 1976	Testing of glass: pendulum impact test on glass used in buildings.
DIN 52338 1977	Testing of glass: ball drop test on glass used in buildings.
DIN 52339 Part 1 1976	Testing of glass: autoclave testing for determining the hydrolytic resistance of the interior surfaces of glass containers and classification, determination by titration. (Draft)
Part 2 1976	As part 1 but flame photometric method. (Draft)
DIN 52346 1978	Testing of glass: vertical load test for containers. (Draft)
DIN 52348 1978	Testing of glass and plastics: abrasion test, sand trickling method.
DIN 58925 Part 1 1965	Optical glass: terms, classification.
Part 2 1965	Optical glass: terms for optical properties.
DIN 58926 1973	Blanks for optical elements, lenses: permissible deviations, marking.

7.8.2 Glass-to-metal seals

DIN 41107 1974	Compression type glass-to-metal seals.
DIN 41109 Part 1 1977	Glass-to-metal seals for electrotechnical use.
Part 3 1977	Glass-to-metal seals for electrotechnical use, with seal bushings.
DIN 41119 Part 1 1973	Compression type glass-to-metal seals for electrotechnology; for rectangular metal housing with two lead-throughs.
Part 3 1975	Compression type glass-to-metal seals for electrotechnology; with soldering lugs, rectangular metal housing with two lead-throughs.
DIN 41129 Part 1 1977	As DIN 41119 Part 3 but for seals of form A, and cylindrical metal housing.
Part 3 1977	As DIN 41119 Part 3 but for seals of form AL, and cylindrical metal housing.
DIN 52327 Part 2 1977	Testing of glass: determination of stresses in glass-to-metal strip seals.

7.8.3 Ceramics

DIN 7000 1969	Acid-resistant stoneware for chemical plant: flange pipes, adapter pipes, intermediate pieces.
DIN 7031 Part 1 1971	Acid-resistant stoneware for chemical plant: armoured flanged pipes.
Part 2 1971	Acid-resistant stoneware for chemical plant: armoured flanged fittings.

DIN 7011–7022 inclusive and 7024 are also for various aspects of chemical stoneware products for chemical plant.

DIN 40680 Part 1 1968	Ceramic components for electrical engineering, admissible tolerances. (Updated draft June 1980)
Part 2 1970	Ceramic components for electrical engineering, admissible shape tolerances. (Updated drafts, August 1976, and June 1980)
Part 3 1976	Ceramic components for electrical engineering: admissible tolerances of position. (Draft)
DIN 40685 Part 1 1974	Specifications for ceramic insulating materials for electrical purposes: classification, requirements, types.
Part 2 1974	Specifications for ceramic insulating materials for electrical purposes: test methods.
DIN 41110 1971	Ceramic protection tubes for electrical engineering.
DIN 43725 1966	Electrical temperature measuring instruments: refractory insulating tubes for thermocouples.
DIN 44926 Part 1 1973	Ceramic parts for electric heating elements: multiple hole tubes, dimensions.
Part 2 1973	Ceramic parts for electric heating elements: open multiple hole tubes, dimensions.
DIN 44975 1954	Electric ovens, resistance heated ovens, ceramic tubes.
DIN 51065 Part 2 1976	Testing of ceramic materials: determination of bulk density of granular material.
DIN 51090 1971	Testing of ceramic materials: bend test on wall and floor tiles.
DIN 51091 1976	Testing of ceramic materials: determination of the chemical resistance of unglazed ceramic tiles for walls and floors. (Draft)
DIN 51092 1976	Testing of ceramic materials: determination of the chemical resistance of the glaze of glazed tiles for walls and floors. (Draft)
DIN 51093 1976	Testing of ceramic materials: determination of the thermal shock resistance of ceramic tiles for walls and floors. (Draft)
DIN 51102 Part 2 1976	Testing of ceramic materials: determination of acid resistance, method with granulated test material.

DIN 51103 1975   Testing of ceramic materials: determination of alkali resistance, method with granulated test material.

DIN 58835 Part 1 1977 Surgical implants: ceramic materials for surgical implants based on alumina. (Draft)

7.8.4 Ceramic-to-metal seals

DIN 41108 1971   Ceramic lead-throughs for electrical engineering: ceramic tubes for.

DIN 41315 1971   Ceramic lead-throughs for electrical engineering.

7.8.5 Hardmetals

Standards for hardmetal tools are in the group DIN 4950–4990, 8010–8013. With some modifications, the ISO scheme is based on the DIN scheme.

7.9

EN (European) Standards

There is a limited range of draft European Standards (Euro-Norms) in the ceramics area. These are available through National Standards bodies.

EN 98 1977	Ceramic tiles: determination of dimensions and surface quality. (Draft)
EN 99 1977	Ceramic tiles: determination of water absorption. (Draft)
EN 100 1977	Ceramic tiles: determination of modulus of rupture. (Draft)
EN 101 1977	Ceramic tiles: determination of scratch hardness of surface according to Mohs' scale. (Draft)
EN 102 1977	Ceramic tiles: determination of resistance to abrasion, unglazed tiles. (Draft)
EN 103 1977	Ceramic tiles: determination of linear thermal expansion. (Draft)
EN 104 1977	Ceramic tiles: determination of resistance to thermal shock. (Draft)
EN 105 1977	Ceramic tiles: determination of crazing resistance. (Draft)
EN 106 1977	Ceramic tiles: determination of chemical resistance of unglazed tiles. (Draft)

Printed in the UK for HMSO
Dd737871 3/85 10170 (1917)